BIOPHYSICAL
AND
PHYSIOLOGICAL
SYSTEMS ANALYSIS

Based on Lectures to Graduate Students

BIOPHYSICAL
AND
PHYSIOLOGICAL
SYSTEMS ANALYSIS

Based on Lectures to Graduate Students

Erol Başar

Institute of Biophysics
Hacettepe University, Ankara

1976

Addison-Wesley Publishing Company
Advanced Book Program
Reading, Massachusetts
London • Amsterdam • Don Mills, Ontario • Sydney • Tokyo

ISBN 0-201-00846-7
ISBN 0-201-00847-5 pbk.

Reproduced by Addison-Wesley Publishing Company, Inc., Advanced Book Program, Reading, Massachusetts, from camera-ready copy prepared by the author.

Copyright © 1976 by Addison-Wesley Publishing Company, Inc.
Published simultaneously in Canada.

Manufactured in the United States of America

ABCDEFGHIJ-MA-79876

to FERİHA

for her magnificent devotion to the intellectual pursuits of her children.

Contents

Preface

This book is written to explain the advantages of taking a systems approach to the interpretation of medical and biological effects, despite their well-known complexity. There is increasing attention to this kind of approach in biology; therefore, this book should appeal to research scientists and graduate students in *biophysics* and *physiology,* biomedical engineering, electroencephalography, as well as those in mathematics, physiological psychology. Physiologists, especially cardiovascular physiologists, neurophysiologists, and EEG-analysts may find some useful ideas for further research in the specific examples given. The organization of the book will be explained in Chapter 1.

More than twenty-five years have passed since the
first publication of Norbert Wiener's revolutionary and now
famous book: *Cybernetics, or Control and Communication in
the Animal and the Machine* (1948). With the publication of
this book and the research upon which it was based, Wiener
launched a very significant and important new inter-
disciplinary science concerned with the application of what
is now called Systems Theory in the study of biological
systems. Wiener established the relevance of all three major
branches of systems science (information and communication
theory, control theory, and computer science) to physiological
systems and pointed the way for future research in
cybernetics.

Nine years ago, I began work on the analysis of biological systems, and in the course of my research, I have
had the opportunity to conduct experiments on a variety of
biological systems, including intensive work on the
circulatory system, smooth muscles, and the brain. During
this period, I have always thought it necessary to combine
methods of abstract systems theory with methods of classical
physiology while collecting rules and methods for a
"Biological Systems Analysis Program" which would help
biosystems investigators, who try to understand biological

phenomena. I also have seen how important and useful it is
for the systems scientist to have profound physiological
knowledge before investigating a physiological problem,
related to his mathematical knowledge. Only when the systems
scientist has amassed all available knowledge of the system
he wishes to study can he design a program of analysis for
his biological experiment.

In different chapters of the book I describe various
experiments in order to create new insight to various
physiological phenomena. However, the book should not be
considered as a collection of studies of different biological systems. Although the major aim of the biological systems
investigator is to find answers to different biological
questions, he must also try to detect some general features
common to all the biological phenomena under review. For
example, it is a well known fact that a large number of
biological systems have intrinsic rhythmic behavior.
However, the role of intrinsic oscillation of a biological
system in the response of the system to external stimuli, its
relation to control and communication are problems not
frequently discussed in the literature. In this book I try
to fill this gap which usually exists in the study of biological systems, and I also emphasize that the investigator

should always consider this aspect of biological systems in performing his experiments. This view plays a major role in the whole book.

I have chosen examples from my own research areas in presenting biological systems analysis. These examples are not necessarily the best that could be given, but they are the examples I could explain best.

The main parts of the book stem from lectures which I gave four years ago to a group of graduate students. Most of them are now doing research in our laboratories in various areas of biological systems analysis. I think they are successful as they are now able to design experiments which have been published in recognized journals. This is the encouraging factor which has given me the idea of organizing my lecture notes in the form of a book entitled "*Biophysical and Physiological Systems Analysis.*"

Erol Başar

ACKNOWLEDGMENTS

The author is grateful to a great many people. A special vote of thanks is due Dr. CANAN EROĞLU, who has devoted herself for two years to the organization of the difficult camera-ready manuscript; without her help the book would never have been completed. Before starting the manuscript I discussed my rationale with Dr. MEHMET RONA, who encouraged me to take the first steps. Dr. ÇİĞDEM ÖZESMİ played a major role in suggesting the need for such a book. Mrs. NECLA DEMİR, who has carefully reviewed the manuscript, and Mrs. PATRICIA BİLİR, who has corrected the language of the manuscript and prepared the index, contributed essential help. Mrs. ELMAS ARSLAN typed part of the manuscript and solved secretarial problems. I am also indebted to Dr. PEKCAN UNGAN, co-author of the sixth chapter, for his untiring and valuable criticisms and suggestions. Miss REZZAN DURUSAN and Mrs. SİREL KARAKAŞ also supported the organization with their various contributions. The authors and publishers who have contributed so much by their kind permission to use their illustrations are acknowledged in figure legends. Again, I wish to express my deepest appreciation to all these people.

SPECIAL ACKNOWLEDGMENT

Most of the research described in this book was carried out in the laboratories of the Institute of Biophysics at the young Hacettepe University in Ankara. Endowed with unique dynamic personality, The Rector h.c. and founder of Hacettepe University, Prof. Dr. Dr. İHSAN DOĞRAMACI, has contributed enormously to the development of our laboratories. Dr. DOĞRAMACI's support also is indirectly reflected in this volume.

Chapter 1

Introduction

1.1 STATEMENT OF THE PROBLEM AND AIMS OF THE BOOK

In this book, we will establish "A General Biological Systems Analysis Program" and then describe various experiments and analyses, the designs of which are based on the nature of various biological phenomena and show the application of the proposed analysis program.

One of the aims of this book is to try to instill in the reader a feeling of when and how he should apply methods of systems theory and what kind of knowledge he can acquire by the use of these methods. We do not attempt to give detailed accounts of the theory of the mathematical and physiological methods used, as we assume the reader to have general knowledge of these. Neither are the classical systems theory methods, such as linear systems theory, frequency characteristics, Fourier and Laplace transforms, given in detail. There are many excellent books on engineering and mathematics for this purpose and the reader is referred to books or original articles for further information (TRUXAL, 1955; SOLODOVNIKOV, 1960). For detailed physiological information the reader is also referred to original articles or books. On the contrary, methods which are used only in the experiments described in the present book will be explained more throughly, because the sources are not easily available to the reader in most of the cases. As will be mentioned in Chapter 3, adequate application of the biological systems analysis program of this book should provide the investigator in bioscience with a new approach to the understanding of the system studied: this means, the experimenter will know much more about the components of the system under study once he has performed the experiments and accomplished his analysis.

Knowledge of the systems frequency characteristics alone cannot enable the investigator to understand the biological system studied. In other words, when he uses the tools of systems analysis, the investigator obtains only a mathematical description of his system. This knowledge does not help him to identify fully different biological or phys-

ical components of the biological system. However, a
successful biological systems analysis should allow the
investigator to identify the biological, physical, or chemical components which play a role in the functions of the
system studied. Only when the investigator combines methods,
rules, and patterns of thought of bioscience and technical
sciences and makes use of already acquired knowledge will
he be able to perform successful analysis. Successful
biological systems analysis should also enable the investigator to obtain new knowledge or to establish new theories
which can not be obtained with classical concepts of physiology. These are the most important concepts this book tries
to point out.

1.2 ORGANIZATION OF THE BOOK

This book is written for all research scientists and
students interested in biological systems analysis. The book
assumes that the reader has basic background in physiology
and basic concepts of general systems analysis. At the
beginning of those chapters in which a new problem is stated,
the general physiological features of the systems to be
studied are given. For the well-trained physiologist, this
material will recall those physiological details pertinent
to a systems analytical approach to the problem. This knowl-

edge is not necessarily enough for the reader who is not specially trained in this branch of physiology. Such readers should refer to the references. At the end of each chapter a discussion of methods and of results are given.

The book is divided into nine chapters, of which *Chapter 1* is introductory.

Chapter 2 deals with *basic concepts* and *definitions* such as the system concept, black boxes.

In *Chapter 3* the *biological systems analysis program* is presented. This program, which is applied in the following chapters, remains the heart of the book. The rules and methods of the program are handled in detail in *section 3.2,* which is cited repeatedly in other chapters of the book.

In *Chapter 4* the reader will find the application of the rules and concepts given in the biological systems analysis program to the *circulatory autoregulation* phenomenon. The systems studied are the kidney and the coronary system of the heart. The application of systems theory methods to these circulatory organs makes possible criticism of different autoregulation theories and also leads to a new working hypothesis.

Chapter 5 serves both as a key chapter for the autoregulation theory developed in Chapter 4, and also includes findings consistent in themselves and very important to the *smooth muscle* physiologist. Mechanical contraction of smooth muscle preparations such as the portal vein and the taenia coli are studied here, again with tools of systems theory. The smooth-muscle physiologist will find a systems theoretical classification, as well as hints and new approaches for the description of smooth muscle rhythmicity.

Chapter 6 is, perhaps, the most noteworthy chapter for the reader interested in general problems arising from the study of biological systems. In this chapter an attempt is made to classify the *nonlinearities* seen in biological systems and to understand their sources. This chapter, which brings new points of view to nonlinear biological systems analysis, serves also as a complement to Chapters 4 and 7. One of the main subjects of the chapter is the study of biological systems showing self-oscillatory behavior due to external stimulation.

Chapter 7 deals with the dynamics of *brain rhythmic* and *evoked potentials*. An important part of the biological systems analysis program of section 3.2 is applied by measuring electrical spontaneous and evoked activities in

various structures of the cat brain. Studies are described
of the auditory pathway, reticular formation, and the
hippocampus; some further measurements from the visual
pathway are also discussed. Systems analysis of electrical
signals from the brain allows the derivation of rules and
principles for the interpretation of evoked potentials, and
prediction of oscillatory waveforms as components of evoked
potentials. Moreover, a framework is developed for the understanding of signal transport in the brain. This framework,
which includes *resonance* phenomena and a concept which will
be called "common selectivities," will be considered to be
very useful tools for modeling theories of brain potentials.

Chapter 8 presents a summary of the methods applied
throughout the book. The methods and concepts developed in
the various chapters will be discussed and compared in this
chapter.

Chapter 9 is a recapitulation of the main points and
offers suggestions for future ways of research.

1.3 HOW THIS BOOK SHOULD BE READ

This book may be read in four different ways:

(1) The reader may start with the second chapter and read all the chapters in the order presented. This manner of reading is recommended to the reader who seeks a broad yet profound knowledge for the use and conceptual understanding of biological systems analysis.

(2) The reader may start with the second and third chapters in order to become familiar with the biological systems analysis program. He then may study the fourth chapter, the fifth chapter, and section 6.3. (The fifth chapter, although it deals with a different problem, also serves as a complement to Chapter 4.) This sequence is recommended to the reader interested only in the study of the circulatory system or to the reader who wishes to gain quickly enough insight to start on his own research problem. Chapters 7, 8, and 9 then may complete the program.

(3) The reader interested only in the study of brain potentials may start with Chapters 2 and 3 and then proceed directly to Chapter 7. He should then continue with Chapter 6. The evoked potential analyst who wants to immediately concentrate on a problem may omit the reading of Chapters 4 and 5 on the first round, but may return later when looking for an

elucidation of the general concepts of biological systems analysis.

(4) The reader interested in nonlinear behavior of biological systems may start with Chapter 6, devoted to important aspects of general biological systems analysis. He may obtain the necessary knowledge for the understanding of the phenomena from the sections 4.5, 4.8, 7.1, 7.6, 7.12 and 7.16.

We recommend to all readers "not to omit" *Chapter 8,* which tries to synthesize the ideas in different chapters.

REFERENCES

Solodovnikov, V.V.: Introduction to the Statistical Dynamics of Automatic Control Systems. Dover Publications Inc., New York (1960).

Truxal, J.G.: Automatic Feedback Control System Synthesis. McGraw-Hill Book Company, New York (1955).

Chapter 2

Definitions and Concepts

In this book we will deal with biological systems. We will consider the biological systems under study as black boxes having an input and output and will try to understand various properties of these systems using the relationship between input and output signals. This chapter will provide the most important definitions, so that the reader may refer to these definitions or concepts, which he will encounter in every part of the book.

2.1 SOME DEFINITIONS OF THE "SYSTEM"

The system and the related concepts can first of all be defined in an abstract manner; as ASHBY (1952) describes it:

> "A system is defined *as any set of variables* that the experimenter selects from those available in the real machine."

Furthermore, a variable is defined as a measurable quantity which at every instant has a definite numerical value.

> "All the quantities used in physics, chemistry, biology, physiology, and objective psychology, are variables in the defined sense. Thus the position of a limb can be specified numerically by coordinates of position, and movement of the limb can move a printer on a dial. Temperature at a point can be specified numerically and can be recorded on a dial. Pressure, angle, electric potential, volume, velocity, torque, power, mass, viscosity, humidity, surface tension, osmotic pressure, specific gravity, and time itself, to mention only a few, can all be specified numerically and recorded on dials."

GRODINS (1963) gives a more concrete definition:

> "We may define a system as a collection of components arranged and interconnected in a definite way. The components may be physical, chemical, biological, or a combination of all three."

MILSUM (1966) goes even further and introduces the performance of function. He states:

> "A *system* in this context is defined as any collection of "communicating" materials and processes which together perform some function in which the investigator is interested. The system's behavior is determined by:
> 1. The characteristics of the components or subsystems.
> 2. The structure of communication between components, which usually involves feedback paths.
> 3. The *input* signals or variables to the system. These are initially assumed to be independent variables under the investigator's control,

but some may in fact be controlled by the outputs of other systems.

The results of the system's operation upon the inputs are the *outputs*. Any variable of the system may be considered an output, dependent only upon the particular interest of the system's investigator. Note that neither input nor output variables need particularly be material flows; variables such as voltage, temperature and pressure qualify equally well as the liters per second of blood flow.

In consequence, a system may be represented symbolically as an input-output device; one conventional symbol is a block with incoming and outgoing arrows to represent the relevant variables. Any system may always be broken down into smaller, connected subsystems if one so wishes, as in {Fig. 2.1}.

The living cell is a convenient example of a system, its boundary being formed by the membrane. Internally the cell has many subsystems, such as nucleus and mitochondria, and communication occurs between them through the actions of the various biochemical materials. The input variables relevant to a particular study are selected from the large number of possible ones which the investigator could manipulate, including environmental concentrations of the various inflowing chemicals, environmental temperature, and pressure. The output variables relevant to the study could include internal concentrations or output flow rates of internally synthesized chemicals, metabolic rate, and transmembrane potential."

This description by MILSUM (1966) is the most adequate one for the experiments and analyses which will be presented in Chapters 4, 5, 6 and 7 of this book. The reader, in our examples of the circulatory system (Chapter 4), smooth muscles (Chapter 5) and the brain (Chapter 7), will

see the importance of communicating materials and processes

which together perform some function, and the importance of

the choice of systems and subsystems.

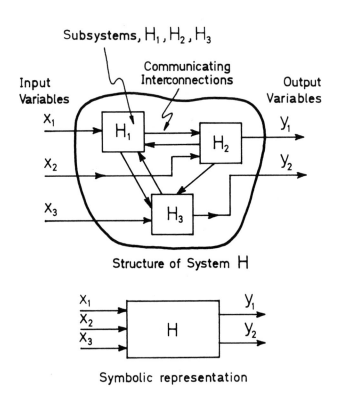

Fig. 2.1 System. (After MILSUM, 1966. Used with permission of McGraw-Hill Book Company.)

A Brief Classification of Systems in General

UNGAN (1974) classifies the systems as follows:

"Theoretically, a system can be represented by
a symbolic analytical relation in the form of

$$D \{ r(t) \} = e(t)$$

where, $r(t)$: the selected output quantity as
a function of time,

$e(t)$: the selected input quantity as a
function of time,

D   : an operator for the input-output
relation.

Systems are grouped into five main cathegories regarding their different aspects and the operator which stands for their input-output relation. These cathegories and their brief explanations are as follows:

1) *Lumped Systems:* In such systems, the phys-ical dimensions of the elements, which consti-tute it, are very small compared to the wave length of the input-output quantities. Their D operator is scalar. Otherwise, D can only be expressed by vectors and the system is "dis-tributed".

2) *Time Invariant Systems:* If the elements of the system do not change their values with time, this system is called "time invariant". In this case D operator is independent of time. Otherwise the system is "time varying".

3) *Linear Systems:* These systems must meet the homogenity and superposition criteria, and their D operators are independent of both input and the output quantities. Other systems are "nonlinear".

4) *Causal Systems:* A system which does not give any output unless an excitation is applied to its input is defined as "causal". Otherwise the system is "uncausal". If an uncausal system is, in addition, free, linear and time invariant, it is called "autonomus". Some systems which are known as "autonom systems" in physiology do not satisfy these additional criteria. Therefore, any confusion should be avoided.

5) *Passive Systems:* In such systems, all the elements are passive (i.e., the time integral of the energy which is given to the system by each of these elements is less than or equal to zero). If there are dependent or independent active elements or energy sources, the system is *active*."

2.2 STATE OF A SYSTEM

"The *state* of a system at a given instant is the set
of numerical values which its variables have at that instant"
(ASHBY, 1952). An example may be given from Chapter 7, where
different states of the brain (waking and sleep stages) are
described, using the terminology of sleep studies.

A variable is a function of time, and a *system* of n
variables will usually be represented by x_1, x_2,....., x_n.
The state of a system at time t is the set of numerical
values of $x_1(t)$,....., $x_n(t)$. A transition can be specified
only after an interval of time, finite and represented by t.
It is represented by the pair of states, one at time Δt and
one at the specified time later.

2.3 THE "BLACK BOX" AND THE "WHITE BOX"

The expression *"black box"* usually refers to an
apparatus, for example an electronic network, having one
input and one output and performing a defined operation,
but from which there is no information concerning the structure and processes giving rise to the defined operation.
In a black box only the input and output functions are known
and not the structure or processes performing the input-
output relation.

The *"white box"* can be defined as a network which is built in such a way that according to its construction a defined input-output relation is guaranteed. In other words, we know the structure and the input-output relation exactly of such a white box.

2.4 ELUCIDATING THE BLACK BOX

We will call the success of all the procedures (technical or mathematical) which contribute to the understanding of the structure or processes which make possible the realization of the defined operation (defined input-output relationship) performed by the black box, *"the elucidation of the black box."*

2.5 CONCEPT OF THE "GREY BOX"

Although the expressions "black box" and "white box" are often used in scientific literature, the concept of *"grey box"* is not used at all by systems scientists. However, the systems scientist, especially the investigator of biological systems, usually deals with grey boxes (somewhat elucidated black boxes) and not with completely black boxes: we call an apparatus or a system a grey box which performs a defined operation and from which we have some information concerning the structure or processes making possible (realizing) the defined operation. In a grey box we have partial information concerning the structure and processes which realize the input-output relation.

The expression, "grey box", will seldom be used in this book. However, in the analyses given in the different chapters to follow the concept of the grey box will often be used, without explicit emphasis of this concept. For example, in Chapter 4, in the analysis of the circulatory autoregulation, knowledge of the smooth muscle vasculature in the arterial wall is a typical case in point. The investigator really has a grey box to study, since he has quite a lot of information concerning the structure of the system under study.

REFERENCES

Ashby, W.R.: Design for a Brain. Chapman and Hall Ltd., London (1952).

Grodins, S.F.: Control Theory and Biological Systems. Columbia University Press, New York (1963).

Milsum, J.: Biological Control Systems Analysis. McGraw-Hill Book Company, New York (1966).

Ungan, P.: Systems theoretical analysis of potentials evoked in the cat auditory cortex. Thesis, Hacettepe Univ., Ankara (1974).

Chapter 3

Biological Systems Analysis Program

3.1 THE BLACK BOX

As we have seen in the preceding chapter, a system may be defined as a collection of components arranged and interconnected in a definite way. The components may be physical, chemical, biological or a combination of all three. The block diagram of Fig. 3.1 indicates that there are three basic quantities involved in any investigation: input (stimulus), the system and the output (response). If the stimulus and response are known or are measured variables, it should be possible to estimate the properties of the system.

If only the input and the output of the system are known and we are asked to determine the abstract frequency characteristics and properties of the system, we are con-

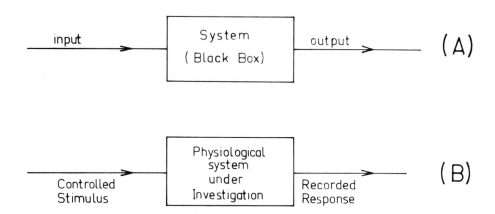

Fig. 3.1 (For explanations see text p. 17, 18)

fronted with the inductive *"black box"* problem. This kind

of problem is the most difficult and the most often encoun-

tered problem in physiological investigations. In the fol-

lowing chapters (Chapter 4, Chapter 5 and Chapter 7) we

will treat three examples of physiological problems by

black box induction.

Alone, the determination of the abstract frequency

characteristics or the transfer function of the biological

systems under study usually causes experimental and some-

times also conceptional difficulties. This is partly due to

the fact that the biological preparations under study often

have short life-times, or the parameters measured   change

rapidly. For example, the brain investigator has the problem

of rapid changes of behavior and sleep stages; the investi-

gator working with isolated organ preparations has the

problem of anoxia or the problem of metabolic insufficiency.
But, on the other hand, knowledge of the abstract frequency
characteristics is only a useful tool for the mathematical
representation of the biological system: the mathematical
representation (transfer function or the law of the system)
does not tell much concerning the biological, physical or
chemical properties of the system. It merely helps to
identify the frequency positions of all the components
without determining the exact nature (biological, physical
or chemical nature) of these components. Using the measured
frequency characteristics, (i.e. having knowledge of different system components), the investigator should search
for other parameters or methods in order to have a clearer
idea of the inside of the black box (studied system). In
other words, he has to try to *elucidate the black box*. Since
the determination of systems mathematical characteristics
alone does not allow statements about the biophysical
(biological and physical, the combination of biological and
physical) nature of the phenomenon, we have the difficult
problem of establishing a *"biological systems analysis
theory"*. This theory should contain the classical analysis
tools of general systems theory, but it should also deal
with some supplementary experimental methods and *"methods*

of thought" according to the special nature of the living systems.

In this book we will try to establish two programs for the determination of a systems theory of biological mechanisms or processes. First of all we will classify the measured data of biological processes in two categories:

1- Stationary biological processes

2- Nonstationary biological processes

In other words the variables (or outputs) of the biological systems will have stationary or nonstationary characteristics. For example, the heart beat presents a stationary process under normal conditions, i.e. a process which remains the same during a certain time. The periodicity and the shape of the cardiac pressure output, ECG, and other different parameters, do not change during minutes or even hours when the whole body is not influenced by external conditions. On the contrary, the electrical activity of the brain is a typical example of nonstationary biological processes. The spontaneous electrical activity of the brain changes permanently, without changes in external conditions. Within a fraction of a second the spontaneous activity can change from one stage to another (see Chapter 7).

Therefore the investigators who perform experiments in order to study the electrical activity of the brain have to consider the electrical activity of the brain as a nonstationary biological process.

We do not assume that the rules and methods of the programs of biological systems analysis which we will present in this book will be responsive to all kinds of problems arising in the study of biological systems. But the application of these methods is usually necessary, and they can supply the biological systems investigator with useful information.

First of all we will establish a biological systems analysis program for *stationary physiological processes*.

Before establishing "A program for biological systems analysis", we will first assume that this program will have two main classes of methods:

1. *Abstract Methods of General Systems Theory*

2. *Specific Methods for Living Systems*

Fig. 3.2 presents these two main classes of methods schematically along with their subdivisions. When the rules or methods of these two categories (or groups of methods) are combined, efficient results to elucidate the

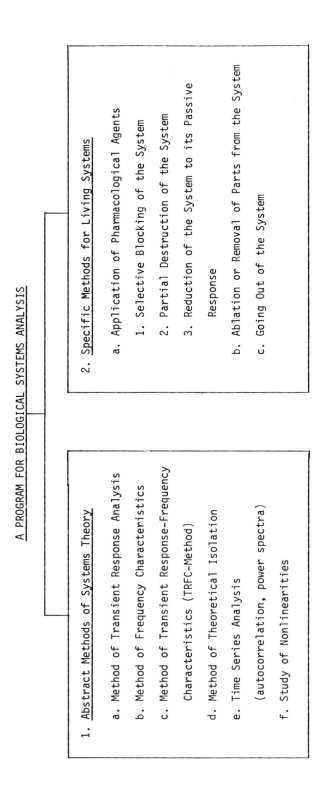

Fig. 3.2

black box studied can be obtained. We will now define all
these rules and methods, giving examples in order to clarify
what they are and how to use them.

3.2 ABSTRACT METHODS OF GENERAL SYSTEMS ANALYSIS

a. Method of Transient Response Analysis

This method consists of the study of a system through
the application of either step or impulse functions at the
input of the system. Fig. 3.4 shows transient responses
(response to impulse and step functions) of the electronic
circuit of Fig. 3.3.

The method of transient responses has the following
advantages. The observer immediately sees the responses of
the system under study when sudden changes (jumps or steps)
in the input function do occur. The greatest disadvantage
of the method stems from the fact that distinct components
of the system studied are not visible in the transient
response. When two, three or more components exist in the
system response, the observer cannot distinguish these
different components without further mathematical analysis.
In Chapters 4 and 7 we see these disadvantages, studying
basic examples. Usually physiologists prefer the method of
transient analysis, but their peak identification is often
erroneous. Simple-looking system transient responses some-

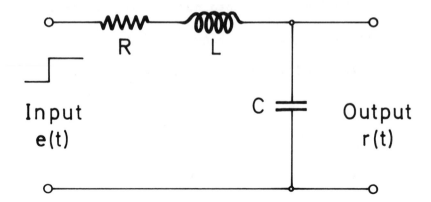

Fig. 3.3. A resonant electronic network (RCL-circuit).
         e(t): Input function (excitation),
         r(t): Response function.

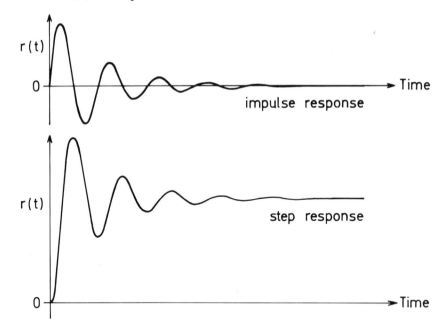

Fig. 3.4. Impulse and step responses of the network of
         Fig. 3.3. Although the network of Fig. 3.3 has
         only one resonance maximum in the frequency
         domain, the transient responses (impulse or step
         responses) depict several peaks (or waves).

times have a large number of components and vice versa, a

large number of peaks in the transient response do not

necessarily reveal the existence of a large number of system

components. (For verification of these remarks the reader

should see the examples in Chapter 7.)

b. *Method of Frequency Characteristics*

This method consists of the measurement of the ampli-

tude and phase characteristics of the system under investi-

gation. Functions $|G(j\omega)|$ and $\phi(\omega)$, which determine the

relative amplitude and phase of the forced oscillations as

functions of the frequency ω ($\omega=2\pi f$), are called, respec-

tively, amplitude and phase characteristics of the system.

The method of determining the amplitude, $|G(j\omega)|$, and the

phase angle, ϕ, is as follows: we apply a sinusoidal signal,

having a frequency, f, to the system. After a certain period

sufficient for the damping of the transient, only forced

oscillations will remain, having the frequency of the signal

(linearity of the system assumed). We measure the frequency,

f, of the applied signal, its amplitude, the amplitude of

the output (forced oscillations of the system under study)

and the phase difference between input and output. We perform

our measurements, gradually increasing the frequency from

$f=0$ to $f=f_0$, where the amplitude of the output becomes so

small that our measuring apparatus no longer responds.
Curves of the ratio of the output amplitude to the amplitude
of the applied signal and those of the phase difference
between output and the applied signal will represent the
amplitude and phase characteristics of the system respectively (SOLODOVNIKOV, 1960).

Fig. 3.6 shows the amplitude frequency and phase
frequency characteristics of the electronic circuit of
Fig. 3.5.

Although this measuring method is usually valid only
for linear systems, it can also be applied to nonlinear
systems. This is argued with examples in Chapter 6.

From the transient responses of the electronic
circuit presented in Fig. 3.5, we cannot immediately derive
or understand the different components which exist in the
system. But the frequency characteristics clearly depict the
number and frequency positions of the subsystems under study.
The amplitude maxima in Fig. 3.6 allow us to understand the
different components of this system without the need of
further analysis. This is the advantage of the frequency
characteristics method (FC-Method) against the transient

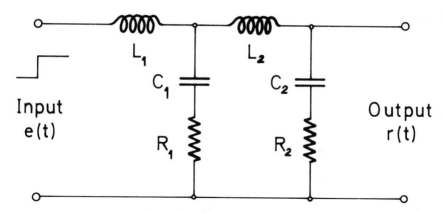

Fig. 3.5. An electronic network with two RCL-Circuits.
       e(t): Input function (excitation),
       r(t): Response function.

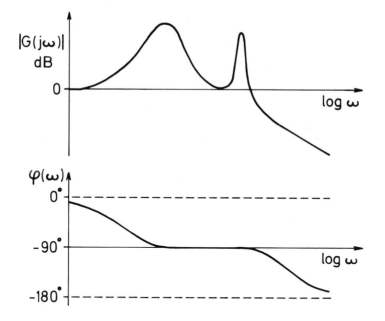

Fig. 3.6. Amplitude and phase characteristics of the
       electronic network of Fig. 3.5. The Amplitude
       Characteristic depicts two different maxima.

response method. The disadvantage of the FC-Method is the difficulty arising from the necessity of time-consuming experiments. As we will see in the next section, this difficulty can be greatly reduced using the TRFC-Method (Transient Response-Frequency Characteristics Method).

The frequency characteristics method enables the experimenter to analyze the components or subsystems of the system studied in the frequency domain. We will see a few examples of how the frequency characteristic curves allow component analysis and explanations concerning the biophysical system studied. However, we should emphasize here, that not all the components, or subsystems, can always be detected by this method. Biological systems are usually complicated and, especially, *compound systems*. Often one of the subsystems or components can mask other smaller subsystems and make them immeasurable. Therefore we would like to point out that in cases like this (as is also the case in other circumstances), the experimenter must be very careful during the analysis of his system. This is one of the greatest problems for the experimenter when he tries to elucidate his black box. The knowledge of the frequency characteristics offers the biological systems analyst a very important tool. But this is only *a tool* and *not a key*

for everything. Therefore in "the biological systems
analysis program" proposed in this book, we try to enlarge
the classical mathematical systems theory methods in order
to be able to elucidate the black box under study. JOHN VON
NEUMANN (1966) in his ingenious work "Theory of Self-Reproducing Automata" describes the relation of mathematics and
physics as follows:

> "In pure mathematics the really powerful meth-
> ods are only effective when one already has
> some *intuitive connection* with the subject,
> when one already has, before a proof has been
> carried out, some *intuitive insight*, some
> expectation which, in a majority of cases,
> proves to be right."...."A very great difficulty
> in any new kind of mathematics is that there
> is a vicious circle; you are at a terrible
> disadvantage in applying the proper pure math-
> ematical methods unless you already have a
> reasonably intuitive heuristic relation to the
> subject and unless you have had some substantive
> mathematical successes in it already."

We may translate this point of view to the analysis
of biological systems. We can see examples of this point of
view in studying some biological systems.

We do not study in this book, in detail, the method
of frequency characteristics; we also do not analyze the
relationship between transfer function and sinusoidal

response. There are excellent books and reviews on this matter. The reader should refer to BLESSER (1969), TRUXAL (1955), GRODINS (1963), SOLODOVNIKOV (1960).

c. TRFC-Method (Method of Transient Response-Frequency Characteristics)

General systems theory states that any linear system can be fully described either in the time domain or in the frequency domain (with frequency characteristics). All information concerning the frequency characteristics of a linear system is contained in the transient response of the system and, conversely, all information concerning the time response of the system is contained in the frequency characteristics of the system. In other words, knowledge of the transient response of a system allows one to predict how this system would react to different input (stimulation) frequencies, if the stimulating signal were sinusoidally modulated. If the step response of a system (time response of the system to a step function) or the impulse response is known, the frequency characteristics, $G(j\omega)$, of this system can be obtained with a Laplace transform (one sided Fourier transform) of the following form:

$$G(j\omega) = \int_0^\infty d/dt \ \{c(t)\} \ exp(-j\omega t) \ dt \tag{1}$$

or

$$G(j\omega) = \int_0^\infty exp(-j\omega t) \ d\{c(t)\} \tag{2}$$

$$G(j\omega) = \int_0^\infty exp(-j\omega t) \ \lambda(t) \ dt \tag{3}$$

$G(j\omega)$ represents the frequency characteristics of the system; $c(t)$ = step response of the system; $\lambda(t)$ = impulse response; $\omega = 2\pi f$, where f is the frequency of the input signal.

The amplitude frequency characteristics, $|G(j\omega)|$, and the phase angle, $\phi(\omega)$, can be obtained by numerical evaluation with the help of a digital computer. The numerical evaluation of the transform (2) is as follows:

$$|G(j\omega)|$$

$$= \sqrt{\left(\sum_{n=1}^N (\cos\omega t_n) \cdot \Delta c(t_n)\right)^2 + \left(\sum_{n=1}^N (\sin\omega t_n) \cdot \Delta c(t_n)\right)^2} \tag{4}$$

$$\Phi(\omega) \;=\; \text{arc tg} \left[\frac{- \displaystyle\sum_{n=1}^{N} (\sin\omega t_n) \cdot \Delta c(t_n)}{\displaystyle\sum_{n=1}^{N} (\cos\omega t_n) \cdot \Delta c(t_n)} \right] \tag{5}$$

More details concerning this mathematical method are given in references (BAŞAR and WEISS, 1968).

Although this transform is valid only for linear systems, it can be applied to nonlinear systems as a first approach. In the study of the circulatory system (Chapter 4) and in the study of the dynamics of the brain (Chapter 7), this method gave good results, although the systems under investigation have nonlinear characteristics. (The reliability of the TRFC-Method will be discussed in following chapters.)

We recommend here the use of the TRFC-Method, especially since the analysis of biological frequency characteristics takes up so much time, and errors resulting from the length of measurements are larger than the errors due to system nonlinearities. During investigation of brain evoked potentials it is quite impossible to obtain frequency characteristics because of the rapid transition of the brain's activity from one stage to another. In Chapter 4 we will give a very striking example of the necessity of using the TRFC-Method (the obtaining of frequency characteristics in the study of the coronary system of the heart, section 4.6).

In mathematical literature, the TRFC-Method is simply called one-sided Fourier transform or the Laplace transform. We use the expression TRFC-Method in order to indicate that this method gives all the characteristics needed in the time and frequency domains. In particular, the physiology investigator is used to observing his experimental parameters in the time domain by obtaining the transient responses of the studied system. Using this method, he has, on one hand, the most often used physiological transient responses. Moreover, he can analyze the frequency contents or the components in the frequency domain. Therefore we find it more useful and descriptive to call this method the TRFC-Method.

d. The Method of Theoretical Isolation (TI-Method)
or Ideal Filtering Method.

The theoretical isolation method is the ideal theoretical filtering of the transient response of a system in such a way that a selective blocking of one or more components (or subsystems) is obtained. Ideal filters are defined as transmission systems which within a predetermined band of frequencies, transfer the input signal without any change in amplitude and with a fixed (independent of frequency) time shift. Outside this band they have zero transmission (or vice versa, depending on whether the filter has a band-pass or a band-stop characteristic). They are not physically realizable, but they should be considered as useful analytical tools when the contribution made to a signal by a frequency band is to be deduced without any distortion.

Let us assume a system $G(j\omega)$ which should result from the interconnections of the subsystems $G_1(j\omega)$, $G_2(j\omega)$, $G_3(j\omega)$,..., $G_K(j\omega)$,..., $G_N(j\omega)$ - in such a way that:

$$G(j\omega) = G_1 \cdot G_2 \cdot G_3 \cdots G_K \cdots G_N \qquad \text{(see Fig. 3.7)}$$

If we already know the amplitude frequency characteristics of the system $G(j\omega)$ under study, and we further want to know how the transient system response would be

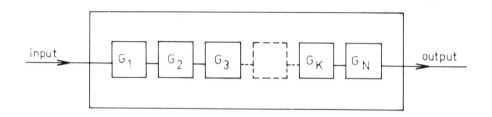

Fig. 3.7. For explanation see text

affected if one or more of the components of the system

were missing, we first of all determine the frequency

band limits of the component to be eliminated (or the

component which should be removed from the system). For

example if the subsystem (or component) $G_K(j\omega)$ is to be

rejected from the system $G(j\omega)$ of Fig. 3.7, the process

used consists of the following steps:

1. Method of Transient Response-Frequency Character-

istics (TRFC-Method): the amplitude characteristic, $|G(j\omega)|$,

of the system under study is obtained by means of Laplace

transform (or one-sided Fourier transform) using the

transient evoked response, c(t), with the method previously

described (section 3.2 (c)).

$$|G(j\omega)| = |L(d\{c(t)\}/dt)| \qquad (1)$$

$$= \left| \int_0^\infty exp(-j\omega t)\ d\{c(t)\} \right| \qquad (2)$$

2. Frequency band limits of theoretical filters are

determined according to the frequency and band-width of

amplitude maxima in the amplitude characteristic, $|G(j\omega)|$.

3. After determination of ideal filter characteristics

in the frequency domain, $G_F(j\omega)$, the weighting function,

$g_F(t)$, of this filter is computed by means of the inverse
Fourier transform:

$$g_F(t) = F^{-1}\{G_F(j\omega)\}$$

$$= \frac{1}{2\pi} \int\limits_{-\infty}^{+\infty} \Big(|G_F(j\omega)|\ exp(-j\omega\tau)\Big) exp(j\omega t)\ d\omega \qquad (3)$$

By taking τ to be equal to zero, any fixed or frequency-
dependent time shift (which would have been inevitable in
the case of a real electrical filter) can easily be avoided.

4. The experimentally obtained transient evoked
response, $c(t)$, is theoretically filtered by means of the
convolution integral using the weighting function, $g_F(t)$, of
adequately determined ideal filter:

$$c_F(t) = g_F(t)*c(t)$$

$$= \int\limits_{-\infty}^{+\infty} g_F(\tau)\cdot c(t-\tau)\ d\tau \qquad (4)$$

$c_F(t)$ is the filtered evoked response.

Since the time response is available in the form of
discrete data whose sampling interval is Δt, the integrals

(2), (3) and (4) are replaced with iterative summation.
Evaluation of integrals (2) and (3) is achieved by using
Fast Fourier Algorithm.

The entire process is given below schematically:

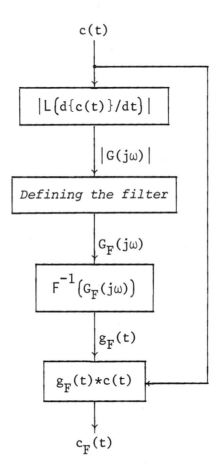

c(t)

$$|L(d\{c(t)\}/dt)|$$

$|G(j\omega)|$

Defining the filter

$G_F(j\omega)$

$$F^{-1}(G_F(j\omega))$$

$g_F(t)$

$$g_F(t)*c(t)$$

$c_F(t)$

(After BAŞAR and UNGAN, 1973)

Amplitude and phase characteristics of an ideal
pass-band filter and its weighting function are shown in
Fig. 3.8.

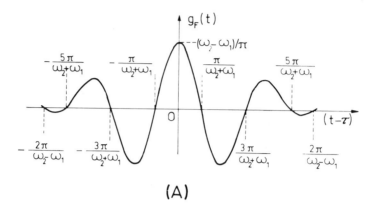

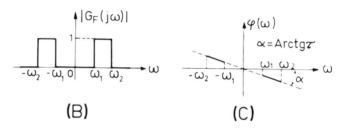

Fig. 3.8. Weighting function (A), amplitude (B) and phase
          (C) characteristics of an ideal pass-band filter.
          (After BAŞAR and UNGAN, 1973)

The method of theoretical isolation has a very important advantage in the study of biological systems: usually
it is very difficult to remove or attenuate subsystems from
the biological system under investigation. But, if the frequency characteristics of the system are known, we can do it
theoretically by using the TI-Method. This is the theoretical version of the method of selective blocking by application of pharmacological agents or by surgical ablation
techniques. Fig. 3.9 describes the theoretical isolation
method schematically with systems theory symbols.

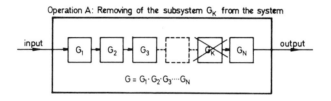

Operation A: Removing of the subsystem G_K from the system

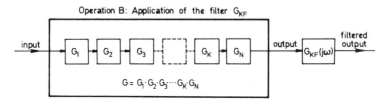

Operation B: Application of the filter G_{KF}

Fig. 3.9 A schematical explanation of theoretical isolation
performed using the method of Ideal Filtering. The
contribution of the subsysystem G_K to the overall
system output is eliminated by direct removal of G_K
in the operation A. The same result is achieved by
the operation B using a properly defined ideal
filter, $G_{KF}(j\omega)$, without disturbing the system
under study. (After BAŞAR et al., 1975a)

Although some electronic filtering methods have

already been used in the study of brain waves and evoked

potentials, the theoretical filtering method presented

here gives us the possibility to choose amplitude and phase

frequency characteristics of the filters separately. There-

fore, the investigator can apply ideal filters *without phase*

shift. It is also possible to use filters with exact char-

acteristics and change them adequately according to the

amplitude characteristic of the system under study. There-

fore the use of theoretical filters is much simpler and more

flexible than the use of electronic filters.

Definition of different ideal filters:

Low-pass filters are filters which provide attenuation in frequencies higher than a desired cutoff frequency, f_c. For example, a low-pass filter with $f_c=10$ Hz provides attenuation in frequencies between 10 and ∞ Hz. An ideal low-pass filter allows zero transmission, i.e. provides infinite attenuation in frequencies higher than f_c.

Pass-band filters are filters which allow, in a desired frequency band, the maximum transmission from input to output. In other frequency bands, the output is negligible compared to the input (in an ideal filter, in other frequency bands, the transmission is zero).

Stop-band filters are filters which provide attenuation in a desired frequency band so that the output is negligible compared to the input. For example, a stop-band filter between 10 and 20 Hz acts in such a way that the output between 10 and 20 Hz is negligible compared with the input. An ideal stop-band filter allows zero transmission, i.e. provides infinite attenuation for frequencies within the band limits.

We should mention here that the choice of filters used can be made independently of any frequency characteris-

tics. The choice can be arbitrary. We will also see an
example where, with the help of filters, we will check the
accuracy of the power spectra of free-running smooth muscle
oscillations (Chapter 5). Important examples are given in
Chapter 7. This chapter, especially, shows how powerful this
method is when one intends to achieve a component analysis
in the study of the biological systems.

> e. *Study of the Intrinsic Oscillatory Behavior of
> Biological Systems. Autocorrelation Function and
> Power Spectrum.*

Most biological systems show intrinsic oscillatory
behavior. Often, the oscillatory character of measured
biological data is not strong enough, and the biology
investigators do not consider them as important parameters
of the biological systems. However, there are a large number
of biological systems where the oscillatory character plays
a major role in the understanding of their functional
structure. The brain, the circulatory system and smooth
muscles are biological systems where the intrinsic oscillatory behavior has been investigated carefully. Visual
inspection alone of the time histories of the recorded
biological oscillation does not give information of noise
content, real periodicities or multiperiodicities revealed

in a system. Therefore the use of autocorrelation functions and power spectral density functions finds important
application in the study of biological oscillators.

Autocorrelation Function

The autocorrelation function for random data describes
the general dependence of the values of the data at one time
on the values at another time (BENDAT and PIERSOL, 1967).
Fig. 3.10 illustrates a sample time history record x(t).

An estimate for the autocorrelation function between
the values of x(t) at times t and t+τ may be obtained by
taking the product of the two values and averaging over the
observation period T. The resulting average product will
approach an exact autocorrelation function as T approaches
infinity. The autocorrelation function is defined mathematically as follows:

$$R_{xx}(\tau) = \lim_{T \to \infty} \frac{1}{T} \int_0^T x(t) \cdot x(t+\tau)\ dt \qquad (1)$$

Given a sample of a physical (and/or biological)
time history record x(t) from a stationary random signal,
the autocorrelation function $R_{xx}(\tau)$ for the signal is
estimated as follows:

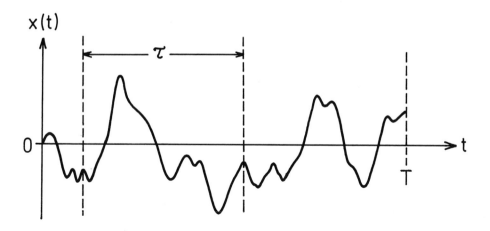

Fig. 3.10. A sample time history record x(t).

$$R_{xx}(\tau) = \frac{1}{T} \int_{0}^{T} x(t) \cdot x(t+\tau) \ dt \qquad\qquad (2)$$

In words, the autocorrelation function is estimated by the following operations:

1. The signal is delayed by a time displacement equal to τ (the lag time).

2. The signal value at any instant is multiplied by the value which has been recorded τ seconds before.

3. The instantenous product value (of # 2) is averaged over the sampling time T.

By moving the lag time τ over the sampling time T, a

plot of the autocorrelation function $R_{xx}(\tau)$ versus lag time
(an autocorrelogram) is obtained.

The estimated autocorrelation function for discrete
data at the displacement rh according to (2) is defined by:

$$R_r = R_{xx}(rh) = \frac{1}{N-r} \sum_{n=1}^{N-r} x_n \cdot x_{n+r} \qquad (3)$$

$$(r = 0, 1, 2, \ldots, m)$$

where

h = sampling interval (N=T/h)

r = lag number

m = maximum lag number

R_r= estimate of the autocorrelation function at lag
number r (corresponding to the displacement τ=rh).

The most important application for the evaluation of
the autocorrelation function of biological (or physical)
data is to determine the influence of values at any time
over values at a future time. The autocorrelation function
can be viewed as an average measure of the relation of the
value of random processes at one instant of time to the value
at another instant of time τ seconds later. A sine wave, or
any other deterministic data, will have an autocorrelation

function which persists over all time displacements.

Therefore autocorrelation measurement clearly provides a

powerful tool for detecting deterministic data which might

be masked in a random background.

Power Spectral Density Function

The autocorrelation function can be viewed as a

measure of the frequency content of the sample function. The

frequency content can be displayed more explicitly by forming

the Fourier transform of the autocorrelation function.

Specifically, for stationary data, the two functions (power

spectrum and autocorrelation function are related by a

Fourier transform as follows:

$$S_{xx}(f) = 2 \int_{-\infty}^{\infty} R_{xx}(\tau) \; exp(-j\pi f\tau) \; d\tau$$

$$= 4 \int_{0}^{\infty} R_{xx}(\tau) \; cos(2\pi f\tau) \; d\tau$$

(4)

(WIENER-KHINCHIN relation (SOLODOVNIKOV, 1960))

The estimated power spectral density function for

discrete data is defined by:

$$S_k = 2h \left(R_0 + 2 \sum_{r=1}^{m-1} R_r \cdot cos\{\frac{\pi rk}{m}\} \cdot (-1)^k \cdot R_m \right) \tag{5}$$

$$(k = 0, 1, 2, \ldots, m)$$

The values of power spectral density are then
smoothed according to the Hanning method as follows:

$$S_0 = 0.5\,S_0 + 0.5\,S_1$$

$$S_k = 0.25\,S_{k-1} + 0.5\,S_k + 0.25\,S_{k+1} \qquad (k = 1,\, 2,\, 3,\, \ldots,\, m-1)$$

$$S_m = 0.5\,S_{m-1} + 0.5\,S_m$$

For the mathematical details and more theoretical
background on the autocorrelation and power spectral density
functions, the reader should refer to literature (BENDAT and
PIERSOL, 1967; SOLODOVNIKOV, 1960).

We want to point out here that any study of the
oscillatory behavior of biological systems should include the
use of the mathematical tools described above. Although the
power spectral density function supplies the investigator
with more explicit results, the autocorrelation function
supplies him with a direct measure for the periodicities of
the studied signals.

f. *Study of Nonlinearities*

The search for sources of nonlinearities can give
useful information about the nature of the biological system
under study. Therefore the study of nonlinearities can serve

as a key to the understanding of the system.

The nonlinear behavior of biological systems and the knowledge we derive from the nonlinearities will be handled in an extended manner in Chapter 6. Therefore, the reader should refer to Chapter 6, in order to have an understanding of the biological nonlinearities and in order to use these considerations as a tool in biological systems analysis. We mention here only that the study of nonlinearities should be considered as an important part of the "Biological Systems Analysis Program" which is given in the present chapter.

3.3. SPECIFIC METHODS FOR LIVING SYSTEMS

The specific methods for living systems presented under Fig. 3.2 of our biological systems analysis program are usually well known and applied by biologists, physiologists, biochemists and pharmacologists. Therefore we will mention them without going into details.

a. Application of Pharmacological Agents.

From the point of view of systems description we can classify the application of pharmacological agents into different categories.

1. Selective Blocking of the System:
One of the components (or subsystems) of the system under

study is blocked. This blocking can be reversible or

irreversible depending on the nature of the agent used.

Fig. 3.11 shows the systems theoretical explanation of a

hypothetical system $G(j\omega)$ where one of the components is

blocked.

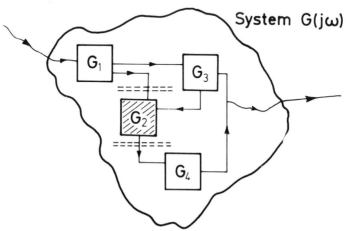

Fig. 3.11 System schematical representation which shows the
         blocking of the subsystem G_2 of the system $G(j\omega)$.
         The pharmacological agent blocks the signal
         transfer between G_1 and G_4.

   2. Partial Destruction of the System:

One of the components of the system under study is

removed or destroyed (Fig. 3.12). (Examples in Chapters 5

and 7.)

   3. Reduction of the System to its Passive Response.

All the biological components of the system under

study are removed or blocked (Fig. 3.13). Examples:

1. After perfusion of a circulatory system with papaverine,

the vasoactive activity of the system is destroyed. The
circulatory system then acts as a physical system with
only hydrodynamic properties. 2. When an isolated frog nerve
is killed with ammonium or strychnine, the nerve still acts
as an electrical cable when electrical stimulation is
applied to one end of it.

b. *Ablation or Removal of Parts from the System.*

Thalamectomy (removal of thalamus), isolated cortex
preparations, and lesion making in different structures of
the brain are examples for this case.

c. *Going Out of the System.*

Search for the mechanisms responsible or for components outside of the studied system (explanation and examples in Chapter 4 and 7).

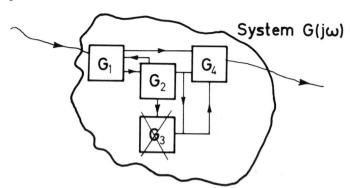

Fig. 3.12. Systems schematical description which shows the
destruction of the component G_3 of the system
$G(j\omega)$.

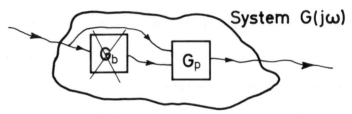

Fig. 3.13. The system will be reduced to its passive
           response.
           G_b= Biological components of the studied system.
           G_p= Physical components of the studied system.

3.4. SYSTEMS ANALYSIS PROGRAM FOR NONSTATIONARY

BIOLOGICAL PROCESSES OR MECHANISMS.

For the study of nonstationary biological processes
we propose a program which in the main has the same features
as the program for stationary mechanisms. But in the study
of nonstationary processes, the signals or measured variables
of the system must undergo a preliminary signal processing.
Some of these methods are often used in communication engineering, in oceanography, in the study of seismic waves, in
nuclear physics etc. In the study of biological systems these
methods find their main application field in brain research.
Some of these preliminary signal processing methods are

   1. Signal averaging

   2. Wiener filtering

   3. Selective averaging

The signal averaging method is one of the methods with
extended area of application in the study of the evoked

potentials of the brain (Chapter 7). The method of Wiener
filtering has been very recently proposed in the study of
electrical activities of the brain. The method of selective
averaging will be described in Chapter 7, and helps us to
select the signals from different brain stages.

To give an example, we can mention the signal
averaging method: when we want to analyze the transient
evoked responses of the brain, before applying the program
of Fig. 3.2, we first obtain the evoked potentials with the
signal averaging, Wiener filtering or selective averaging
method. After this preliminary signal processing, the potential which we want to analyze can be considered as a
response signal which does not contain background noise
and which represents the response in an almost stationary
stage. Only then can we apply the proposed biological signal
analysis program.

In this chapter we do not describe these preliminary
signal processing methods, explained in detail in Chapter 7.
In Chapter 7, we show several examples of the problems of
brain electrical activity. (We need those examples in order
to make these methods fully understandable.)

REFERENCES

Başar, E., A. Gönder, Ç. Özesmi, and P. Ungan: Dynamics of brain rhythmic and evoked potentials. I. Some computational methods for the analysis of electrical signals from the brain. Biol. Cybernetics 20, 137-143 (1975).

Başar, E., and P. Ungan: A component analysis and principles derived for the understanding of evoked potentials of the brain: studies in the hippocampus. Kybernetik 12, 133-140 (1973).

Başar, E., und Ch. Weiss: Analyse des Frequenzganges druckinduzierter Änderungen des Strömunswiderstandes isolierter Rattennieren. Pflügers Arch. 304, 121-135 (1968).

Bendat, J.S., and A.G. Piersol: Measurement and Analysis of Random Data. John Wiley and Sons Inc., New York (1967).

Blesser, W.B.: A Systems Approach to Biomedicine. McGraw-Hill Book Company, New York (1969).

Grodins, S.F.: Control Theory and Biological Systems. Columbia University Press, New York (1963).

von Neumann, J.: Theory of Self-Reproducing Automata. University of Illinois Press, (1966).

Solodovnikov, V.V.: Introduction to The Statistical Dynamics of Automatic Control Systems. Dover Publications Inc., New York (1960).

Truxal, J.G.: Automatic Feedback Control System Synthesis. McGraw-Hill Book Company, New York (1955).

Chapter 4

The Circulatory Autoregulation

In this chapter we really begin the biological systems analysis proper, in the sense that we are going to describe a biological system in a completely systems theoretical way. We have chosen this example because it is relatively simple, although not the simplest possible example. It is sufficiently complicated that it can stand as a prototype which can be generalized for the analysis of almost all biological systems. Thus, although we are dealing with a particular example, all the rules we mention are immediately generalizable, and these will be given so that one can see the general characteristics of a biological systems description. We begin with the phenomenon of the regulation of blood flow and the circulatory autoregulation.

4.1. INTRINSIC REGULATIONS OF CIRCULATION.

The circulatory system does not require continual control by the nervous system. Indeed, the circulation of a dog whose head has been guillotined and whose spinal cord has been destroyed by alcohol injection, still has intrinsic controls over arterial pressure, cardiac output, blood volume and local blood flow. It is these controls that regulate the circulation continuously, and that are mainly responsible for adjusting the blood flow in each individual tissue to accord with the tissue need (GUYTON, 1971). The ability of local tissue blood vessels to adjust their blood flow in response to the needs of the surrounding tissues is called *local blood flow regulation*.

The principles of vascular control, vascular activity, and the definitions concerning distensibility, resistance and capacitance of vessels are explained in a detailed and brilliant form by FOLKOW and NEIL (1971). In the mentioned book, which is written especially on circulatory phenomena, the reader will find excellent explanatory illustrations.

Usually the mechanism of local blood flow regulation maintains flow through each tissue almost exactly at that level required to supply the need of the tissues. The blood

flows first through very small arterioles and meta-arterioles
(terminal arterioles) before passing into the capillaries.
The arterioles have a strong muscular coat. The meta-
arterioles are surrounded by sparse but highly active smooth
muscle fibers. Finally, at each point where a capillary
leaves a meta-arteriole, a small muscular precapillary
sphincter surrounds the origin of the capillary (Fig. 4.1A,
B, C). The smooth muscle cells are usually arranged
circumferentially or helically in the wall (Fig. 4.1D).

The smooth muscle of the meta-arteriole of the
precapillary sphincters ordinarily has a high degree of
intrinsic tone: even without nervous impulses or hormonal
stimulation, the smooth muscle remains contracted to a
considerable degree. The function of the vascular smooth
muscle is to produce *active tension* by contraction under
physiological control and so change the diameter of the
lumen of the vessel and accordingly, the flow through the
vessel. The greatest manifestation of the control of smooth
muscle over the size of the lumen is in the arterioles,
where it is abundant. The arterioles, because of their small
lumenal size, can increase the total resistance to flow much
more than can the constriction of larger vessels.

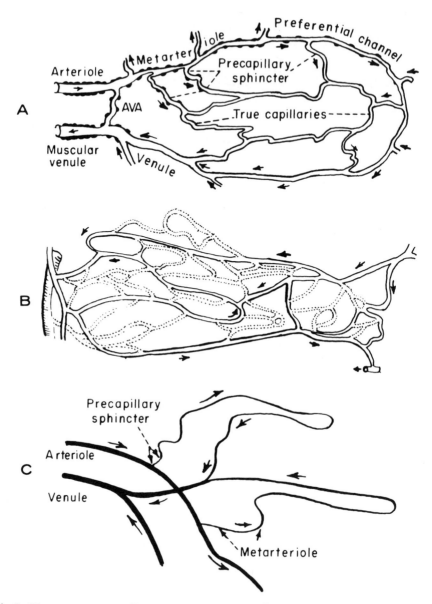

Fig. 4.1 Three types of pattern of terminal vascular beds.
        A, muscle, with the preferential channels. The
        location of smooth-muscle control vessels is
        indicated. B, the mesentery. The true capillaries
        are shown by the dotted lines. C, the unique hairpin
        capillary loops of the human nail bed. (After
        ZWEIFACH, Transactions of the Third Conference on
        Factors Regulating Blood Pressure in 1950)

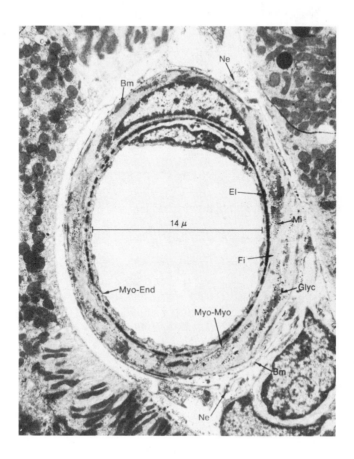

Fig. 4.1D Cross-section from an arteriole (aff. arteriole of
          the rat kidney) with the muscle layer composed
          of several smooth muscles, the nucleus of one seen
          at top. The muscle layer is surrounded by a base-
          ment membrane (Bm) and just outside this, non-
          myelinated sympathetic nerves (Ne) are seen. A thin
          elastic membrane (El) separates the smooth muscle
          layer from the endothelial cells, the nucleus of
          one seen at upper margin of endothelium.
          Membraneous contact are seen between muscle cells
          (Myo-Myo) and between muscle cells and the
          endothelium (Myo-End: "myoendothelial junctions").
          In the smooth muscle cells mitochondria (Mi) and
          particulate glycogen (Glyc) are scattered through-
          out the cytoplasm which is largely dominated by
          the myofilaments (Fi). (Courtesy of Dr. J. Rhodin,
          New York Medical College.) (After FOLKOW and NEIL,
          1971)

Terminal vascular beds differ greatly in different
regions of circulation. Microscopic observation of the
living microcirculation, as by ZWEIFACH (1939) and his
colleagues, and the modern method of injection of plastic
material to give casts of the small vessels, have begun
to give us the true picture (Fig. 4.1A, B, C). The reader who
is interested in the new findings in microcirculation is
referred to a recent review article by ZWEIFACH (1973).

Fig. 4.1D shows the cross-section from an arteriole
(afferent arteriole of the rat kidney), with the muscle layer
composed of several smooth muscles, the nucleus of one of
which may be seen at the top.

Watching a living vascular bed under the microscope
reveals that the flow in the capillaries is not steady, nor
uniform in direction. Instead, there is vasomotion, in which
individual capillaries are seen to close completely and then
reopen. This phenomenon is probably a result of the contraction of the arterioles.

4.2. AUTOREGULATION OF BLOOD FLOW WHEN THE ARTERIAL
PRESSURE CHANGES

Autoregulation has often been defined as the
intrinsic tendency of an organ to maintain constant blood

flow despite changes in arterial blood pressure (JOHNSON, 1964a). Fig. 4.9A shows an example of the autoregulation of the kidney (increase in the arterial pressure over values of 90 mm Hg, not any increase in flow).

The earliest experiments which gave evidence of an autoregulatory type of behavior were reported by BAYLISS in 1902. The question *"How does autoregulation occur"* is one of the most difficult questions to resolve among cardiovascular problems. The autoregulation of blood flow is observed in different organs such as the kidneys, the liver, the brain, the coronary system of the heart, hind limb, etc.

In this chapter we will apply the methods of systems theory to the autoregulating organs such as the rat kidney and the coronary system of the rat heart. We will describe experiments which should contribute to understanding the mechanism of autoregulation. But before doing this, we will review briefly the architecture of the vascular bed of the coronary system and of the kidney. It is not our aim in this chapter to resolve fully the problem of autoregulation, but we will try to make a systems approach which will help to understand the systems dynamics, and we will try to find the biological and physical correlates of the dynamic behavior of the circulatory autoregulation.

4.3 ARCHITECTURE OF THE TERMINAL VASCULAR BED IN THE

CORONARY VASCULAR SYSTEM AND IN THE KIDNEY

Coronary Vascular System: Vascular network in the
walls of the heart.

The coronary circulatory system is the vascular
network which exists in the walls of the heart for its own
nourishment. The course and distribution of the major
coronary arteries in all mammalian groups is remarkably
similar. The basic anatomical patterns are thus comparable
in the smallest to the largest mammals (GREGG and FISHER,
1963).

The main coronary arteries, the left and the right,
arise from the sinus of Valsava, near the aortic valvular
ring. The left coronary artery supplies the left ventricle
plus the anterior half of the septum. The right coronary
artery supplies the right ventricle and the posterior half
of the septum. There are many anastomoses of the two systems
at the apex, and the left coronary artery can also supply
the apex of the right ventricle. (:: Arteriovenous
anastomoses are direct connections between terminal arteries
and veins. The anastomoses short-circuit (or act as a shunt)
around the capillary system fed by their arterioles. Fig. 4.2
shows the structure of arteriovenous anastomoses ::).

The capillary network which the arteries supply is unusually rich, so that each heart muscle cell is very close to a capillary. Venous drainage follows the usual pattern of venules, collecting veins and finally the single coronary veins reaching the right atrium at the coronary sinus, where about 90% of the coronary flow empties. A schematical representation of the coronary vascular system is shown in Fig. 4.3. For detailed information on the functional anatomy of the blood supply to the heart see references (GREGG and FISHER, 1963).

Kidney and Functional Architecture of the Renal Circulation.

The circulatory network in the kidneys has the following course: Renal artery → interlobar artery → arcuate arteries → the afferent arterioles → the glomerulus → the efferent arterioles → capillary network around the tubuli → interlobar vein → renal vein.

Major distribution of the renal artery in the dog is shown in Fig. 4.4, while Fig. 4.5 shows division of the interlobar artery into arcuate arteries (Arc I, Arc II, Arc III). The afferent arterioles usually supply one glomerulus.

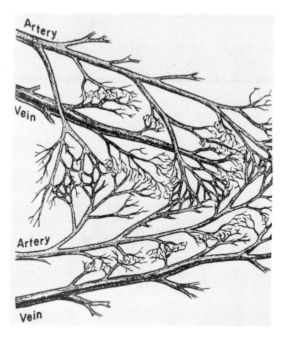

Fig. 4.2 Anastomoses of the coronary arterial system.
         (After GUYTON, 1971)

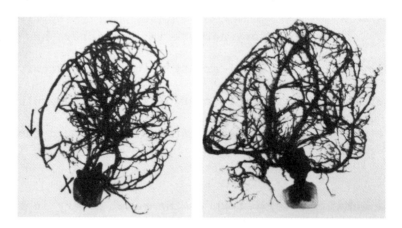

Fig. 4.3 Casts of the coronary arterial system of the dog
         Heart. (From A. C. Burton: PHYSIOLOGY AND BIOPHYSICS
         OF THE CIRCULATION, 2nd edition. Copyright © 1972
         by Year Book Medical Publishers, Inc., Chicago. Used
         by permission. Courtesy of D. Busby.)

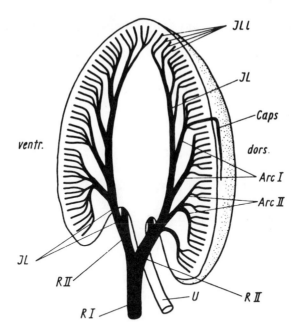

Fig. 4.4   Horizontal section through the dog kidney. RI and
RII: renal artery and primary branches; Arc I and
Arc II: primary and secondary arcuate arteries; JL:
interlobar artery; JL1: interlobular artery; Caps:
capsular artery; U: aorta. (After VON KÜGELGEN,
et al., 1959)

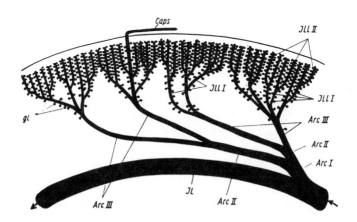

Fig. 4.5 Schema of the finer arterial supply of the dog
kidney. gl: glomerulus with vas afferens. (After
VON KÜGELGEN, et al., 1959)

Each kidney contains about 1,000,000 *nephrons* the functional units of the kidney. In physiological literature, usually not the entire kidney, but merely the activities of a single nephron are discussed in order to explain the function of the kidney. GUYTON (1971) describes the functional architecture of the renal circulation as follows: the nephron is composed basically of (1) *a glomerulus* through which fluid is filtered out of the blood, (2) *a long tubule* in which the filtered fluid is converted into urine. Fig. 4.6 illustrates the basic anatomy of the nephron: blood enters the glomerulus through the afferent arteriole and then leaves through the efferent arteriole. The glomerulus is a network of 50 parallel capillaries enclosed in Bowman's capsule. After blood passes into the efferent arteriole from the glomerulus, most of it flows through the peritubular capillary network that surrounds the tubules. As we see in Fig. 4.6, there are two capillary beds supplying the nephron; (1) the glomerulus and (2) the peritubular capillaries. These two sets of capillaries are separated from each other by the efferent arteriole.

The basic function of the nephron is to clean the blood plasma of unwanted substances as it passes through the nephron. The mechanism by which the nephron clears the plasma

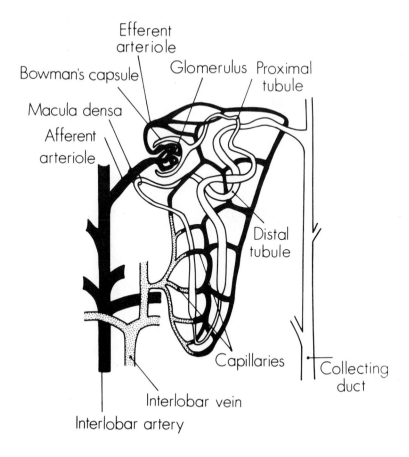

Fig. 4.6   Schematical representation of a nephron.
          (Modified after SMITH, 1959)

of unwanted substances is: (1) it filters a large proportion

of the plasma through the glomerulus into the tubules; (2) as

the filtered fluid flows through the tubules, the unwanted

substances fail to be reabsorbed while the wanted sub-

stances, especially water and many of the electrolytes, are

reabsorbed back into the plasma of the peritubular capil-

laries. The wanted portions are returned to the blood. The

unwanted portions pass into the urine. For more detailed

information on the functions and functional anatomy of the
kidneys see references (GUYTON, 1971; SMITH, 1959).

4.4. DIFFERENT HYPOTHESES OF AUTOREGULATION

Here we will review briefly some of the important
hypotheses of autoregulation.

Myogenic Hypothesis

JOHNSON (1964a) describes the myogenic hypothesis as
follows: the myogenic hypothesis supposes that there is an
intrinsic mechanism in the smooth muscle cells of the arteries or arterioles which responds to an increase in internal
pressure or tension in the wall with contraction. When the
transmural pressure across the vascular bed is increased by
increasing arterial or venous pressure around the organ, it
follows from the myogenic hypothesis that these vessels
should constrict. In other words, the vascular system of
the organ should respond to the pressure increase with a
maintained constriction.

Tissue Pressure Hypothesis

According to the tissue pressure hypothesis, autoregulation occurs in the low pressure vessels by the pressure
of tissue fluid on them. JOHNSON (1964a) describes one of
the several models of tissue pressure hypothesis as follows:

Elevation of arterial pressure in a capillary system will cause an outflow of fluid from the capillaries into the extravascular space. This outpouring of fluid will cause the perivascular pressure to increase because of a rigid container, or capsule, around the organ, which resists deformation (as is the case in the kidney). The tissue fluid will then encroach upon the blood vessels in the circuit. Since the venous vessels have the lowest internal pressure and little rigidity, they would be the most vulnerable to change in tissue pressure and should be the primary site of the change in resistance in the system, exhibiting tissue pressure autoregulation (JOHNSON, 1964a). Tissue pressure autoregulation can be demonstrated in a physical model because it does not require active response of blood vessels. This is a passive type of autoregulation.

Cell Separation Hypothesis

This hypothesis suggests a separation of the cells and plasma en route through the renal vascular bed (PAPPENHEIMER and KINTER, 1956). According to this hypothesis, the interlobar arteries and afferent arterioles act, producing skimming of plasma from the peripheral layers of the blood stream into the deep glomeruli, leaving a high hematocrit in the outer glomeruli. Autoregulation would occur by virtue of

the change in viscosity and, therefore, resistance to blood
flow as the blood passes into the other regions of the renal
cortex. As blood pressure and blood flow increase, viscosity
would also increase, tending to keep the blood flow constant
(JOHNSON, 1964a). This is also, like the tissue pressure
hypothesis, a passive type of autoregulation. Cell separation autoregulation can be demonstrated in a physical model
which does not incorporate the active response of blood
vessels.

Metabolic Hypothesis

The metabolic hypothesis is an active type of
autoregulation theory. The various metabolic hypotheses
are primarily based on the supposition that a decrease in
blood flow causes vascular relaxation by the accumulation of
vasodilator metabolites in the tissue or by a decreased
nutrient supply. A possible metabolic scheme of autoregulation is described by JOHNSON (1964b) as follows:

> "In a capillary system, reduction of arterial
> pressure may lead initially to decreased blood
> flow which increases the concentration of
> vasodilator tissue metabolites, causing vascu-
> lar relaxation. Decreased blood flow would also
> decrease tissue pO_2, possibly altering the
> metabolism of the tissue and increasing the
> production of vasodilator metabolites (BERNE,
> 1964)."

Another version of this theory can be described in the

following manner:

> "The lowered tissue pO_2 weakens the "tone" of
> the vascular smooth muscle and this leads to
> a metabolic type of autoregulation " (JOHNSON,
> 1964a).

Renin Angiotensin Hypothesis in the Kidney

THURAU assumes that any satisfactory understanding of

renal autoregulation must be based on an appreciation of the

role which renal blood flow plays in urine formation

(THURAU, 1964). The active sodium reabsorption in the

tubules of the kidney accounts for the major part of renal

metabolism, and if the kidney responds with vasoconstriction

when metabolism increases, this would lead to a reduction in

sodium load by means of decreased renal blood flow and

glomerular filtration rate.

THURAU (1964) proposes the following autoregulation

hypothesis:

> "Pressure increase in the arterioles leads
> first to an increase of the glomerular fil-
> tration rate and therefore to an increase of
> tubular Na^+ (sodium) load. The increase of the
> Na^+ concentration in the tubules consequently
> leads to the increase in sodium concentration
> in the loop of Henle. It is postulated that
> the macula densa segment of the nephron and
> the afferent arteriole are functionally con-

nected in such a way that the chemical composition of the intratubular urine at the
macula densa site, once it has passed the
proximal convolution and the loop of Henle,
regulates renin release, thus affecting the
tone of the afferent arteriole and the renal
flow resistance: a high sodium concentration
at the macula densa segment stimulates renin
release and a low sodium concentration inhib-
its renin release. (:: It has occasionally
been inferred that renin has to be secreted
into the blood stream in order to catalyse
the reaction of renin to Angiotensin I, which
is converted by an enzyme to Angiotensin
II::)."

To summarize, THURAU suggests that vasoconstriction
in the kidney is linked to metabolism in such a way that
renin angiotensin could be the transmitter system between
change in metabolism and the vascular smooth muscle.

4.5   PROBLEM AND THE EXPERIMENTAL PROCEDURES

The investigations which we will review in this
chapter were carried out using two different autoregulating organ preparations, the isolated and artificially perfused rat kidney and the coronary vascular
system of the isolated rat heart. For the perfusion, an
osmotically and colloidosmotically isotonic solution of
Haemaccel (Behringerwerke), a plasma substitute, was used.

In the case of the kidney, pressure signals, such as
slow ramps, pressure steps and sinusoidal pressure changes

of different frequencies were applied to the renal artery

through the aorta (Fig. 4.7).

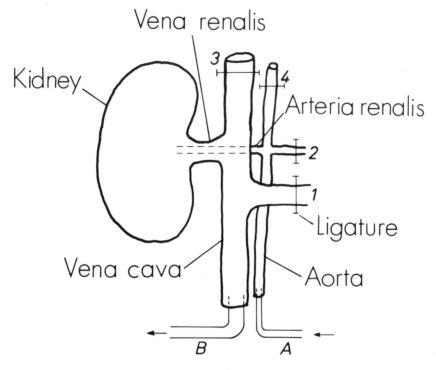

Fig. 4.7   Schema of the isolated right kidney of the rat.
           (A): The input pressure is applied in the aorta.
           (B): The flow is measured in vena cava.

The pressure was measured with a pressure transducer and the

flow recorded with the help of an electromagnetic flowmeter

in the venous side (vena cava) (Fig. 4.8A). During the studies

of the coronary vascular system, the isolated heart

preparation shown in Fig. 4.8B replaces the kidney in the

experimental setup. In this case, the input signals (pressure)

were applied to the aorta, and the flow through the coronary

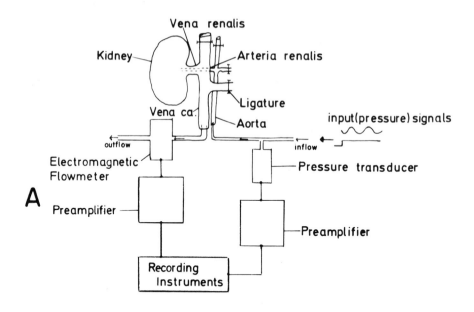

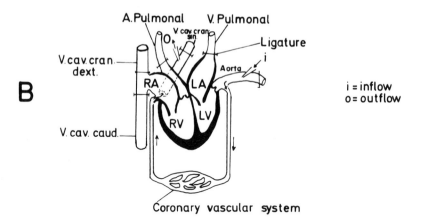

Fig. 4.8 (A): Schematical drawing of the experimental setup
with the isolated kidney preparation.
(B): Schematical drawing of the isolated rat heart.
During experiments on coronary system the
heart preparation replaces the kidney prepa-
ration in the experimental setup shown above.
(After BAŞAR, 1974 from T.-I.-T. Journal of
LIFE SCIENCES, Vol. 4, 1974 published by
TOWER INTERNATIONAL TECHNOMEDICAL INSTITUTE,
PHILADELPHIA)

vascular system was measured in the vena cava cranialis

sinistra. (Details of the experimental setup and organ pre-

paration have been published elsewhere, BAŞAR et al., 1968a,b.)

Fig. 4.9A shows the pressure-flow relationship of the

autoregulating rat kidney. Along the abscissa is the pres-

sure in mm Hg and along the ordinate, the corresponding flow

($\dot{V}$) in ml/min.g (g of kidney). As we see, the flow remains

relatively constant above pressure values of 100 mm Hg. On

addition of papaverine to the perfusion medium the autore-

gulation is abolished, (or the pressure induced autoregula-

tion is abolished and the autoregulating system is reduced to

its passive form).

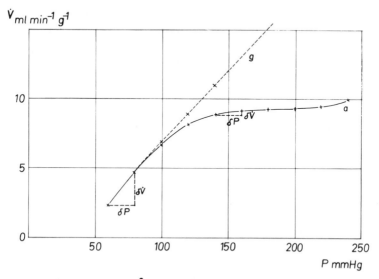

Fig. 4.9A   Flow-pressure ($\dot{V}$/p) relationship in the autoregulating isolated rat kidney. Upon addition of
papaverine to the perfusion medium the autoregulation is abolished (curve (g)). (After BAŞAR
et al., 1968b)

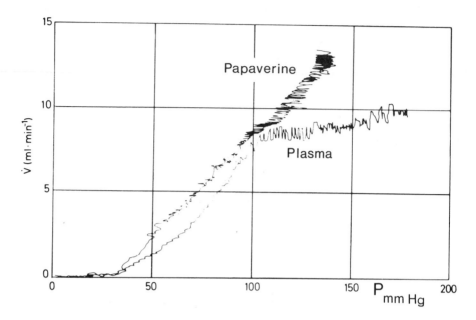

Fig. 4.9B Flow-pressure ($\dot{V}$/P) relationship in the autoreg-
         ulating coronary system of the rat heart. The
         curve indicated with "plasma" is the
         autoregulation curve obtained when the heart is
         perfused with standard medium (plasma substrate).
         Upon addition of papaverine to the perfusion
         medium the autoregulation is abolished. (After
         BAŞAR et al., 1968a)

Fig. 4.9B shows the flow-pressure relationship of the

autoregulating coronary system. Recording was made with an

X-Y plotter. The heart was fluttering at the time of this

recording. The recording time was about 1 min. (The pres-

sure was raised during 1 min period from 0 mm Hg to 180 mm

Hg.) Here again, the addition of papaverine abolishes auto-

regulation. The noisy character of the curves is due to the

spontaneous fluttering of the isolated rat heart.

4.6. DYNAMIC CHARACTERISTICS OF THE AUTOREGULATING

KIDNEY AND CORONARY SYSTEM

We now consider the pressure as the input and the flow as the output of the autoregulating organs under study. Our aim is the determination of the dynamics of both autoregulating organs (kidney and coronary system) using deterministic input signals.

Fig. 4.10A shows the response to a pressure step (or step function) of the autoregulating kidney. The input pressure was increased from 90 to 180 mm Hg. The flow reaches a maximal value, then it diminishes going through a minimum 5-10 secs after the pressure step. It rises slightly again and reaches a constant value about 45-60 secs after the pressure step.

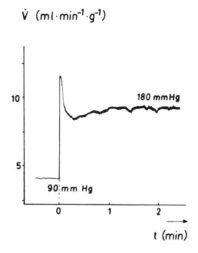

Fig. 4.10A Flow response of the isolated rat kidney to a pressure step from 90 to 180 mm Hg. (After BAŞAR and WEISS, 1968)

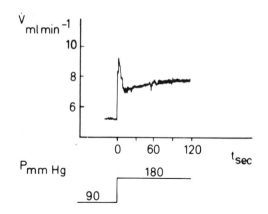

Fig. 4.10B Flow response of the coronary system of the
           isolated rat heart (upper curve) to a rectangular
           pressure step from 90 to 180 mm Hg. (After BAŞAR
           and WEISS, 1969)

The response of the autoregulating coronary system

(fibrillating heart) to an arterial pressure step in the

same range is basically similar (Fig. 4.10B). Only the first

seconds of the step responses are different, as we see in

Figs. 4.11A and 4.11B, where both responses are presented

with a longer time resolution. With the addition of papaverine

to the perfusion medium, curves with proportional behavior

are obtained (Fig. 4.12).

    Fig. 4.13 shows the frequency characteristics of the

autoregulating rat kidney. These frequency characteristics

are obtained using similar step responses as in Fig. 4.10A

and the TRFC-Method of section 3.2. Along the abscissa is the

frequency in logarithmic scale. Along the ordinate are:

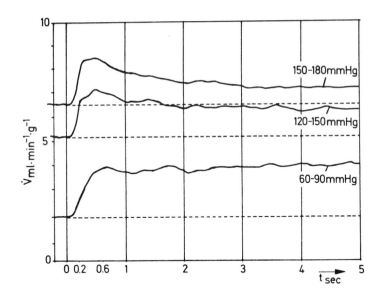

Fig. 4.11A. The first 5 seconds of flow response of the
            isolated rat kidney. The pressure values at
            the curves indicate the minimal and maximal
            values of the applied arterial pressure steps.
            (After BAŞAR and WEISS, 1968)

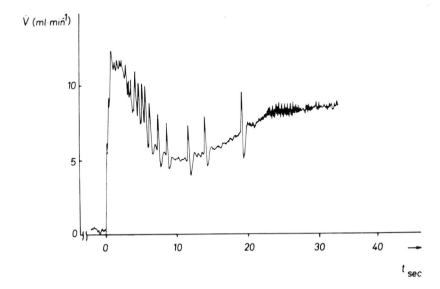

Fig. 4.11B. The first 30 seconds of the flow response of the
            rat coronary system to a pressure step from 30
            to 180 mm Hg. (After BAŞAR et al., 1968a)

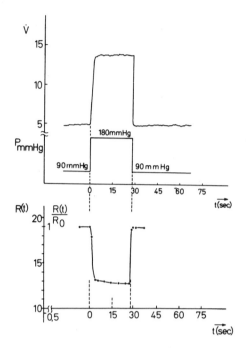

Fig. 4.12. Flow response (upper curve) of a kidney to a
rectangular upward and downward pressure step.
The kidney was perfused with a medium containing
papaverine. (After BAŞAR and WEISS, 1969)

(A) the system gain (or the flow amplitude) in decibels,

(B) phase angle in degrees. The system gain shows a maximum

between 0.2 and 0.4 Hz, a minimum between 0.007 and 0.03 Hz

and has low-pass characteristic at values higher than 0.4 Hz.

The phase angle has positive values between 0.01 and 0.1 Hz.

At the low frequencies, where the gain of the system has

stationary values, the gain (the flow amplitude) is much

smaller than the maximum around 0.2-0.4Hz. The curves of

$|G(j\omega)|$ are normalized in such a way that the gain at 0 Hz is

considered to be equal to 1 (or log 1=0). Fig. 4.16 shows

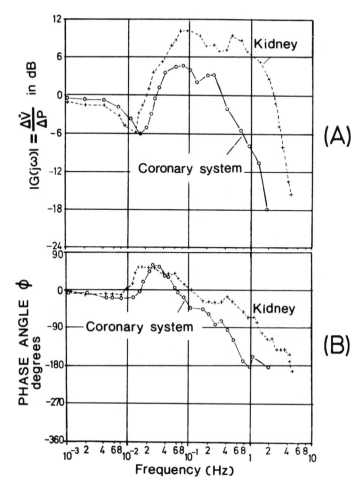

Fig. 4.13 Frequency characteristics of the autoregulating
          kidney and of the coronary system. These curves
          are computed using the TRFC-Method from step
          responses by application of arterial (input)
          pressure steps from 100 to 180 mm Hg. (A) Amplitude
          characteristics $|G(j\omega)|$ (the gain) (B) Phase char-
          acteristics. The phase angle is plotted in degrees.
          Along the abscissa is the input (pressure) fre-
          quency in logarithmic scale. Along the ordinate
          is the flow amplitude in decibels. The curves are
          normalized in such a way that the amplitude of
          flow at 0 Hz is equal to 1 (or log 1=0). (After
          BASAR et al., 1968a)

the frequency characteristics of a non-autoregulating kidney
which was perfused with a papaverine-containing medium. The
gain has constant values up to a frequency of 0.2 Hz; then it
diminishes. The curves of experiments with papaverine are
normalized in such a way that the flow at 0 Hz of the normal
curves is taken equal to 1.

Fig. 4.14 presents the frequency characteristics of an
autoregulatory coronary system. Here again, the frequency
characteristics are computed using the pressure step responses. The amplitude and phase characteristics are very
similar to those of the autoregulating kidney. The system
gain shows a minimum of flow (maximum of vascular resistance) between 0.007 and 0.03 Hz. The maximum of gain is here
shifted to slightly lower frequencies: the amplitude maximum
is at about 0.1 Hz. The phase angle also has positive values
between 0.01 and about 0.1 Hz. When the coronary system is
perfused with papaverine, the system gain shows low-pass
behavior as in the case of the kidney. In the coronary
system, the papaverine low-pass characteristics have a cutoff
frequency which is slightly shifted to lower frequencies between 0.08 and 0.1 Hz. The phase angle does not have positive values between 0.01 and 0.1 Hz.

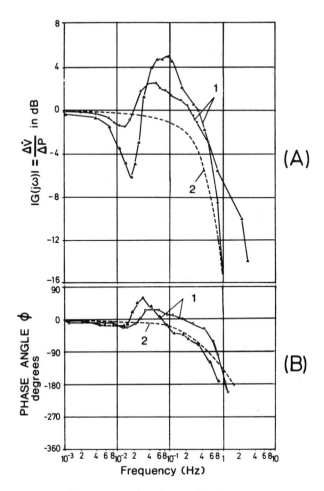

Fig. 4.14 Frequency characteristics of the coronary system
of the isolated rat heart: (1) autoregulating
coronary system preparations (2) coronary system
preparation which is perfused with papaverine
containing medium. These curves are computed
using the TRFC-Method from step responses by
application of arterial (input) pressure steps
from 100 to 180 mm Hg. (A) Amplitude character-
istics $|G(j\omega)|$ (the gain) (B) phase characteris-
tics. The phase angle ϕ is plotted in degrees.
Along the abscissa is the input (pressure)
frequency in logarithmic scale. Along the ordinate
is the flow amplitude in decibels. The curves are
normalized in such a way that the amplitude of flow
at 0 Hz is equal to 1 (or log 1=0). (After BAŞAR
et al., 1968a)

In Chapter 6, nonlinear properties of the autoregulating kidney are described in detail. The experiments described in Chapter 6 show that the autoregulating kidney behaves as a linear system only if the input pressure is modulated with amplitudes (ΔP) around 20-30 mm Hg ($\Delta P \sim 20$-30 mm Hg). In other words, the linearization of the system is possible when the amplitude of the input signal can be maintained low enough.

In order to see the effects of the nonlinearities, a series of experiments were performed applying pressure steps of 30 mm Hg in different input pressure ranges. The pressure was changed in form of step functions between the following input pressures:

(1) Pressure step from   60 to   90 mm Hg

(2)   "   " "   120 "   150 "   "

(3)   "   " "   150 "   180 "   "

(4)   "   " "   240 "   270 "   "

Fig. 4.15 describes such an experiment. In the lower curves, the pressure steps in different pressure ranges (1)-(4) are shown. The upper curves show the flow responses to pressure steps in three different pressure ranges. Figs. 4.16, 4.17 and 4.18 show the frequency characteristics computed with the help of TRFC-Method using the step responses of Fig. 4.15.

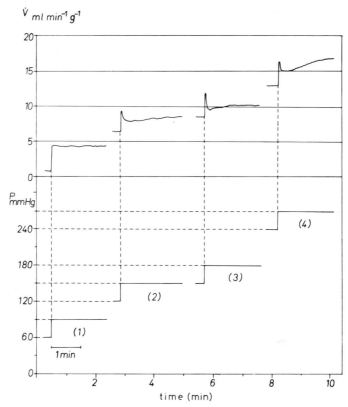

Fig. 4.15. Pressure step responses of the kidney in different
           pressure ranges. Lower curves (1), (2), (3), (4)
           present the input steps; curves at the top, the
           corresponding flow responses. (See also the text,
           p. 82)

We use the following nomenclature:

Frequency characteristic	computed from a step response after a pressure step:				
G_1 $(j\omega)$	from	60	to	90	mm. Hg
G_2 $(j\omega)$	"	120	"	150	"
G_3 $(j\omega)$	"	150	"	180	"
G_4 $(j\omega)$	"	240	"	270	"
G_p $(j\omega)$	"	100	"	180	"

(with papaverine
perfused kidney)

Also, we denote the relative amplitudes as:

$$|G_n| = \frac{|G_n(j\omega)|}{|G_n(0)|}$$

(n=1,...,4 and n=p)

Fig. 4.16 shows that below the pressure of 100 mm Hg the kidney has frequency characteristics resembling those of the papaverinized kidney. The amplitude characteristics shown in Fig. 4.17 are very similar to those obtained in nonlinear experimental conditions as in the case in the experiment of Fig. 4.13 (autoregulation range). In pressure ranges between 240 and 270 mm Hg (nonphysiological conditions), where the autoregulation is no longer maintained (or is again abolished), the amplitude frequency characteristic is similar to that of the autoregulating kidney, between 0.01 and 5 Hz. But, the amplitude values below 0.01 Hz do not remain constant as they do in the autoregulation range (Fig. 4.18). The amplitude increases in lower frequencies and reaches values higher than the amplitude at 0.4 Hz.

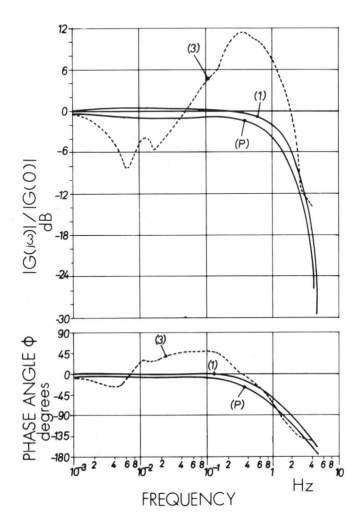

Fig. 4.16 Frequency characteristics of the isolated rat
kidney. The curves (1) present amplitude and phase
characteristics of G_1 (jω), curves (P) amplitude
and phase characteristics of G_p(jω). The dashed
curve (3) is plotted for comparison. For definitions and nomenclature see p. 84. Along the
abscissa is the input (pressure) frequency in
logarithmic scale. Along the ordinate is the flow
amplitude in decibels and the phase angle φ in
degrees. The curves are normalized in such a way
that the amplitude of flow at 0 Hz is equal to 1
(or log 1=0).

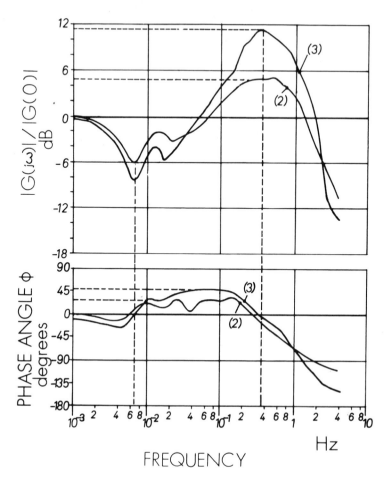

Fig. 4.17 Frequency characteristics of isolated rat kidney.
Curves (2) present amplitude and phase characteristics of $G_2(j\omega)$, curves (3) present amplitude and
phase characteristics of $G_3(j\omega)$. For nomenclature
see p. 84. Along the abscissa is the input
(pressure) frequency in logarithmic scale. Along
the ordinate is the flow amplitude in decibels and
the phase angle in degrees. The curves are
normalized in such a way that the amplitude of flow
at 0 Hz is equal to 1 (or log 1=0).

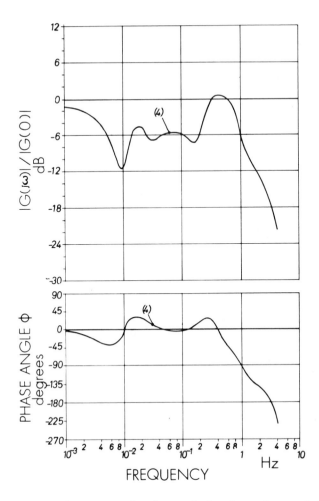

Fig. 4.18   Frequency characteristics of isolated rat kidney.
Curves (4) present amplitude and phase characteristic of G4(jω). For nomenclature see p. 84.
Along the abscissa is the input (pressure) frequency in logarithmic scale. Along the ordinate
is the flow amplitude in decibels and the phase
angle in degrees. The curves are normalized in
such a way that the amplitude of flow at 0 Hz is
equal to 1 (or log 1=0).

4.7 AUTOOSCILLATIONS OF FLOW IN THE KIDNEY

1. Definition of Flow Autooscillations

We define the flow autooscillations as the maintained
rhythmic changes of flow in different circulatory areas of
isolated organs when the circulatory area under study is
perfused with constant arterial pressure. Autooscillations
of different circulatory areas in isolated organs, as well
as in organs in situ, have been studied by several authors.
To give some examples we mention GEBERT et al. (1968),
KOEPCHEN et al. (1963), SELLER et al. (1967), GOLENHOFEN
et al. (1970).

The autooscillations of flow in the kidney were
observed by BASAR and WEISS (1970). Fig. 4.19 illustrates
typical records of flow fluctuations of an isolated rat
kidney ($\dot{V}$, flow measured in vena cava). The perfusion pressure
in all three cases amounts to 180 mm Hg. Visual inspection
of these records indicates that the periodicity of flow waves
varies between 10 and 20 secs. However, visual analysis does
not allow one to make any statement regarding either the
exact values of this periodicity or the complexity (for
example, multiperiodicity) of these waves. Upon the addition
of the vasomotor paralyzing substance, papaverine, to the
perfusion fluid, these periodical fluctuations disappear.

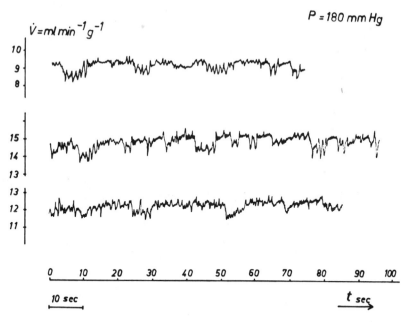

Fig. 4.19. Time histories of spontaneous fluctuations of
          flow in three different isolated rat kidney
          preparations. (After BAŞAR and WEISS, 1970)

2. Autocorrelogram

A typical plot of autocorrelation versus time displacement (R_{xx} versus τ) for the time histories of a
perfused isolated rat kidney is presented in Fig. 4.20.
The value of R_{xx} does not diminish to zero by increasing
time lag, but it oscillates with a period of nearly 15 secs.
It should also be noted that $R_{xx}(0) > R_{xx}(\tau)$.

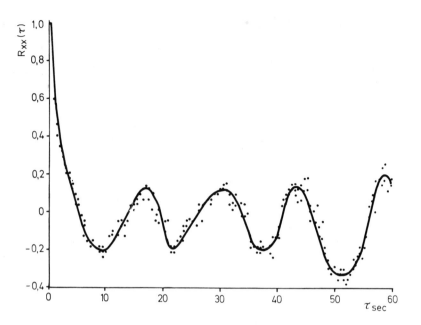

Fig. 4.20. Autocorrelogram for the time histories of a
           perfused isolated rat kidney. Along the abscissa
           is the time in seconds, along the ordinate is the
           autocorrelation function $R_{xx}(\tau)$. (After BAŞAR and
           WEISS, 1970)

3. Power Spectra

Typical plots of power spectral density are presented

in Fig. 4.21. The important features of these plots are two

sharp peaks at frequencies centered at about 0.04-0.07 Hz

and 0.09-0.12 Hz. At all other frequencies S_{xx} has values

close to zero.

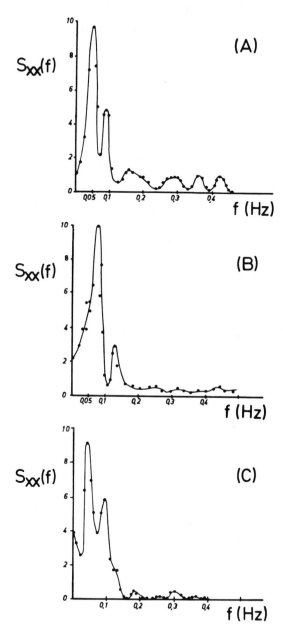

Fig. 4.21. Plots of power spectral density versus frequency.
Along the abscissa is the frequency, f, along the
ordinate is the power spectral density, $S_{xx}(f)$.
The curves A, B and C are obtained during
experiments with three different kidney preparations. (After BAŞAR and WEISS, 1970)

4.8   COMPONENTS OF THE CIRCULATORY AUTOREGULATION
      DYNAMICS: THEIR PHYSIOLOGICAL AND PHYSICAL
      CORRELATES

In section 4.3 we have seen that the functional
architecture of the kidney and of the coronary vascular
system are quite different. *The kidneys have a complicated
filtering and reabsorbing system while the coronary system
serves only as the blood supply for the nutrition of the
heart, in the form of a large arterioles-and-capillaries
system.*

The common features in both systems are: (1) the
existence of capillary networks and (2) the existence of
smooth muscle cells in the walls of the arterioles (see
also Fig. 4.1D). The coronary system does not have glomeruli
or nephrons. A physical (or hydrodynamic) similarity in
both systems is the fact that the blood vessels act in both
systems as capacitive and resistive networks. The application of deterministic pressure signals to both systems is
the way of obtaining of the time-dependent laws of flow in
both systems.

Consider now the amplitude frequency characteristics of the autoregulating kidney and of the coronary
system. In section 3.3 we described a method which consisted

of reducing the system to its passive components (or physical
components). The addition of papaverine to the perfusion
medium is an example of the application of this method.
Papaverine is a substance which paralyzes the smooth muscle
activity. The function of the vascular smooth muscle is to
produce active tension by contraction under physiological
control and so change the diameter of the lumen of the vessel
(see section 4.1). Therefore, when the kidney or the coronary
system is perfused with papaverine, the physiological
control of the vascular lumen and consequently, the control
of flow, ceases. Under these conditions, both systems can
be considered, from the point of view of circulation, as
inactive biological or pure physical systems.

We return to the amplitude frequency characteristics
of both systems which we obtained by perfusion with
papaverine (Figs. 4.14 and 4.16). In the case of the kidney,
the flow amplitude (and therefore the vascular resistance)
remains constant between the lowest frequencies and a frequency of about 0.4 Hz. (:: Definition of vascular resistance or the resistance to flow: resistance to flow is
defined mathematically as R= $\delta P/\dot{V}$ in which $\dot{V}$ is blood flow,

δ P is the pressure difference between the two ends of the vessel, and R is the resistance. A pressure difference between the two ends of the vessel causes blood to flow from the high pressure area to the low pressure area while resistance impedes flow ::). When the input frequency is higher than 0.5 Hz, the amplitude of flow decreases rapidly with increasing frequency. Similar amplitude characteristics are obtained in studies of the coronary system. The papaverinized coronary system amplitude characteristics also have a low-pass shape: the amplitude remains constant up to a frequency of about 0.1 Hz; then it decreases rapidly with the increasing input frequency.

What does this mean? In general systems theory, the amplitude characteristics presented by papaverine curves of Figs. 4.14 and 4.16 are called "low-pass" characteristics. In electronics, the network illustrated in Fig. 4.22A has the low-pass function. In hydrodynamics, the recipients of the circulation system shown in Fig. 4.22B have low-pass function.

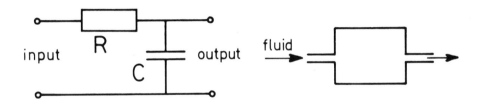

Fig. 4.22A. Low pass circuit   Fig. 4.22B. Hydrodynamic
            R: Resistor   low-pass-element.
            C: Capacitor   V: Volume of the
       For explanations see   recipient
       text above.   For explanation see
                                         text above.

In other words, the amplitude characteristics of a

coronary vascular bed and of a kidney which are perfused

with papaverine simply present the transfer characteristic

of a hydrodynamic system's response of the coronary vascular

bed and of the kidney. We see that in the coronary system the

cutoff frequency of the frequency response lies at about

0.1 Hz, while the cutoff frequency of the kidney character-

istic is at about 0.4 Hz. These results (i.e. the abstract

system's characteristics) indicate that the heart prepara-

tion must have a greater capacitive effect than the kidney

preparation. This is also the case when both preparations

are compared anatomically. The perfusion fluid of the

coronary system, which is measured in the vena cava cranialis

sinistra, flows through the right atrium of the heart prepa-

ration (Fig. 4.8B). Therefore, it was to be expected that

the physical characteristics of the coronary system preparation would have a lower cutoff frequency than the kidney.
Furthermore, this finding shows us that we may not expect to
have reliable biological information of higher than these
cutoff frequencies (0.1 Hz for the coronary system preparation; 0.4 Hz for the kidney). The low-pass characteristic of
the physical systems (physical properties of the vascular
systems) will certainly filter out all the information which
would exist in higher frequencies. The hydrodynamic
properties of these circulatory organs play the role of
low-pass filters in frequencies higher than 0.1 Hz and
0.4 Hz.

In the papaverine-treated kidney a pressure-flow
relationship resembling that in passive elastic tubes has
to be expected. Recently WETTERER and KENNER (1968) have
discussed a four-terminal electrical analog network
containing only passive elements which describes the
hydrodynamic properties of elastic tubes (Fig. 4.23):

Principally, all elements contained in the analog
network of Fig. 4.23 ought to be effective in the kidney
(and coronary system) whether paralyzed or non-paralyzed.
However, in our results from the paralyzed organs, only a
low-pass effect between 0.001 and 5 Hz was observed

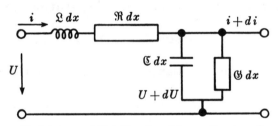

$\mathfrak{R}\,dx$ = Resistance $\triangleq$ Frictional resistance (laminar flow)
$\mathfrak{L}\,dx$ = Inductance $\triangleq$ Effective mass (inertance)
$\mathfrak{C}\,dx$ = Capitance $\triangleq$ Relationship between pressure and vol-
    ume (elastance)
$\mathfrak{G}\,dx$ = Derivation $\triangleq$ Sidewise outflow
U (voltage) $\triangleq$ P (pressure; I (current) $\triangleq$ $\dot{V}$ (flow).

Fig. 4.23 Analog network. (After BAŞAR and WEISS, 1969)

(Figs. 4.14 and 4.16). The biological conclusion which we draw from our results is derived from the parts of the pressure and flow curves which occur about 0.3-0.4 sec after the pressure step. At this time the influence of passive hydrodynamic factors on the shape of the flow curves should be small indeed. We are therefore reasonably certain that our inferences, as far as the properties of the active pressure-induced biological mechanism are concerned, are valid.

Now we will try to understand what happens between input frequencies of 0.001 and 0.1 Hz in both organs. In this frequency range the amplitude and phase characteristics of the kidney and of the coronary system show remarkable similarity: the flow amplitude has an important minimum around 0.02 Hz. The minimum flow corresponds to a maximum of

the resistance to flow in the circulatory system. This means
that the *pressure-induced active increase of the vascular
resistance* reaches a maximum in this frequency range. We
want to emphasize the expression *active*. We have seen that
the studied systems (kidney and coronary systems), which were
reduced to their passive elements, did not show any change
in the vascular resistance between 0.001 and 0.1 Hz
(Figs. 4.14 and 4.16).

What can this mechanism be which increases actively
the vascular resistance? In order to answer this question
we will apply the rule of *going out of the system*. We have
already applied this rule in studying both systems, the
coronary vascular bed and the kidney. We are already
searching for the responsible components outside of these
systems. The coronary system does not have functional units
called "nephrons" as are present in the kidney (Fig. 4.6).
The only common functional anatomical feature of both
circulatory systems is the existence of arterioles, venules
and capillaries, as we have already stated (section 4.3).
We also know that at each point where a capillary leaves a
meta-arteriole, a small muscular sphincter surrounds the
origin of the capillary. The existence of smooth muscle
cells in both circulatory areas is perhaps the most common

feature in the vascular architecture of both organs. Furthermore, it is already established that smooth muscle responds to mechanical stretch with active contraction (BURNSTOCK and PROSSER, 1960; JOHANSSON and MELLANDER, 1975; see also Chapter 5). This means that the increase of pressure in a circulatory area would cause (1) passive stretch of the vascular smooth muscle and then (2) an active contractile response of these muscles. What are the time and frequency characteristics of this contraction mechanism? This question is answered by the findings of GOLENHOFEN (1965) on smooth muscles and by our findings given in Chapter 5. GOLENHOFEN (1965) measured the amplitude frequency characteristics of guinea-pig taenia coli with sinusoidal passive stretching of this smooth muscle preparation.

Fig. 4.24 shows the measured amplitude characteristics of the tension developed in guinea-pig taenia coli. We see that in the frequency range of 0.02 Hz, where the frequency characteristics of the kidney and the coronary system show a maximum of the active resistance to flow, the smooth muscle responds with a maximum of tension. In other words, the smooth muscle characteristics fit in well with the characteristics of the circulatory systems under study (Fig. 4.24).

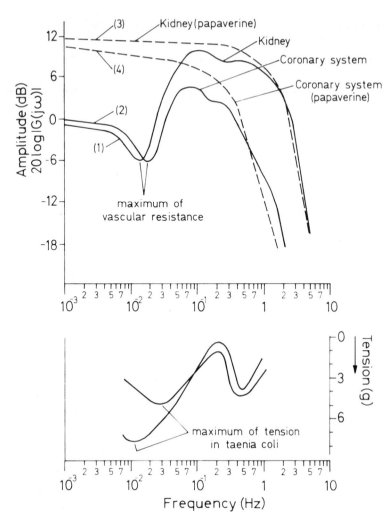

Fig. 4.24. Curve (1): Amplitude characteristic of the autoregulating rat kidney. Curve (2): Amplitude characteristic of the autoregulating coronary system
of the rat heart. Curves (3) and (4): Amplitude
characteristics of the same kidney and the same
coronary system preparations after addition of
papaverine to the perfusion medium. Along the
abscissa is the input (pressure) frequency in
logarithmic scale. Along the ordinate is the flow
amplitude in decibels. The curves are normalized
in such a way that the amplitude of flow at 0 Hz
of curves (1) and (2) is equal to 1 (or 20 log
1=0). At the bottom: frequency dependent tension
changes of isolated strips of taenia coli of the
guinea-pig.

We have also determined the amplitude frequency characteristics of the tension developed in a vascular smooth
muscle preparation: typical amplitude frequency characteristics of the tension induced by passive stretch in the portal
vein depict maxima centered at frequencies around 0.02 Hz,
thus supporting the results of GOLENHOFEN (1965) (see
Fig. 5.12 of section 5.8).

GOLENHOFEN (1965) measured another maximum of tension
in the vicinity of 0.5 Hz. In the circulatory preparations
which we studied, the frequency range around 0.5 Hz does not
allow us to make statements concerning biological phenomena.
According to his findings and according to our findings of
the kidney and coronary system and vascular smooth muscle,
we may state that the maximum of vascular resistance in the
vicinity of about 0.02 Hz is of myogenic nature.

Let us now give an additional explanation concerning
the autoregulatory mechanism by simply studying the frequency characteristics of the system. Our tentative explanation
for the shape of the amplitude characteristics is based on
the assumption that the mechanism of pressure-induced change
of vascular resistance is rate-sensitive: at the lowest
frequencies studied, (0.001-0.005 Hz), the slope of pressure
changes is too small to be fully effective as a vasocons-

trictive stimulus. Accordingly, the vascular resistance is comparatively low. (We know from smooth muscle studies that the vasculature responds with contraction to passive stretch.) With increasing frequency, the mean slope of the pressure change becomes steeper, thus acting as an adequate stimulus. A maximum of flow resistance is reached at about 0.008-0.03 Hz (the *Minute-Rhythm* frequency range of vascular smooth muscle). At higher frequencies, due to the relatively slow reaction time of the muscular response, the effect decreases progressively and the flow resistance falls again. Finally, at still higher frequencies, the flow resistance increases steeply due to the inertia of the fluid volume in the perfusion system.

According to the above interpretation, a minimum slope of the pressure stimulus would be a prerequisite for pressure-induced changes of flow resistance. With decreasing frequency, the flow resistance should decrease further to its minimum, reaching at least a value corresponding to the maximum of amplitude at about 0.3-0.4 Hz. But in our curves (Fig. 4.24) the flow resistance remains considerably below these values, at 0.3-0.4 Hz. This means that, the autoregulatory mechanism has a rate-sensitive component (sensitive to dp/dt), since the steepness of the pressure has an increasing

effect on vasoconstriction. But this rate-sensitive component alone cannot explain the entire mechanism of autoregulation. The vascular resistance is still high (the flow
amplitude, low) at the lowest frequencies. This result is in
accordance with previous findings. THURAU and KRAMER (1959)
observed pressure-induced increase of vascular resistance in
the kidney even at extremely slowly increasing perfusion
pressures (83 mm Hg/min). According to this evidence we
assume the presence of two components in autoregulation of
flow:

   (1) A rate-sensitive component

   (2) A rate-insensitive but *long-lasting* component

   The amplitude characteristics of Fig. 4.18 support
this consideration. In the non-physiological pressure range
above 220 mm Hg, where autoregulation is abolished, the
rate-sensitive component still exists. But the rate-
insensitive component is non-existent. At the lowest frequencies, the vascular resistance reaches minimal values.
(Flow amplitude reaches large values.) However, although the
long lasting autoregulation is abolished, the kidney responds
with an increase of vascular resistance to sudden increase
of pressure. *The rate-sensitivity to pressure change*
(sensitivity to dp/dt) remains, whereas the long lasting

component no longer exists (see also BAŞAR and WEISS, 1969).

4.9. PHYSIOLOGICAL IMPLICATIONS AND TOWARD A NEW
MYOGENIC CONCEPT OF CIRCULATORY AUTOREGULATION

In the previous section we have seen that above frequencies of 0.1-0.4 Hz, the amplitude frequency characteristics of the kidney and of the coronary system do not give any reliable information on biological processes in play. We have also seen that the frequency responses of both organs between the values of 0.001 and 0.1 Hz mainly reflect vascular smooth muscle response. The fact that the maximum of the active increase of the smooth muscle tension lies in a frequency range of about 0.02 Hz has led us to this conclusion.

We now turn to a different kind of problem and a different kind of approach: we first identified the different components revealed by the dynamic characteristics of the organs under study. We will now try to establish a working hypothesis based on the *dynamic* results, taking into consideration all the physiological implications.

Let us first review and describe once more the concept of the myogenic hypothesis of autoregulation. We defined the *myogenic mechanism* as the *intrinsic mechanism in the smooth muscle cells* of the arteries or arterioles which responds to

an increase in the internal pressure or tension in the wall

with contraction (section 4.3). BAYLISS (1902), who first

discovered the phenomenon of circulatory autoregulation,

suggested the following myogenic explanation of autoregula-

tion: the distension or the passive stretch offered by the

increase of blood pressure acts as a facilitating stimulus

on vascular smooth muscle, intensifying its activity. From

the physiological literature, we know that the vascular

smooth muscle responds with contraction to a passive stretch

(SPARKS and BOHR, 1962; GOLENHOFEN, 1965). Also the experi-

ments of BAŞAR et al. (1974a,b) which we described in

Chapter 5, support this contention. However, largely because

of the special design and function of the vessels, there

appear to be some serious obstacles, at least at first glance,

to the full acceptance of Bayliss' hypothesis. These obsta-

cles necessitate careful analysis and interpretation of

actual events. Folkow describes these obstacles as follows

(FOLKOW, 1964):

> "1. Blood flow autoregulation, if caused by the
> Bayliss mechanism, would seem to demand a main-
> tained shortening of the contractile elements
> as a response to distension. However, then the
> contraction would seem to abolish its own stim-
> ulus, which is a paradoxical situation (see
> also GASKELL and BURTON, 1953).

2. Bayliss' mechanism implies a positive feedback, which inherently would lead to exceed-
ingly high blood pressure and resistance levels.
Since this evidently does not occur, it must be
concluded that either there are effective brake
mechanisms, or the principle is physiologically
untenable."

In order to deal with these obstacles, let us first
mention the more modern concepts of the myogenic hypothesis
based on studies of vasomotion (FOLKOW, 1964). There are
many observations that the precapillary sphincters constrict and dilate periodically (CHAMBERS and ZWEIFACH,
1947) and that this activity is asynchronous (NICOLL, 1964).

FOLKOW (1964) states that the ratio of the con-
stricted and dilated phases of the sphincters may change
under nervous, physical, hormonal and metabolic influences.
A sudden change of vasomotor tone or of perfusion pressure
will influence all elements at the same moment, bringing
part of them into asynchronous action. This would result in
an oscillation of the average vascular tone, which could
continue until the original asynchrony is restored due to
differences in frequency of the units. PEÑAŹ et al. (1968)
propose to call this theory "vasomotion theory" of the
autoregulation instead of myogenic.

Based on findings of vascular autooscillations and
vascular smooth muscle autooscillations, we will design a

theory similar to the vasomotion theory.

In section 4.7 we have seen that in autoregulating
isolated kidney preparations, the perfusion flow showed
periodical oscillations. Autooscillations of flow (or the
vascular autooscillations) disappeared when the autoregulation of the organs under study was abolished (BAŞAR and
WEISS, 1970). The vascular autooscillations also disappeared
when the arterial pressure of the isolated kidney was held
below 100 mm Hg, i.e. below the pressure range of autoregulation.

Fig. 4.25 compares the power spectra of the kidney
flow oscillations with the power spectra of the isolated
smooth muscle contractions. Fig. 4.25A presents the power
spectrum of the isolated kidney flow oscillations. The
mechanical autooscillations of the guinea-pig taenia coli
and of the guinea-pig portal vein are presented in
Fig. 4.25B and 4.25C. First of all, we want to confine
our attention to the activities (or mechanisms) higher than
0.03 Hz. One sees that in all these organs (preparations)
the oscillatory activities are centered on frequencies of
about 0.06 Hz and about 0.1 Hz. In these frequency ranges
the power spectra show striking similarities. Since perfusion
flow of kidneys was measured for about only 100 secs, it

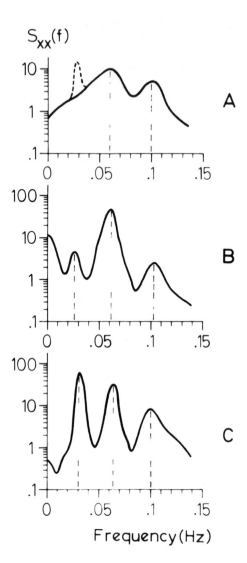

Fig. 4.25 (A): Power spectral density of flow fluctuations
        (vascular autooscillations) in the isolated rat
        kidney (solid line) and arterial flow fluctuations
        in the hind limb (dashed curve) (WEISS and
        THIEMANN, 1974).
        (B): Power spectral density of guinea-pig taenia
        coli contractions.
        (C): Power spectral density of guinea-pig portal
        vein contractions.
        Along the abscissa is the frequency in Hz, along
        the ordinate is the power spectral density S_{xx} (f)
        in relative units.

is not possible to make statements concerning the rhythm

around 0.02 Hz. However, the amplitude characteristics of

the kidney and of the coronary system of the rat heart

showed a maximum of vascular flow resistance of about

0.008-0.02 Hz which corresponds to the frequency range of

the slow smooth muscle rhythm (or the Minute-Rhythm)

(Figs. 4.13, 4.14, 4.17, 4.24, and 4.25). Moreover, recently

WEISS and THIEMANN (1974) recorded arterial and venous flow

curves from an isolated rat hind limb. The dashed curve in

Fig. 4.25, taken from their results, indicates the power

spectrum, which has a distinct maximum at a frequency of

0.03 Hz. These facts allow us to state that the flow auto-

oscillations are due to the spontaneous contractions of

vascular smooth muscles. We have seen that smooth muscle

cells play a very important role in the arteriolar archi-

tecture (section 4.1). From Chapter 5 and from Fig. 4.25A,

B and C, we know that spontaneous contractions of smooth

muscle are similar to flow oscillations. We may then state

that the flow oscillations do reflect the spontaneous ac-

tivity of smooth muscle.

Further to the known facts, we are able to make

another observation. We know that the autooscillations of

flow should have myogenic origin since the vascular smooth

muscle rhythmic activity is completely reflected in the
power spectra of autooscillations. Moreover, we also know
that the smooth muscle rhythmic activity depicts three components, Minute-Rhythm (0.02 Hz), the 0.06 Hz component and
the 0.1 Hz component. In Chapter 5 we describe the following
analysis. We filtered the time histories of spontaneous
contraction of the portal vein smooth muscles by means of
the theoretical filtering method of section 3.2 (the method
of theoretical isolation). Fig. 5.8 illustrates the results
of the theoretical ideal filtering. In Chapter 5 we also
describe that in a typical contraction period, the distension
(decrease of the contraction) of the slower component (i.e.
of the 0.02 Hz Minute-Rhythm) is usually followed by tension
increase (contractions) of greater frequencies. The filtered
components of Fig. 5.8 also confirm these experimental
observations: during the distension period of the slower
rhythm, tension increase of a faster rhythmic component is
always observed. The periodicities of all these components
are such that the faster rhythms have nearly half the period
of the slower rhythms (0.02-0.03 Hz rhythm, 0.05-0.08 Hz
rhythm, 0.09-0.2 Hz rhythm). So, the activities of the
contractile components (or of the different rhythms) are
arranged in the time domain in such a way that they are

always in counter phase (see Fig. 5.9). This phenomenon

can eliminate the serious obstacles mentioned by

FOLKOW (1964). Our new hypothesis is as follows:

>"Two or three contractile mechanisms acting with
>different phase shifts (or acting in counter
>phase) could solve the problem of the main-
>tained contractile vasoconstriction elements
>in spite of the distension. During the contrac-
>tion of one element, the other elements exert
>distension. This way, one or two contracted
>elements may exist while the other ones relax.
>Fig. 4.26 explains these assumptions. In this
>illustration the smooth muscle rhythmicity
>components of Fig. 5.8 are superimposed in
>order to compare the direction of their ac-
>tivities more easily. During the contraction
>period of the slowest rhythm (1) (40 Second-
>Rhythm or Minute-Rhythm), the element-producing
>rhythm (2) contracts twice and relaxes only
>once, while rhythmicity (3) shows three con-
>tractions and about three relaxations (the
>first 20 seconds). This schema shows that, due
>to the effects of different contraction mech-
>anisms, the diameter of the lumen of a blood
>vessel can be maintained small without all of
>the components of the smooth vasculature
>remaining continuously (and progressively)
>contracted, and accordingly, not being stim-
>ulated without distension. The shape of the
>vessel lumen would then change without impor-
>tant change in the diameter. Due to the dis-
>tension of different contractile elements, the
>stimulation resulting from the increased arte-
>rial pressure (i.e. from the increased passive
>stretch) would not cease to act in the arteri-
>al wall."

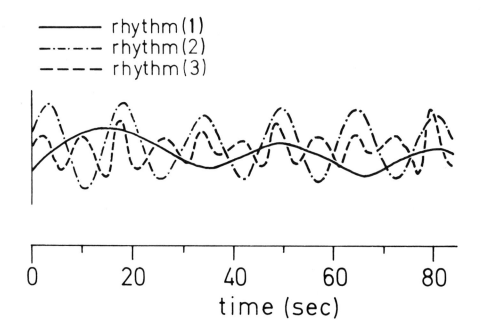

Fig. 4.26 See also Fig. 5.8. For explanations see text p.156.

Multi Component Vasomotion Theory of Autoregulation

We summarize the multi-component vasomotion theory of the circulatory autoregulation as follows:

(1) The peripheral vascular bed responds to an arterial pressure increase above 100 mm Hg, with a fast contraction having a latency shorter than 0.5 sec. The first

and prompt response results from a rate-sensitive mechanism
and exists only if the pressure increase time is short
(dp/dt is large).

(2) This first rate-sensitive component is responsible
only for the first seconds after pressure increase. A second
rate-insensitive component, which has a maximal contraction
response of about 0.01-0.03 Hz in the frequency domain, is
the dominant component of the active increase of vascular
resistance. This component fits in the frequency domain
together with the Minute-Rhythm of vascular smooth muscle.

(3) The increased vascular resistance can be maintained at the same level due to the different contractile
components of vascular smooth muscle, which act in opposite
phases, thus causing distension and/or stimulating each other.

The considerations above and the formulated working
hypothesis are fully supported by a recent analysis on
dynamics of vascular smooth muscle. JOHANSSON and MELLANDER
(1975) studied the effects of static and dynamic passive
stretch and shortening on electrical activity and active
force in the isolated rat portal vein. These authors found
that the contractile activity of the vessel was strongly
dependent on muscle length and was strongly influenced by

variations in the rate of change in length (dL/dt) in a well-

defined, graded manner. In other words a rate-sensitive

component was also mentioned in their findings. The analysis

of JOHANSSON and MELLANDER (1975) leads these authors to

the following conclusion:

> "Myogenic reactivity (e.g., myogenic autoreg-
> ulation of blood flow) has been considered
> mainly in relation to changes in blood pres-
> sure from one steady level to another. No
> doubt, such a *static component of the myogenic*
> response does exist, as also evidenced by the
> present study, but the *dynamic component* appar-
> ently is much more prominent. This concept can
> explain how prompt myogenic vasoconstrictions
> or vasodilations are accomplished during the
> phasic period of a blood pressure change and
> how such responses are graded in relation to
> the rate of the pressure change. Such precise
> effects are implicit in the phenomenon of blood
> flow autoregulation. If the static myogenic
> constrictor response evoked during the plateau
> of a blood pressure rise failed to maintain
> vascular tone at the new increased level, the
> vessel would again be transiently distended
> which, in turn, would create the stimulus for
> a repetitive dynamic myogenic constrictor
> response. The damping and asynchrony of such
> cyclic variations in tone in different sections
> of the vascular tree are factors that contri-
> bute to the maintenance of an overall rela-
> tively stable level of blood flow in the tis-
> sue. It has sometimes been said that a positive
> feedback mechanism is inherent in the myogenic
> theory (the pressure rise causes constriction
> and an increase in resistance which, in turn,
> causes an additional pressure rise, etc.). The
> present data show that any extreme effects of
> such a mechanism will not ensue, since there
> is an upper biological limit of the dynamic

response at high rates of stretch. Furthermore, the chemical metabolic control system acts as a brake on the myogenic control, since intense vasoconstriction is counteracted by the consequent local accumulation of vasodilator metabolites."

The independent conclusion of JOHANSSON and MELLANDER (1975), who revealed different *static* and *dynamic* components in the myogenic response, definitely enhances the myogenic concept which we developed using the systems theoretical approach of this chapter.

4.10. DIFFERENT HYPOTHESES OF THE CIRCULATORY AUTOREGULATION IN VIEW OF SYSTEMS THEORY RESULTS

The considerations of section 4.9 lead us to a new concept of the myogenic hypothesis. We come to the multicomponent vasomotion theory conclusions by going step by step through systems theoretical findings. The conclusion of the oscillating myogenic model stems from experimental results and from the evidence of systems theory criteria. However, some of the hypotheses of autoregulation, introduced in section 4.4, are not completely excluded by systems theory results presented in previous sections. We will discuss these theories in the same order as we presented them in section 4.4.

1. Myogenic Hypothesis

In section 4.8 we have already explained how the systems theoretical results support the myogenic hypothesis of autoregulation. A new model of myogenic hypothesis, where vascular autooscillations play a major role, is described in section 4.9.

2. Tissue Pressure Hypothesis

The experiments with papaverine-treated kidneys and coronary system reject the possibility of the role of the tissue pressure hypothesis of autoregulation. As described in section 4.4, the tissue pressure autoregulation is a passive type of autoregulation. If the tissue pressure plays a significant part in autoregulation, the autoregulatory mechanism should not be abolished after paralyzing the vasculature of the organs under study with papaverine. At present, during papaverine experiments, the organs are reduced to their passive responses. Autoregulation of the passive (paralyzed) organs is not observed, thus showing the irrelevancy of the tissue pressure hypothesis.

3. Cell Separation Hypothesis

This is also a passive type of autoregulation hypothesis. In the experiments we have described, the organs were prepared with a cell-free solution of Haemaccel. The autoregulation was maintained when the organs were perfused with this cell-free medium. Therefore, the cell separation mechanism cannot be considered as a causal factor for the circulatory autoregulation.

4. *Metabolic Hypothesis*

This is an active hypothesis of autoregulation. Systems theory findings in previous sections do not reject the possibility of metabolic components. However, time and frequency characteristics of assumed metabolic components or causal factors are unknown. The validity of the assumed metabolic components as causal factors of autoregulation can be checked only if time and frequency characteristics of these components are known. Any metabolic hypothesis of autoregulation must fit in with the frequency characteristics of the autoregulatory organs described in section 4.6.

However, we would like to state that the fast rate-sensitive component with a reaction time shorter than 0.5 sec can certainly not be identified as having a metabolic origin.

5. *Renin Angiotensin Hypothesis*

The fast rate-sensitive component also cannot be

explained with the renin-angiotensin hypothesis. The response occurring 0.5 sec after the pressure step (increase) is certainly too short for the passage time of sodium ions in the tubuli of the kidney and the activation of renin release.

It is as yet unknown whether the increase of Na^+ load in the macula densa area of the kidney, the release of renin and the production of Angiotensin I-II would accommodate the 0.01-0.03 Hz component of the frequency characteristics of the autoregulating kidney. In the case that the renin-angiotensin mechanism could fit together with the kidney frequency characteristics, this mechanism would play only an auxillary role, since we have already shown that the myogenic components alone are able to play the major role in autoregulation and can cause maintained increased vascular resistance due to autooscillation of smooth muscle. The same mechanism of smooth muscle causes autoregulation in the coronary system as well (without the need of the angiotensin mechanism).

We should mention here also the experiments by LEICHTWEISS et al. (1967) who perfused rat kidneys with paraffin oil. The kidneys perfused with paraffin oil (i.e. kidneys where the sodium containing plasma is not circulating in the nephrons) showed typical autoregulation char-

acteristics. The findings of LEICHTWEISS et al. (1967)

reveal that the renin-angiotensin mechanism does not play a

major role in the circulatory autoregulation.

4.11 DISCUSSION OF METHODS AND CONCLUDING REMARKS

We should point out once more that the extended myo-

genic theory of autoregulation, which we developed in section

4.9, is not the only possible explanation of the phenomenon

of circulatory autoregulation. However, this theory can cer-

tainly explain almost perfectly, within the studied time and

frequency ranges, the role effected by vascular smooth muscle

and the myogenic nature of the active increase of vascular

resistance. Moreover, this new theory eliminates the obsta-

cles predicted by the critics of the earlier myogenic theory.

Proponents or defenders of other theories are obliged to

show that the mechanisms which they predict can accord

with the time and frequency characteristics of autoregula-

tion, as we have illustrated.

According to IBERALL et al. (1971), high frequency

oscillations around the mean level of the regulated value of

a biological system may be characteristic of autoregulation.

IBERALL (1971) and coworkers describe the necessity of oscillations for furnishing the regulation of a biological system premised by homeostasis. They tend to postulate that the generation of oscillations of particular periods is likely to be an intrinsic characteristic of the regulatory processes of the biological system. Our findings provide further support for this hypothesis, since we observe different high frequency oscillations in a strong autoregulatory process. We will return to the important hypothesis of IBERALL et al. (1971) in Chapter 8, where we give a general discussion on biological systems.

Two of the *specific methods for living systems* were used:

1) Cells were removed from the circulation by perfusion with Haemaccel to test their possible role in autoregulation.

2) The pharmacological agent papaverine was applied to remove all dynamic vascular action from the system. This accomplished two things. First, by abolishing autoregulation, it showed that the passive hypothesis of tissue pressure control of autoregulation must be false. Second, it allowed us to identify the frequency characteristics of the physical component of the system, separately from the biological component.

In Chapter 3 we proposed a biological systems analysis
program, and we assumed that the application of the rules
and methods given in this program could help the investigator
to obtain a clearer idea of the inside of the black box
under study. In the present chapter we applied most of the
rules given in that program. We will now discuss briefly
the applied methods and what their results can teach us.
A general discussion of methods will be given in the last
chapter; therefore, we discuss here only the methods as
they are applied to the peripheral circulatory mechanisms,
without general implications.

The determination of time and frequency characteristics of a biological system is usually of basic importance
when the investigator tries to identify the dynamic components of the studied mechanism. The most important concept
in the examination of time and frequency characteristics
of a biological system can be formulated as follows: given
a mechanism which might be responsible for the occurrence
of a defined biological phenomenon, let us suppose that
we are able to measure the time and frequency characteristics
of the proposed mechanism. If this mechanism takes longer
to occur than the studied biological phenomenon itself, then
we would not be justified in discussing this mechanism as

the causal factor. For example, if the smooth muscle dynamics
do not correspond with the dynamics of flow in the process
of active increase of vascular resistance, we could not
assume the myogenic mechanism as being the causal factor of
autoregulation. It is not logical to consider a mechanism
which requires ten minutes to cause vasoconstriction as the
causal factor of autoregulation. The mechanism or mechanisms
should relate in time and frequency domain to the measured
autoregulation characteristics. To summarize, *comparison of
time and frequency characteristics of the mechanisms predicted to be (or to work) in coordination, is necessary.*

The use of the TRFC-Method was necessary during the
autoregulation studies discussed in this chapter. By direct
measurement of the frequency characteristics of the kidney
we were able to obtain only incomplete curves (although
they are in approximate agreement with curves obtained using
the TRFC-Method). The isolated heart preparation has a short
life-time, and as the heart beats spontaneously, it can be
caused to fibrillate for only a few minutes. For this reason,
the frequency characteristics could be determined only by
the use of the TRFC-Method.

As the results of Chapter 6 will show, the system
nonlinearities do not cause serious obstacles in the deter-

mination of frequency characteristics using the TRFC-Method.
The knowledge which we obtain from the frequency characteristics is not influenced by minor quantitive differences
existing between the linearized and nonlinear responses.
On the contrary, the information which we obtain from nonlinear behavior of the system under study fully supports
the contentions in this chapter. We therefore suggest that
the systems investigator must seriously consider the nonlinearities of the system under study. For further information the reader should study the section 6.1.

The example of circulatory autoregulation clearly
depicts the necessity for searching for causal components
outside the biological system under investigation (i.e.
the necessity of *going out of the system*). It would be
difficult to understand the origin of the maximum of
vascular resistance of the kidney if we did not have information on the dynamics of smooth muscles. Additionally,
the fact that the same maximum of vascular resistance
exists in the coronary system, also, leads the investigator
to search for a common mechanism in both organs.

REFERENCES

Başar, E.: Biological systems analysis and evoked potentials
    of the brain. T.-I.-T. Journal of Life Sciences, Vol. 4,
    37-58 (1974).

Başar, E., C. Eroğlu, and P. Ungan: Time series analysis of
    guinea-pig taenia coli spontaneous activity. Pflügers
    Arch. 347, 19-25 (1974a).

Başar, E., C. Eroğlu, and P. Ungan: An analysis of portal
    vein spontaneous contractions. Pflügers Arch. 352,
    135-143 (1974b).

Başar, E., G. Ruedas, H.J. Schwarzkopf und Ch. Weiss:
    Untersuchungen des zeitlichen Verhaltens druckabhängiger
    Änderungen des Strömungswiderstandes in Coronargefässystem
    des Rattenherzens. Pflügers Arch. 304, 189 (1968a).

Başar, E., H. Tischner und Ch. Weiss: Untersuchungen zur
    Dynamik druckinduzierter Änderungen des Strömungswider-
    standes der autoregulierenden isolierten Rattenniere.
    Pflügers Arch. ges. Physiol. 299, 191 (1968b).

Başar, E. und Ch. Weiss: Analyse des Frequenzganges druckin-
    duzierter Änderungen des Strömungswiderstandes isolierter
    Rattennieren. Pflügers Arch. 304, 121-135 (1968).

Başar, E., and Ch. Weiss: Rate sensitivity of the mechanism
    of pressure induced change of vascular resistance.
    Kybernetik 5, 241-247 (1969).

Başar, E., and Ch. Weiss: Time series analysis of spontaneous
    fluctuations of the flow in the perfused rat kidney.
    Pflügers Arch. 319, 205-214 (1970).

Bayliss, W.M.: On the local reactions of the arterial wall to
    changes in internal pressure. J. Physiol. (London) 28,
    220 (1902).

Berne, R.M.: Metabolic regulation of blood flow. Circulation
    Research 15 (suppl. I): I-261, (1964).

Burnstock, G., and L.C. Prosser: Responses of smooth muscles
    to quick stretch; relation of stretch to conduction. Am.J.
    Physiol. 198, (5): 921-925 (1960).

Burton, A.C.: Physiology and Biophysics of the Circulation.
    Year Book Medical Publisher, INC. (1965),(1972).

Chambers, R., and B.W. Zweifach: Intercellular cement and
    capillary permeability. Physiol. Revs. 27, 435-463 (1947).

Folkow, B.: Description of the myogenic hypothesis. Supplement
    I to Circulation Research. Vols. XIV and XV (1964).

Folkow, B. and Neil, E.: Circulation. Oxford University Press
    (1971).

Gaskell, P., and A.C. Burton: Local postural vasomotor reflexes
    arising from the limb. Circulation Research 1, 27 (1953).

Gebert, G., P. Konold, and H. Seboldt: Eigenschaften und
    Beeinflussbarkeit der mechanischen Spontanaktivität
    isolierter Arterien. Pflügers Arch. 299, 285-294 (1968).

Golenhofen, K.: Rhythmische Dehnung der glatten Muskulatur
    von Blinddarm des Meerschweinchens. Pflügers Arch. 284,
    327-346 (1965).

Golenhofen, K., and D.V. Loh: Intracellulare Potentialmes-
    sungen zur normalen Spontanaktivität der isolierten Portal
    Vene des Meerschweinchens. Pflügers Arch. 319, 82-100
    (1970).

Gregg, D.E., and L.C. Fisher: Blood supply to the heart. In,
    W.F. Hamilton (Ed.): Handbook of Physiology. Section 2:
    Circulation, Vol. II. (1963).

Guyton, A.C.: Textbook of Medical Physiology, W.B. Saunders
    Company. Philadelphia (1971).

Iberall, A., M. Weinberg and A. Schintler: General Dynamics
    of the Physical Chemical Systems in Mammals. NASA Report
    Cr- 1806 (1971).

Johansson, B., and S. Mellander: Static and dynamic components
    in the vascular myogenic response to passive changes in
    lenght as revealed by electrical and mechanical recordings
    from the rat portal vein. Circ. Res. Vol. 36, No. 1, (1975).

Johnson, P.C.: Review of previous studies and current theories
    of autoregulation. Supplement I to Circulation Research.
    Vols. XIV and XV. 1-9 (1964a).

Johnson, P.C.: Autoregulation of blood flow. Circulat. Res.
15, No. 2, Suppl. No. 1 (1964b).

Koepchen, H.P., J. Polster, and P. Langhorst: Über zentral-
nervös und durch efferente Reizung ausgelöste rhythmische
Kontraktionen der Gefässmusculatur. Pflügers Arch. 278,
24 (1963).

von KÜGELGEN, A., B. Kuhlo, W. Kuhlo, and J. Otto: Die
Gefässarchitektur der Niere. Stutgart, Thieme (1959).

Leichtweiss, H.P., H. Schröder, Ch. Weiss: Die Beziehung
zwischen Perfusionsdruck und Perfusionsstromstärke an
der mit Paraffinöl Perfundierten isolierten Rattenniere.
Pflügers Arch. ges. Physiol. 293, 303-309 (1967).

Nicoll, P.A.: Structure and function of minute vessels in
autoregulation. Supplement I to Circulation Research
Vols. XIV and XV 245, (1964).

Pappenheimer, J.R., and W.B. Kinter: Hematocrit ratio of
blood within mammalian kidney and its significance for
renal hemodynamics. Amer. J. Physiol. 185, 377 (1956).

Peňaź, J., P. Burianek and B. Semrád: Dynamics aspects of
vasomotor and autoregulatory control of blood flow. In,
O. Hudlicka (Ed.): Circulation in Skeletal Muscle.
Pergamon Press, Oxford (1968).

Seller, H., P. Langhorst, J. Polster, and H.P. Koepchen:
Zeitliche Eigenschaften der Vasomotorik II. Erscheinungs-
formen spontaner und nervös induzierter Gefässrhythmen.
Pflügers Arch. 296, 110-132 (1967).

Smith, H.W.: The Kidney, Structure and Function in Health
and Disease. Oxford University Press, New York (1959).

Sparks, H.V., and D.F. Bohr: Effect of stretch on passive
tension and contractility of isolated vascular smooth
muscle. Amer. J. Physiol. 202, 835 (1962).

Thurau, K.: Renal hemodynamics. Am. J. Med., 36, 698-718
(1964).

Thurau, K., und K. Kramer: Die Reaktionsweise der glatten
Muskulatur der Nierengefässe auf Dehnungsreize und ihre

Bedeutung für die Autoregulation des Nierenkreislaufs.
Pflügers Arch. ges. Physiol. 286, 188 (1959).

Weiss, C., and V. Thiemann: New aspects on the mechanism of
autoregulation of blood flow. In, H. Bischer and D.F.
Bruley (Ed.): Physiology of Oxygen Transport to Tissue.
Plenum Publishing Corporation, New York (1974).

Wetterer, R., und Th. Kenner: Grundlagen der Dynamik des
Arterienpulses. Springer, Berlin-Heidelberg-New York
(1968).

Zweifach, B.W.: The character and distribution of the blood
capillaries. Anat. Res. 73, 475 (1939).

Zweifach, B.W.: Microcirculation. Ann. Rev. Physiol. 35,
117-150 (1973).

Chapter 5

Smooth Muscle Contractions

5.1 MAIN PHYSIOLOGICAL FEATURES; AIM OF THE ANALYSIS

Almost every organ of the body contains smooth muscle, which means that a large share of our overall bodily function is dependent on the characteristics of smooth muscle contraction. Although contraction mechanisms in smooth muscle were investigated by several authors, no evident theories exist which are able to explain the basic mechanism underlying these contractions. In recent lectures at the Symposium on Physiology of Smooth Muscle, the contractile properties of smooth muscle are discussed from anatomical, biochemical and pharmacological aspects (BÜLBRING and NEEDHAM, 1973; BÜLBRING and SHUBA, 1975). We will classify the smooth muscle contractions into two different groups:

129

1- Spontaneous contractions

2- Contractile responses to stretch (evoked contractions)

Spontaneous contractions: Smooth muscles in different organs of the body show intrinsic mechanical activity. These organs are found in the digestive tract (stomach, small intestine, large intestine) in the urogenital tract (uterus, urinary bladder, the scrotum, the penis) and also in the circulatory system (vascular smooth muscles).

Contractile responses to stretch: Smooth muscles do respond to passive mechanical stretch with active contraction (or with an active increase of tension). (BURNSTOCK and PROSSER, 1960; BOZLER, 1947; SPARKS, 1964.)

We must emphasize the important physiological properties of the vascular smooth muscle. This type of muscle shows contractile properties as well as being independent of the CNS; also, these muscles act as effectors of the CNS in many vital functions of the body. As a first example we may cite the vasoconstriction or vasodilatation phenomena which occur depending on contraction or relaxation of vascular smooth muscle upon electrical signals from the CNS.

As another example, we cite a visceral smooth muscle: the muscle in the pelvis of the kidney is self-excitable and transmits impulses along the ureter, causing a peristaltic wave to travel along this tubular structure, thus forcing urine into the bladder. Similar effects occur in the bile ducts, in other gland ducts, in the vas deferens, in the gut and in many other tubular structures of the body (GUYTON, 1971).

Although it is not the aim of this chapter to deal with the functions and all of the kinds of physiological responses of smooth muscle, we will summarize the basic acting ability of smooth muscles as follows:

1- Smooth muscles show spontaneous mechanical activity,

2- Smooth muscles have spontaneous electrical activity,

3- Smooth muscles respond with large contraction to quick stretch,

4- Smooth muscles respond with contraction to electrical stimulation,

5- Smooth muscles respond with contraction or relaxation to pharmacological, chemical or hormonal stimulation,

6- Smooth muscles play important effector roles in the coordination of circulation, water regulation, the urogenital mechanism and the digestive system.

We will not describe and discuss in detail the properties mentioned above in this chapter. Our aim in this chapter is to study the dynamics of smooth muscles such as the taenia coli and portal vein of guinea-pig with methods of systems theory. In order to do this, we will apply first of all, in part, our biological systems analysis program (see Chapter 3). The characteristics of smooth muscle dynamics, the determination of which we will describe in this chapter, were used for the understanding of peripheral circulatory vasoconstriction phenomena and the blood flow autoregulation discussed in Chapter 4.

The results of the application of systems theory to our experimental findings should be important for the smooth muscle physiologist, especially when he tries to classify smooth muscle rhythmicities or coordination phenomena. However, as of now, we are not able to identify the physiological correlates of the contractile components. Suggestions will be given for further experiments to identify the contraction components. At the end of the chapter, some peripheral rhythmic phenomena will be mentioned in order to

emphasize the major role of the smooth muscle in the coordination of various physiological processes.

5.2 METHODS AND EXPERIMENTAL SETUP

Portal Vein

Female guinea-pigs weighing between 450-600 g were
killed by exsanguination. The abdomen was opened, and strips
of portal vein with in situ lengths of approximately 20 mm
were dissected and placed in a 35 C^o Krebs solution of the
following composition (mmol/1): NaCl 118, KCl 4.17, $CaCl_2$ 2.5,
$NaHCO_3$ 14.9, KH_2PO_4 1.18, $MgSO_4$ 1.17, glucose 5.5.

When mounting the portal vein in the perspex chamber
filled with Krebs solution preaerated with a mixture of
95% O_2 and 5% CO_2, one end of the portal vein was connected
to a tension transducer (GRASS force-displacement transducer
FT.03) through a suitably chosen spring. This spring was
used in order to maintain an experimental condition which
was close to the one in situ. The suitability of this kind
of experimental condition has already been pointed out by
GOLENHOFEN (1970). The other end of the strip was anchored
at a fixed point in the perspex chamber. The position of the
perspex chamber relative to the transducer could be adjusted
in order to change the passive tension of the muscle. The

mechanical tension of the portal vein was transduced to an electrical signal with a GRASS-transducer and was further amplified and recorded with a SCHWARZER Polygraph V822. (Experimental setup is shown in Fig. 5.1.)

Taenia Coli

Female guinea-pigs weighing between 450-600 g were killed by exsanguination. The caecum was exposed and strips of taenia coli with in situ lengths of approximately 20 mm were excised as described by GOLENHOFEN (1970), and placed in the 35 C^o Krebs solution. Then, the taenia coli was mounted in the perspex chamber and recordings were made with the help of the experimental setup described above (see Fig. 5.1).

For the experiments described in section 5.8, one end of the preparation was anchored to a point in the perspex chamber that could be moved mechanically with the help of a lever system which is driven electromechanically by means of an electromagnet system energized by a function generator (Fig. 5.1).

5.3 SPONTANEOUS MECHANICAL ACTIVITY OF PORTAL VEIN ANALYZED WITH TIME SERIES ANALYSIS METHODS

Time Histories

Fig. 5.2A-E illustrates five typical records of spontaneous fluctuations of the tension developed in

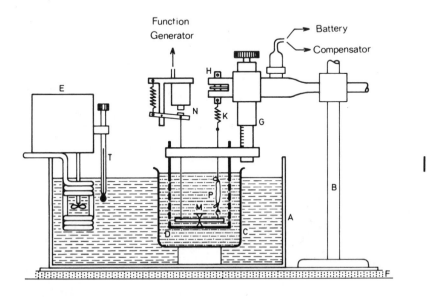

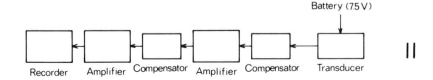

Fig. 5.1 (I): Experimental setup to record the spontaneous
        mechanical tension changes of smooth muscle.
        (A) Aquarium filled with water, (B) Support,
        (C) Muscle bath, (D) Krebs solution, (E) Ther-
        moregulator, (G) Device used to apply passive
        stretch to muscle, (H) Force transducer,
        (K) Spring, (M) Device used to apply mechanical
        tension to muscle, (N) Electromagnetic device
        used to apply mechanical step function to
        muscle (P) Isolated smooth muscle, (T) Thermo-
        meter.
      (II): Schematical diagram of the above experimental
        setup

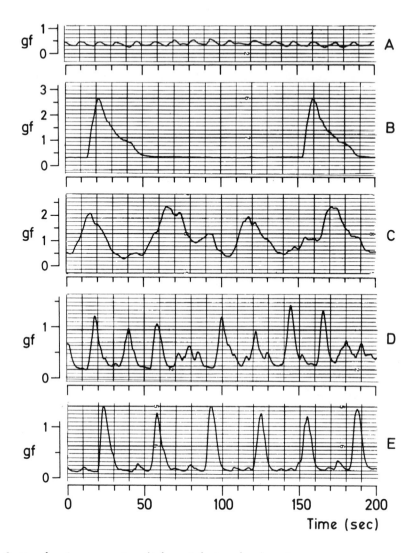

Fig. 5.2 Typical records (time histories) of spontaneous
         tension changes of guinea-pig portal vein. Trans-
         fer spring constant used was 3 g/cm. Tension
         scale shows directly the force created in the
         portal vein strip. (After BAŞAR et al., 1974b)

portal vein. They are typical in the sense that the activities recorded from 20 different portal vein preparations during a total of about 250 hrs of observation could be identified most of the time as one of the types shown in Fig. 5.2. It should also be noted that during a long recording period of about 12 hrs almost all the activity patterns recorded from each individual preparation fitted one of these forms. Furthermore, most of these types of patterns have already been shown in the related literature (see discussion).

Fig. 5.2A presents a pattern which has a frequency of about 0.1 Hz. Fig. 5.2B presents a pattern with a frequency of about 0.01 Hz, while the pattern of Fig. 5.2C presents a contraction period with a frequency of 0.02 Hz. The pattern of Fig. 5.2B has a simple periodic form without wavelets (or superimposed waves), while the pattern of Fig. 5.2C has a more complicated shape. The patterns of 5.2D and 5.2E are complex waveforms, and in these cases it is difficult to define a unique contraction frequency.

In 28% of our data we observed the pattern of Fig. 5.2E. (As will be described in the next section, this pattern is characterized by the power spectrum of Fig. 5.4E.) In 23% of our experiments the pattern of 5.2D was observed.

(This pattern is characterized by the power spectrum of Fig. 5.4D.) The pattern of 5.2C was observed in 19% experiments, and the pattern of 5.2B was recorded in only 12% of our experimental records. The simple higher frequency pattern of Fig. 5.2A was recorded in 18% of our results.

Another noteworthy observation was that patterns similar to those of Fig. 5.2A were recorded at the beginning of the experiments. Contractions with a frequency composition including the 0.01-0.03 Hz band usually appeared 1 hr after the beginning of the recording period.

Autocorrelation Functions

Autocorrelation functions $R_{xx}(\tau)$ of the five typical portal vein contractions, illustrated in Fig. 5.3, were computed (see Chapter 3). All these $R_{xx}(\tau)$ functions had oscillatory behavior with negligible decay with τ.

Power Spectra

Plots of power spectral density versus frequency (S_{xx} vs f) are presented in Fig. 5.4. These plots are called power spectra. Curves A-E of Fig. 5.4 were obtained using time histories A-E of Fig. 5.2, respectively. In the power spectrum shown in Fig. 5.4A, only one maximum around 0.1 Hz is seen. The dominant maximum is at about 0.01 Hz

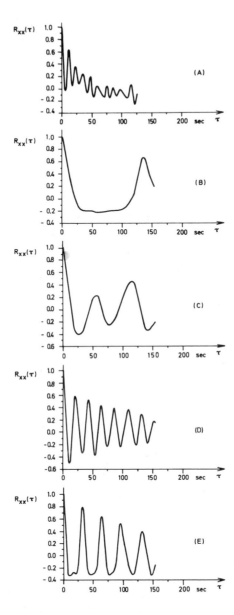

Fig. 5.3 Autocorrelograms of the time histories of spontaneous tension changes of guinea-pig portal
vein. These autocorrelograms A–E are computed
using the time histories of the curves A–E of
Fig. 5.2 respectively. Along the abscissa is
the lag time τ, along the ordinate is the
autocorrelation function $R_{xx}(\tau)$. (After EROĞLU,
1974)

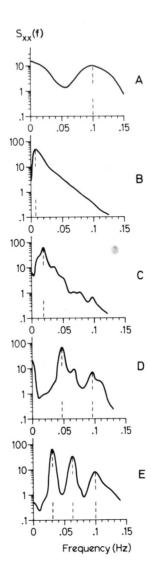

Fig. 5.4 Power spectra of tension changes of portal vein
         which are obtained using the time histories of
         Fig. 5.2. Curves A-E correspond to the patterns
         A-E of Fig. 5.2. Along the abscissa is the fre-
         quency in Hz, along the ordinate is the power
         spectral density $S_{xx}(f)$ in relative units.
         (After BAŞAR et al., 1974b)

for curve B, at about 0.02 Hz for curve C. The power spectrum of 5.4E contains three maxima centered at frequencies of about 0.02, 0.06 and 0.1 Hz. The power spectrum of Fig. 5.4D depicts two maxima at frequencies of 0.05 and 0.1 Hz, but no maximum around 0.01-0.03 Hz. (104 power spectra were evaluated.)

Using the percentages of occurrence of the patterns given in the previous section combined with the information contained in the power spectra, the following results were obtained: 1) the 0.01-0.03 Hz component (which corresponded to the Minute-Rhythm) was existent in 88% of all curves, 2) the 0.05-0.08 Hz component was existent in 60% of all our recordings, 3) the faster 0.09-0.2 Hz component was observed in 47% of all the recordings.

5.4 DISCUSSION OF THE SPONTANEOUS MECHANICAL ACTIVITY OF THE PORTAL VEIN

Spontaneous Contraction Patterns

Contraction patterns similar to those of Figs. 5.2D and 5.2C were reported by different authors. FUNAKI and BOHR (1964) observed a periodicity of contraction in rat smooth muscle in the range of 0.2 Hz; HOLMAN et al. (1968) observed contractions in the frequency range of 0.1 Hz and

0.2 Hz in the smooth muscle of rabbit portal vein. JOHANSSON
and LJUNG (1967) described contractions of rabbit portal
vein between 0.05 Hz and 0.13 Hz. Finally, GOLENHOFEN and
LOH (1970b) described two different kinds of contraction
activities which they called Minute-Rhythm (MR) and Basic
Organ Specific Rhythm (BOR). Moreover, GOLENHOFEN (1970)
has described the frequency range and the conditions for
the manifestation of the Minute-Rhythm. GOLENHOFEN (1970)
states that 1) in isolated preparations, depending on the
experimental conditions, the Minute-Rhythm will appear
stronger, or weaker, or not exist at all, 2) the
length of the preparation must not be shorter than 20 mm
for the manifestation of the MR, 3) the frequency of the
portal vein MR varies between 0.01 and 0.05 Hz, 4) the
higher frequency rhythm BOR has periodicities 0.05-0.07 Hz
and 0.12-0.16 Hz (GOLENHOFEN and LOH, 1970b). Our results
fully support these findings, in addition to confirming
the faster rhythms already demonstrated by HOLMAN et al.,
1968; FUNAKI and BOHR, 1964; JOHANSSON and LJUNG, 1967.
The following question arises: what is the additional
information derived from our studies? This question can be
answered by studying the power spectra of the contractions,
which show that all three rhythmic activities do exist in

the most typical compound pattern.

Power Spectra

The power spectra of Fig. 5.4 show that the rhythmic contractions of portal vein are found mainly in three frequency ranges: 0.01-0.03 Hz, 0.05-0.08 Hz and 0.09-0.2 Hz. These contractions appear either as single rhythmicities (Fig. 5.2A-C) or in the form of complex contraction patterns. The complex contraction patterns similar to those in Fig. 5.2D depict two components, while the patterns similar to those in Fig. 5.2E depict three components.

The following question may arise: do the main maxima (or peaks) revealed by the power spectra stem from different rhythmical mechanisms or, is there any possibility that these peaks present some harmonical elements? This question can be answered through the following reasoning:

a) The power spectra obtained from our experiments depicted maxima of the spectral density either in the form of a distinguished *single* periodicity (Fig. 5.4A-C) or in the form of a distinguished periodicity dominating the others (Fig. 5.4D,E). This means that the periodicities depicted in the spectra of Fig. 5.4D and E could be detected as single activities independent from each other. Furthermore, it often happened that a single preparation showed each of these three single activity patterns (with single periodicities) during different parts of a long recording session (10-12 hrs). Different authors observed rhythmicities in these three frequency ranges as single distinguished periodicities (FUNAKI and BOHR (1964), 0.2 Hz; JOHANSSON and LJUNG (1967), 0.05-0.13 Hz; GOLENHOFEN and LOH (1970b). 0.05-0.07 Hz and 0.12-0.16 Hz). The superposition of these single periodicities gives the compound contraction patterns shown in Fig. 5.2D and 5.2E; this fact can also be decoded from the power spectra of Fig. 5.4D and 5.4E. This calculation is essential in showing that the various peaks of 0.01-0.03 Hz, 0.05-0.08 Hz and 0.09-0.2 Hz of the power spectra do not represent harmonical components.

b) If the power spectra should contain harmonical components which could result from nonlinear distortions in the rhythmic activity, the frequencies of these harmonical components would have to be integer multiples of the fundamental frequency. But in our case, the frequency of the components existing in the power spectra do not depict mathematical relations in this sense. (As nonlinear distortion we mean the deviation from the pure sinusoidal shape of the periodical waves under study.)

c) The power spectrum of Fig. 5.2B shows only one periodicity of 0.01 Hz. The contraction pattern of Fig. 5.2B has a sawtooth-like shape which is known to have rich harmonical composition. However, no additional harmonical peaks appear in the power spectrum of Fig. 5.4B. This is mostly due to the Hanning Smoothing, which we apply in order to supress irrelevant peakings which might be due to harmonics. (Hanning Smoothing is described in section 3.2.)

Time histories of Fig. 5.2D and 5.2E show complex contraction patterns. Accordingly, the corresponding power spectra contain several maxima: the spectrum of Fig. 5.4D depicts two maxima, the spectrum of Fig. 5.4E depicts three maxima. In other words, the smaller superimposed waves in the dominant periodical element of the contraction pattern, rather than the harmonics, give rise to the various maxima in the power spectrum. Therefore, the power spectrum of Fig. 5.4D indicates the existence of two, and the power spectrum of Fig. 5.4E indicates the existence of three distinct components in the complex contraction patterns.

The methods encountered in the smooth muscle literature allow one to determine the approximate period of only the dominating component or the dominating rhythm. But, by applying the mathematical method used in this work,

all of the discrete periodicities contained in a complex
pattern of spontaneous contractions can be detected and
evaluated.

Our discussion may even lead one to interpret
various forms of multiperiodical contractions as different
combinations of these components, with varying relative
magnitudes and phases during different stages of portal
vein contractions and under different experimental conditions. In order to give a more concrete example we consider the contraction pattern of Fig. 5.2E and the corresponding power spectrum of Fig. 5.4E. This is the most
frequently encountered contraction pattern in our portal
vein investigations. GOLENHOFEN and LOH (1970b) describe
this kind of activity also as the most typical portal vein
spontaneous activity. The power spectrum indicates that
not only the dominating Minute-Rhythm, but also the faster
0.06 Hz and 0.1 Hz components can be decoded from this
complex pattern, which results from the superimposition
of the other slower components. When faster components
(0.05 and 0.1 Hz components) are dominant (Fig. 5.4D),
the corresponding contraction pattern has a different
shape. In conclusion, we may say that in the most typical
contraction pattern of the portal vein (which is presented

in Fig. 5.2E) all the different single rhythms already described in the literature (and also given in our study) exist in a superimposed form. The shape of the pattern is determined by the relative magnitudes and phases of different rhythmic components. At the beginning of the experiments, the fastest contraction pattern, between 0.09 Hz and 0.2 Hz, is usually dominant; later, the 0.05-0.08 Hz pattern appears and gains weight. The complex contraction pattern with MR (Minute-Rhythm) appears at earliest 1 hr after the beginning of the experiment.

5.5 SPONTANEOUS MECHANICAL ACTIVITY OF TAENIA COLI ANALYZED WITH TIME SERIES ANALYSIS METHODS

Time Histories

Fig. 5.5A-D illustrates four typical records of spontaneous fluctuations of the tension developed in taenia coli. They are typical in the sense that the activities recorded from 20 different taenia coli preparations during a total of about 300 hrs of observation could be identified most of the time as one of the types shown in Fig. 5.5. Furthermore, during a long recording session, almost all the activity patterns recorded from each individual preparation fitted one of these forms.

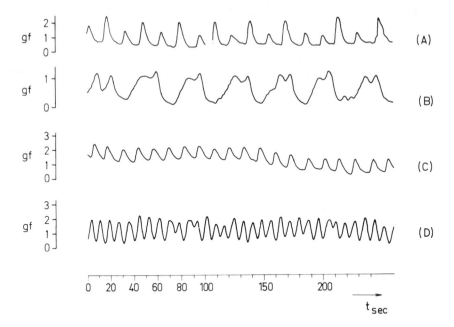

Fig. 5.5 Typical records (time histories) of spontaneous
        tension changes of guinea-pig taenia coli. Trans-
        fer spring constant used was 3 g/cm. Tension
        scale shows directly the force created in the
        taenia coli strip. (After BAŞAR et al., 1974a)

Autocorrelation Functions

Autocorrelation functions, $R_{xx}(\tau)$, of the four

typical taenia coli contraction patterns, illustrated in

Fig. 5.6 were computed. All these $R_{xx}(\tau)$ functions had

oscillatory behavior with negligible decay with τ. The

one which was computed from the time history A of Fig. 5.5

manifested a distinct multiperiodical course.

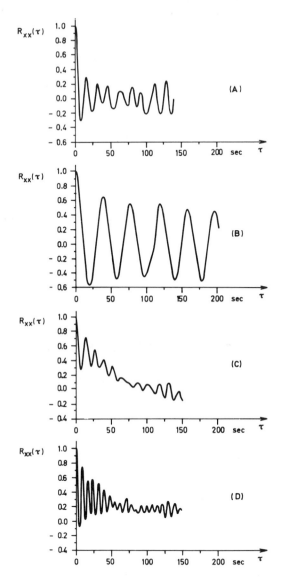

Fig. 5.6 Autocorrelograms of the time histories of spontaneous tension changes of guinea-pig taenia
coli. These autocorrelograms A-D are computed
using the time histories of the curves A-D of
Fig. 5.5 respectively. Along the abscissa is
the lag time τ, along the ordinate is the
autocorrelation function $R_{xx}(\tau)$. (After EROĞLU,
1974)

Power Spectra

Plots of power spectral density versus frequency (S_{xx} vs f) are presented in Fig. 5.7. Curves A-D of Fig. 5.7 were obtained using the time histories A-D of Fig. 5.5, respectively. The dominant peak is at about 0.02 Hz for the curve B, at 0.07 Hz for the curve C and at 0.13 Hz for the curve D. For some of the patterns which were not presented in this study, a maximum was noted at about 0.01 Hz. The power spectrum A contains three main maxima whose values are less different from each other than those of the power spectra B, C and D. The frequencies of these three main maxima are in the vicinity of the above given values.

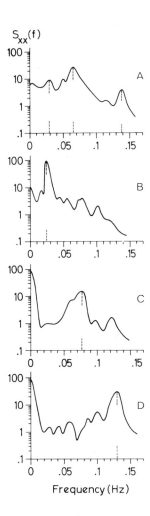

Fig. 5.7 Power spectra of tension changes of taenia coli
which are obtained using the time histories of
Fig. 5.5. Curves A-D correspond to the patterns
A-D of Fig. 5.5. Along the abscissa is the frequency in Hz, along the ordinate is the power
spectral density $S_{xx}(f)$ in relative units.
(After BAŞAR et al., 1974a)

5.6 DISCUSSION OF THE SPONTANEOUS MECHANICAL

ACTIVITY OF THE TAENIA COLI

Autocorrelation Functions

The autocorrelation functions computed from the
time histories A, B, C and D of Fig. 5.5 show oscillatory
behaviors with practically no decay. This fact provides
mathematical and objective evidence that these are
definitely rhythmic contractions well above a negligible
background noise level.

Power Spectra

The power spectra of Fig. 5.7 show that rhythmic
contractions of taenia coli are found mainly around three
frequencies: 0.02 Hz, 0.07 Hz and 0.13 Hz. A number of
complex contraction patterns, containing at least two
components with these frequencies, were observed during
the experimental part of this work. Such a case is
exemplified by the record A of Fig. 5.5. There may arise
a question as to whether these components are real periodical elements of the contraction pattern or whether they
are harmonics of one another, the strongest one being the
fundamental. This can be answered through the following
two lines of reasoning:

a) The frequencies of distortion-oriented harmonical components have to be the integer multiples of the fundamental frequency. But in our case, the frequencies of the components determined by means of the power spectrum do not necessarily show a harmonical display on the frequency scale, as can be seen in Fig. 5.7.

b) Each of these frequencies could be observed in the form of a distinguished periodicity dominating the others (Fig. 5.5B, C and D). Furthermore, it often happened that a single preparation showed each of these three spontaneous activity types with a single dominating periodicity during different intervals of time throughout a long recording session (about 10 hrs). This means that each of these three frequencies could well be the fundamental. Hence, when they are combined and form a complex pattern, there are reasons that they should be considered as real periodical elements. (For these considerations see also the previous section on portal vein.)

The foregoing discussion may even lead one to interpret various forms of multiperiodical contractions as different combinations of these components with varying relative magnitudes and phases during different stages of taenia coli activity and different experimental conditions.

Such a consideration may provide a compromise for discrepent spontaneous taenia coli contractions found in the
literature (BÜLBRİNG and KURIYAMA, 1973; GOLENHOFEN and
LOH, 1970a).

As in the case of the portal vein, the methods encountered in the literature allow one to determine the approximate period of only the dominant component. Upon the application of the mathematical methods presented in this book,
all the discrete periodicities contained in a complex pattern
of spontaneous contractions can be detected and evaluated.

5.7 CONTRACTILE COMPONENTS OF SMOOTH MUSCLE IN TIME AND FREQUENCY DOMAINS. STAGES OF CONTRACTION OF SMOOTH MUSCLE

Inspection and comparison of the different contraction
patterns of Figs. 5.2 and 5.5 showed that the shape of time
histories alone cannot allow any exact statement on the
multiperiodicity of the mechanical spontaneous activity.
The power spectra, however, showed that in most of the
contraction patterns, various periodicities with different
weights are present (Figs. 5.4 and 5.7). Visual inspection
of the pattern of Fig. 5.5A does not allow us to distinguish
the three periodicities which are seen in the power spectrum

of Fig. 5.7A. Therefore, we can assume that different contraction patterns are due to the fact that the equilibrium
of strengths of different rhythmicity components perpetually
changes. As a result we observe different contraction patterns, although usually all the components are present with
different weights. According to this interpretation we
introduce the concept of *"Different Stages of Spontaneous
Activity of Smooth Muscle"*.

In the previous section we have demonstrated the
existence of three different components (or rhythmic
components) of portal vein and of taenia coli. These rhythmic
components were centered in three similar frequency ranges
in portal vein and in taenia coli. Using the ideal theoretical filtering method of section 3.2, we can select or
reject components of contraction patterns presented in
Figs. 5.2 and 5.5. Let us mention the example of Fig. 5.5.
Application of theoretical filters to two of the patterns
of Fig. 5.5 gave the following results:

1) By application of a low-pass filter with a cutoff
frequency of 0.04 Hz to the time history of Fig. 5.5A,
we reject all activities higher than 0.04 Hz. After re-
jection of frequency components higher than 0.04 Hz we
observe the oscillatory behavior of the curve (1) in

Fig. 5.8. These results confirm the existence of a component below 0.04 Hz, although such a component could not be detected by visual inspection of the curve of Fig. 5.5A. Application of a pass-band filter between 0.04 Hz and 0.09 Hz selects another oscillatory component (Fig. 5.8 (2)). A smaller component between 0.09 Hz and 0.2 Hz must also exist, since by application of a high-pass filter which rejects activities slower than 0.09 Hz, a smaller oscillatory behavior is seen (curve (3)), while no activity is left after application of a high-pass filter of 0.2 Hz (curve (4)).

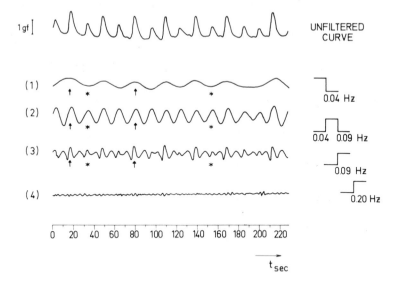

Fig. 5.8 Theoretical filtering of the curve of Fig. 5.5A
        with different ideal filters. The band limits of
        the filters (filter characteristics) applied are
        schematically shown on the right side of the
        filtered curves. (After BAŞAR and EROĞLU, In,
        PHYSIOLOGY OF SMOOTH MUSCLE. Edited by E. Bülbring
        and M.F. Shuba. © . 1975 by Raven Press. New York)

2) Similar theoretical filters were applied to the contraction pattern of Fig. 5.5B. The largest component was the component selected by application of a low-pass filter with a cutoff frequency of 0.05 Hz (curve (1)). The oscillatory component between 0.05 Hz and 0.09 Hz (curve (2)) and the component larger than 0.09 Hz were small in comparison to the slow component in curve (1).

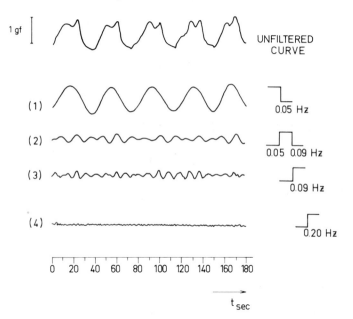

Fig. 5.9 Theoretical filtering of the curve of Fig. 5.5B with different ideal filters. The band limits of the filters (filter characteristics) applied schematically shown on the right side of the filtered curves. (After BAŞAR and EROĞLU, In: PHYSIOLOGY OF SMOOTH MUSCLE. Edited by E. Bülbring and M.F. Shuba. © . 1975 by Raven Press. New York)

The theoretical filtering gave us the same results as those obtained by the study of the power spectra. If we compare the power spectrum of Fig. 5.7 with the filtered

curves of Figs. 5.8 and 5.9, we see that in both cases the
largest periodical components are the activities around
0.02-0.03 Hz and 0.04-0.09 Hz. The analysis, which we extended to all curves obtained, gave further support to the
power spectra. We mention here only two examples.

The isolated components (obtained with theoretical
filtering) of both spontaneous activities shown in Figs. 5.8
and 5.9 have similar oscillatory time courses, although no
resemblance of the unfiltered contraction patterns could be
detected by visual inspection. This is due to the fact that
the corresponding oscillatory components (shown in Figs. 5.8
and 5.9) have different amplitudes (weights) and different
relative phases during different stages of taenia coli
contractions and different experimental conditions. If the
components are in opposite phase they cancel each other.
In other words, these subsystems or mechanisms, which are
responsible for different contraction components, change
the magnitudes of their activities during different contraction stages. Therefore, dissimilar contraction patterns
of the taenia coli (portal vein, too) were observed, although
the periodicities of the components are basically similar.
This is another explanation (or support) for the concept of
the *equilibrium of strengths of different rhythmic components*

stated in the previous section.

It is also possible to assume *"contractile reverberation circuits"*. These reverberatory contractions might
be due to at least three different contraction components.
The filtered components of Figs. 5.8 and 5.9 reveal a
very important point. The interactions between the contraction components seem to be very strong. One can easily see
the following correlation: when the tension maxima in components (1) and (2) of Fig. 5.8 are in phase, component (3)
(component with activity higher than 0.09 Hz) has the largest
magnitude. (See the arrows in Fig. 5.8.) When components (1)
and (2) are in counter-phase (asteriks in Fig. 5.8), component (3) has a small magnitude. This fact can be explained
as follows: when some smooth muscle filaments do contract,
they may act as mechanical stimulators for other contractile
filaments. This stimulation effect can be compensated when
different contraction components are acting in counter-phase.

5.8 TIME AND FREQUENCY CHARACTERISTICS OF SMOOTH MUSCLES DETERMINED BY THE PASSIVE STRETCH-INDUCED TENSION

Experiments were performed in order to determine time and frequency characteristics of the tension developed in smooth muscle to passive stretch. Step functions (stretch stimulation in form of a step function) were applied to the portal vein and taenia coli preparations in order to measure the step responses of smooth muscle and then to evaluate the smooth muscle frequency characteristics with the TRFC-Method described in section 3.2.

Step Responses

Fig. 5.10 shows the responses of the portal vein to a passive stretch in the form of a step function. Upon the sudden stretch, the portal vein responds with a quick increase of tension. The tension reaches maximal values between 2 and 4 sec after quick stretch; it then decreases and reaches a steady-state value after some small fluctuations. (When the spring constant of the force-transducer is low, the fluctuations have larger magnitudes.)

As Fig. 5.11 shows, the response of the taenia coli to step stretch has basically the same time course as the portal vein. The experiments by BURNSTOCK and PROSSER (1960) support our findings.

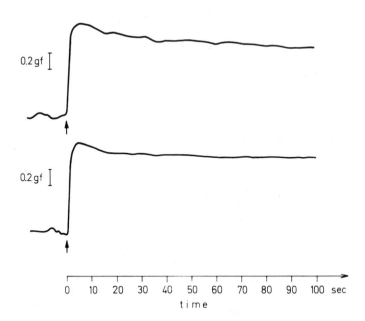

Fig. 5.10 Two typical responses of portal vein to a passive
stretch in the form of a step function. (After
EROĞLU, 1974)

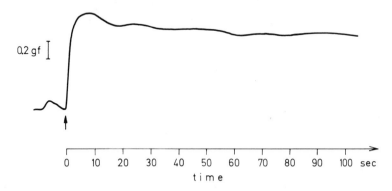

Fig. 5.11 A typical response of taenia coli to a passive
stretch in the form of a step function. (After
EROĞLU, 1974)

Frequency Characteristics

Fig. 5.12 shows two typical amplitude frequency characteristics of the tension developed in the portal vein. The abscissa is the frequency in logarithmic scale; the ordinate is the amplitude (tension amplitude) in relative units and decibels (20 log 1=0).

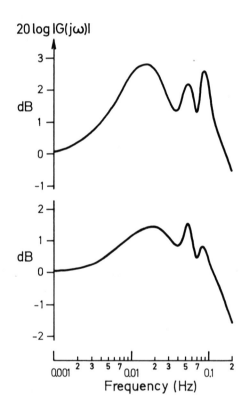

Fig. 5.12 Typical amplitude frequency characteristics of the tension induced by passive stretch in the portal vein. Along the abscissa is the frequency in logarithmic scale. Along the ordinate is the amplitude of the tension in relative units and decibels (20 log 1=0). (After BAŞAR and EROĞLU, In: PHYSIOLOGY OF SMOOTH MUSCLE. Edited by E. Bülbring and M.F. Shuba. © . 1975 by Raven Press. New York)

The amplitude characteristics depict maxima centered usually at frequencies around 0.01-0.03 Hz, 0.05-0.06 Hz and around 0.08-0.1 Hz. In other words, the amplitude characteristics show stretch sensitive components in the same frequency bands revealed by the mechanical spontaneous activity (compare Figs. 5.4, 5.7 and 5.11). However, it is interesting to note that the high frequency components (or amplitude maxima) in the vicinity of 0.1 Hz have relatively larger magnitude in comparison to the components of power spectra obtained using the spontaneous mechanical activity. If one assumes that the amplitude maxima in Fig. 5.11 are due to myogenic resonance phenomena, it can be concluded that the resonance in the higher frequency range of 0.1 Hz is larger than the resonance in the low frequency range of the Minute-Rhythm. This means, forced oscillations have greater selectivities in higher frequencies. In section 5.2, we have mentioned that any increase in the passive tension of the preparations resulted in oscillations of shorter periodicities. The amplitude frequency characteristics serve as a more objective quantification of this observation. In simpler words, the evaluation of frequency characteristics supports the following assumption: *passive stretch of smooth muscles augments the frequency of smooth muscle oscillations.*

5.9 COMPARISON OF THE RHYTHMIC ACTIVITY OF TAENIA COLI AND PORTAL VEIN SMOOTH MUSCLES WITH THE VASCULAR AUTOOSCILLATIONS

In previous studies we have already reported observations on periodical spontaneous activities of the guinea-pig taenia coli and portal vein, and on periodical spontaneous fluctuations in the vascular bed, which were handled with the same mathematical tool described here (also see BAŞAR et al., 1974a; BAŞAR and WEISS, 1970). The most typical power spectrum of spontaneous fluctuations of flow in the kidney, which appears only when the perfusion pressure is higher than 100 mm Hg, is shown in Fig. 5.13A (BAŞAR and WEISS, 1970). Fig. 5.13B shows the power spectrum of the most typical taenia coli contraction pattern. Fig. 5.13C presents the typical portal vein contraction power spectrum. One sees that the peaks around 0.06 Hz and 0.1 Hz are in agreement in all these curves. Since perfusion flow of kidneys was measured for only about 100 sec, it was not possible to make statements concerning the Minute-Rhythm between 0.01 Hz and 0.03 Hz. However, the pressure-dependent amplitude frequency characteristics of the kidney and of the coronary system of the rat heart showed a maximum of vascular flow resistance at about 0.02 Hz, which corresponds to the frequency range of the slow smooth muscle rhythm (BAŞAR et al., 1968; BAŞAR and WEISS, 1970). (See

section 4.6.)

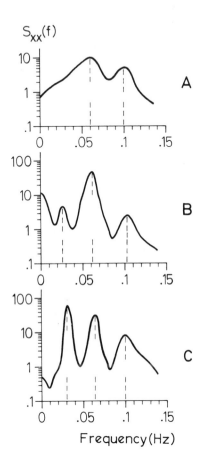

Fig. 5.13 (A): Power spectral density of flow fluctuations
in the isolated rat kidney (vascular autooscillations),
(B): Power spectral density of guinea-pig taenia
coli contractions,
(C): Power spectral density of guinea-pig portal
vein contractions.
Along the abscissa is the frequency in Hz,
along the ordinate is the power spectral
density $S_{xx}(f)$ in relative units.
(After BAŞAR et al., 1974b)

5.10 DISCUSSION OF METHODS

The methods applied in this chapter will not be discussed in detail here as we have done in Chapters 4 and 7 since most of the methodological discussions in sections 4.11, 7.21 and 7.22 are also valid here. However, we will briefly point out what the methods applied added to our knowledge in the study of spontaneous oscillations and evoked contractions of smooth muscles.

Power Spectra

The power spectra analysis brings a new point of view to the difficult task of classification of smooth muscle rhythms. The superimposition and the mutual influence of the rhythms merit important consideration for the functional classification of the rhythms. Therefore, we want to emphasize that the application of power spectral analysis adds an important point of view to the analysis of smooth muscle rhythmicity. Using this method, the investigator obtains the possibility to define the compound contraction patterns in terms of their frequency components. Accordingly, in the classification of rhythmicities, compound patterns should be considered with their spectral compositions and not with the frequency of the dominating contraction rhythm.

Theoretical Ideal Filtering

The theoretical ideal filtering method (TI-Method) has two important applications in these studies of smooth muscle contractions. First of all, the results of theoretical filtering support the data obtained by the power spectra analysis (section 5.7). This use of theoretical filtering is similar to that in studying evoked potentials: as we will see in section 7.9, the theoretical filtering method helps to confirm the amplitude characteristics computed using the TRFC-Method.

Second of all, the application of the TI-Method adds the conceptional knowledge of different stages of smooth muscle contraction. Moreover, the use of the filtered smooth muscle contractile components enables us to formulate a new autoregulation hypothesis, as we explained in detail in the previous chapter (see section 4.9).

Nonlinearities

In the systems theory analysis of smooth muscle, we did not perform any experiments to determine the type of nonlinearities that might be present. (These will be described in Chapter 6 of this book.) Nevertheless our observations support a very important concept of the

behavior of oscillating systems: in a system having two
different oscillations, it is possible for one rhythm to
force the other one into its own rhythm. Under certain
conditions it is possible for one of the rhythms to pull
the other one into one of its harmonic frequencies. (See
description of model circuit, section 6.4.) We have seen
that different smooth muscle contractions have rhythmicities
which are located in frequency ranges corresponding to the
harmonic component of the dominant rhythm, although we can
definitely show that these rhythms are different rhythms
(section 5.4). This observation indeed supports the concepts
derived from the model circuit of section 6.4, and shows
that, in biological systems, the effect of forcing to its
harmonic by the dominant rhythm can be observed under
certain conditions. Another example is given in a recent
study by HYNDMAN (1974) who investigated the role of
rhythms in homeostasis. HYNDMAN (1974) also describes
experiments where the phenomenon of one rhythm pulling
another rhythm to its harmonic is observed. He calls this
phenomenon the producing of an *"harmonic entrainment"*.

5.11 SOME PHYSIOLOGICAL IMPLICATIONS

What are the biological or biochemical correlates of smooth muscle contractile components? This is certainly one of the most fundamental questions which arise in the study of smooth muscles. The smooth muscle experiments described in this chapter were started especially in order to design a new concept for the classification of rhythms and to define the compound contraction patterns with their frequency components. The dynamics of smooth muscle which are presented in this chapter, are an important key to the understanding of the circulatory autoregulation by vascular smooth muscle, as discussed in Chapter 4.

Smooth muscles are also inherent to the gastro-intestinal tract, the urinary system, and the uterus. Knowledge of the dynamics of smooth muscles will therefore provide a powerful tool for increasing our understanding of such phenomena as peristalsis and uterine contractions.

The question, "what are the biological or biochemical correlates of the contractions?" remains yet unanswered by our studies. However, we will mention a study that makes an important step in this direction.

SIEGEL et al. (1972) performed measurements of Na^+

and K^+ exchange on isolated carotid media of dogs. Their
point of view was that spontaneous rhythmic contractions
of blood vessels should occur parallel to spikes and
oscillations of the membrane potential and that these phenomena must be based on corresponding ionic movements.
In fact these authors observed ionic exchanges in power
spectra at the frequency ranges of 0.01 and 0.02 Hz,
which thus correspond to one of the smooth muscle contractions revealed in our curves (Fig. 5.4). Although such
measurements are yet rare, they will become more common
as physiologists interested in the search for the biochemical or bioelectrical nature of smooth muscle activity
become increasingly aware of the importance, and even
necessity, of applying the rules and concepts of systems
theory to their investigations.

REFERENCES

Başar, E., and C. Eroğlu: Spectral analysis of spontaneous activity in smooth muscles. In, E. Bülbring and M.F. Shuba (Ed.): Physiology of Smooth Muscle. Raven Press, New York (1975).

Başar, E., C. Eroğlu, and P. Ungan: Time series analysis of guinea-pig taenia coli spontaneous activity. Pflügers Arch. 347, 19-25 (1974a).

Başar, E., C. Eroğlu, and P. Ungan: An analysis of portal vein spontaneous contractions. Pflügers Arch. 352, 135-143 (1974b).

Başar, E., G. Ruedas, H. Schwarzkopf, und Ch. Weiss: Untersuchungen des zeitlichen Verhaltens druckabhängiger Anderungen des Strömünswiderstandes im Coronargefäßsystem des Rattenherzens. Pflügers Arch. 304, 189-202 (1968).

Başar, E., and Ch. Weiss: Time series analysis of spontaneous fluctuations of the flow in the perfused rat kidney. Pflügers Arch. 319, 205-215 (1970).

Bozler, E.: Response of smooth muscle to stretch. Amer. J. Physiology 149, 299 (1947).

Burnstock, G., and C.L. Prosser: Responses of smooth muscles to quick stretch: relation of stretch to conduction. Amer. J. Physiol. 198, 921 (1960).

Bülbring, E., and H. Kuriyama: The action of catecholamines on guinea-pig taenia coli. Phil. Trans. R. Soc. Lond. B. 265, 115-121 (1973).

Bülbring, E., and D.M. Needham: A discussion on recent developments in vertebrate smooth muscle physiology. Phil. Trans. R. Soc. Lond. B. 265, 1-231 (1973).

Bülbring, E., and M.F. Shuba: Physiology of Smooth Muscle. Raven Press, New York (1975).

Eroğlu, C.: An analysis of spontaneous contraction patterns of smooth muscles in time and frequency domains. Thesis; Hacettepe Univ., Ankara (1974)

Funaki, S., and D. Bohr: Electrical and mechanical activity
of isolated vascular smooth muscle of the rat. Nature
(Lond.) 203, 192-194 (1964).

Golenhofen, K.: Slow rhythms in smooth muscle (Minute-
Rhythm). In, E. Bülbring (Ed.): Smooth Muscle. Arnold
Ltd. London (1970).

Golenhofen, K., und D.V. Loh: Electrophysiologische
Untersuchungen zur normalen Spontanaktivität der
isolierten Taenia coli des Meerschweinchens. Pflügers
Arch. 314, 312-328 (1970a).

Golenhofen, K., und D.V. Loh: Intracellulare Potentialmes-
sungen zur normalen Spontanaktivität der isolierten Portal
Vene des Meerschweinchens. Pflügers Arch. 319, 82-100
(1970b).

Guyton, A.C.: Textbook of Medical Physiology. W.B. Saunders
Company, Philadelphia (1971).

Holman, M.E., C.B. Kasby, M.B. Suthers, and J.A.F. Wilson:
Some properties of the smooth muscle of rabbit portal
vein. J. Physiol 196, 111-132 (1968).

Hyndman, B.W.: The role of rhythms in homeostasis. Kybernetik
15, 227-236 (1974).

Johansson, B., and B.L. Ljung: Sympathetic control of
rhythmically active vascular smooth muscle as studied by
a nerve-muscle preparation of portal vein. Acta Physiol.
Scand. 70, 299-311 (1967).

Siegel, G., H.P. Koepchen, and H. Roedel: Slow oscillations
of transmembrane Na^+ and K^+ fluxes in vascular smooth
muscle. In, E. Betz (Ed.): Vascular Smooth Muscle.
Springer Verlag, Berlin (1972).

Sparks, H.V.: Effect of quick stretch on isolated vascular
smooth muscle. Circulation Res. 15, (Suppl. I), 254-260
(1964).

Chapter 6

Nonlinearities in Biology

by E. Başar and P. Ungan

Nonlinearities in biological systems have not yet been studied thoroughly, although a few studies attempt to define some special cases detected in biological systems (CLYNES, 1961; CLYNES, 1962; SPEKREIJSE and OOSTING, 1970; VAN DER TWEEL and VERDUYN LUNEL, 1965; BORG, 1973).

In this chapter, we attempt to achieve a more general classification of nonlinearities in biological systems. For this purpose, examples are chosen from the investigations which are presented in the different chapters of the present book. It is not to be expected that the mechanisms giving rise to the observed biological nonlinearities will be understood precisely, however, in the examples

given, the reader will find important keys to the consideration of other systems showing different types of
nonlinearities. First of all, the examples given allow
for the extension of the understanding of the system
under study. Moreover, the reader will see in this chapter
that despite the nonlinear character of the biological
systems in general, he can easily use linear analysis methods in order to carry out a nonlinear systems analysis.
In particular, the brain investigator will also find a
probabilistic explanation of the development of averaged
evoked potentials of the brain.

6.1 NONLINEARITIES ENCOUNTERED IN BIOLOGICAL
SYSTEMS

According to TRUXAL (1955) the highly developed
analysis theories for linear systems are a natural result
of the well-behaved characteristics of a *linear system*.
One of the most fundamental characteristics of a linear
system is the validity of the principle of superposition:
if $c_1(t)$ is the response to $r_1(t)$ and $c_2(t)$ to $r_2(t)$, the
response to $r_1(t) + r_2(t)$ is $c_1(t) + c_2(t)$. The superposition principle is, of course, one of the ways of de-
scribing the concept of *linearity*. As a consequence of

the validity of superposition, certain test signals (e.g.,
the step function, the impulse function, or the sinusoidal
function with variable frequency) can be used to measure
system characteristics. The amplitude of the test signal
is immaterial. Another way to describe a linear system is
as follows: if a linear system is excited by a sinusoidal
signal, the output of a linear system cannot contain components at frequencies not present in the input. In other
words, the output signal is a pure sine wave of the input
frequency.

The characteristics described above are absent in
the nonlinear system: the principle of superposition is
not valid; the frequencies present in the output may not
be those of the input; the output to a sinusoidal input
has distortions. Usually, all biological systems have nonlinear behavior. Therefore, nonlinearities in biological
systems should be seriously considered. It is not in
the scope of this book to describe all the nonlinear analysis techniques. The reader is referred to the references
(TRUXAL, 1955). However, in this chapter we will try to
describe some typical biological nonlinearities and try
to understand what these nonlinearities can tell the
experimenter.

As is the case in different chapters of this book, it is expected that the reader has the basic knowledge of the technical and mathematical aspects of systems analysis. Our aim (in this book) is to show the reader how to adapt his technical or mathematical knowledge to the understanding of biological systems behavior.

The basic difference in considering the nonlinearities in technical systems and biological systems comes from the fact that the nonlinearities seen in technical systems play a very important role in the synthesis and stability problems of these systems. Since synthesis of biological systems is out of the question, nonlinearities of biological systems can serve only as keys for the understanding of the nature of these systems.

We will classify the nonlinearities of biological systems into three groups:

1- Time (frequency) independent nonlinearities

2- Time (frequency) dependent nonlinearities

3- Nonlinearities seen when the studied system has a genuine oscillation

6.2 TIME (FREQUENCY) INDEPENDENT NONLINEARITIES

The response of systems which have this type of nonlinearity depends only on *the amplitude* and *not on the frequency* of a sinusoidal input signal. These kinds of nonlinearities are also defined as *static nonlinearities*. SPEKREIJSE and OOSTING (1970) consider a system which shows the distortion produced by a "leaky" diode with character- istic y=f(x) to a sinusoidal input x= A sin ωt. They then classify the static nonlinearities as follows:

> "a) Smooth Static Nonlinearities. These are sys- tems for which the function f(x) and all its derivatives are bounded continuous functions of x in the range of input amplitudes A($|x| \leq$ A). A power series expansion of f(x) is always possible for these systems. This means that if the amplitude of a (sinusoidal) input is decreased, the result is that the amplitudes of the harmonics in the response are reduced in such a way that the attenuation is greater, the higher the order of the harmonic. In other words, the output waveform grows more and more like the input sinusoid as the amplitude of the input is progressively reduced. These sys- tems can therefore be investigated under such conditions that their behavior is approximately linear, i.e. by using "small" signals.

> b) Essential Static Nonlinearities. These are systems for which f(x) or one of its deriva- tives are discontinuous for one or more values of x, such that $|x| \leq$ A. If the average value of the input signal takes a value of x_0, and f(x) or one of its derivatives is discontinuous at x=x_0, then the Fourier expansion of the out- put signal of the nonlinearity to a sinusoidal input includes harmonics whose amplitude spec- trum is independent of the amplitude of the

input signal. In practice this means that if
the input amplitude is progressively decreased
then there is no reduction of the harmonic
content in the output of this type of nonlinearity."

6.3 TIME (FREQUENCY) DEPENDENT NONLINEARITIES

A nonlinear system will be revealed at once by not

replicating the sine wave. If the output signals have dif-

ferent wave shapes by application of different input fre-

quencies we may say that the system has *frequency dependent*

nonlinearities.

Fig. 6.1A illustrates an electronic circuit which

contains a transistor and different RC-circuits connected

to the base of the transistor.

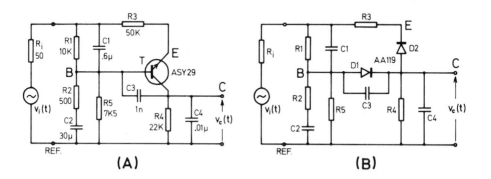

Fig. 6.1 (A): The electronic model circuit for the study
of frequency dependent nonlinear behavior.
(B): The equivalent circuit with two diodes which
represent the junctions of the transistor.

Fig. 6.2 shows input signals applied to the circuit and output signals of this circuit, which are described as follows:

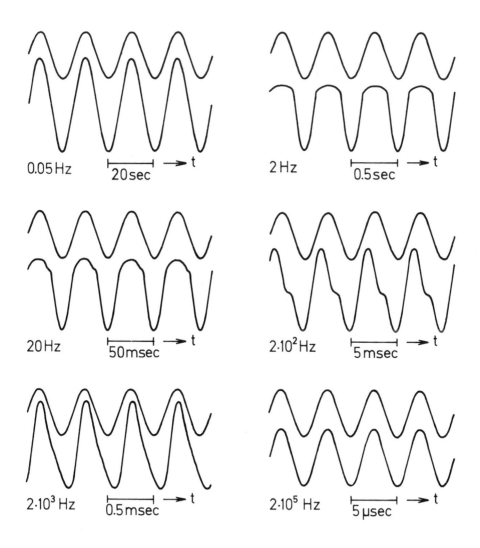

0.05 Hz |—20sec—| →t   2 Hz |—0.5sec—| →t

20 Hz |—50msec—| →t $2 \cdot 10^2$ Hz |—5 msec—| →t

$2 \cdot 10^3$ Hz |—0.5msec—| →t $2 \cdot 10^5$ Hz |—5 µsec—| →t

Fig. 6.2 The output signals of the model circuit given in
Fig. 6.1 (lower curves) for sinusoidal inputs of
different frequencies (upper curves).

1- In input frequencies higher than $2 \cdot 10^5$ Hz
($f > 2 \cdot 10^5$ Hz) the system behaves as a linear system. The
output has a perfect sinusoidal form; i.e. the system behaves linearly in this frequency range.

2- At frequencies around $2 \cdot 10^3$ Hz the circuit already
has nonlinear behavior. The increasing side of the output
wave is steeper than the decreasing side.

3- f=200 Hz. Although the increasing portion of the
output signal has a sinusoidal shape, the decreasing portion
is distorted.

4- 2 Hz $< f <$ 20 Hz . The distortion of the output
has reached a maximum. The response has a full saturation
(or the peak of the output sinusoid is fully clipped).

5- f < 0.05 Hz . The output wave has nearly a pure
sinusoidal form.

At first glance one can state that the nonlinear
properties of this circuit are out of action at frequencies
$f > 2 \cdot 10^5$ Hz or f < 0.05 Hz . As we know, the nonlinear properties of the system of Fig. 6.1A are due to the action of the
transistor T with the help of the RC-couples. Accordingly,
in frequencies $f > 2 \cdot 10^5$ Hz the transistor T is out of action.
And for very low frequencies (f < 0.05 Hz), all the capacitors
are open circuit; thus no RC-couple is left in the circuit

to provide any phase difference between the voltages $v_i(t)$

and $v_b(t)$. We will return to this important point in the

coming paragraphs.

Let us now consider the kidney preparation presented

in Fig. 4.7 (section 4.5) as a black box with frequency

characteristics, $G_k(j\omega)$, as in Fig. 6.3A. The biological

(A)

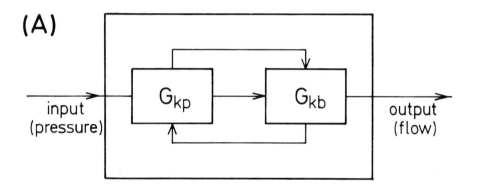

(B)

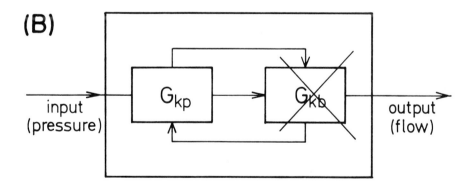

Fig. 6.3 (A): A block schematical representation of main
features of the kidney circulatory system.
(B): Reduction of this system into its passive form.
The actuators (vascular smooth muscles) are
inactivated when papaverine is added to the
perfusion medium. (See also Fig. 3.13 in
Chapter 3.)

system $G_k(j\omega)$ is composed mainly of two subsystems:
G_{kp} and G_{kb}. The subsystem $G_{kp}(j\omega)$ represents the
physical characteristics of the studied system, such as
the capacitors and resistors resulting from the experimental
setup and the capacitors and resistors of the physical part
of the kidney vasculature. The subsystem G_{kb} represents
the active biological system's properties.

Following, experiments are discussed in which sinusoidal pressures were applied to the arteria renalis of an
isolated and artificially perfused kidney: the resulting
flow is considered as the output function of the studied
biological system. (For the experimental setup and physiological functions and characteristics of the circulatory
system of the kidney, the reader will find detailed explanations in Chapter 4.) Figs. 6.4A and B show the response
of the kidney to different pressure input frequencies:

1- At frequencies around 1 Hz (in Fig. 6.4A at
f=0.82 Hz) the output wave ($\dot{V}$, volume current in the vena
renalis) has nearly sinusoidal shape; i.e. the system behaves almost linearly.

2- At frequencies between 0.5 Hz and about 0.13 Hz
the increasing portion of the output wave $\dot{V}$ is steeper than
the decreasing portion of the wave. (Compare the curve for

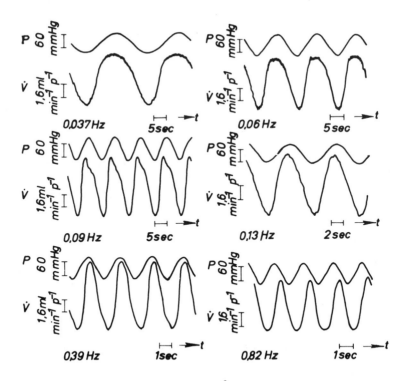

Fig. 6.4A Response patterns (flow, V̇) of the isolated and
          perfused rat kidney to sinusoidally modulated
          input signals (pressure, P) of various frequencies.
          The minimal pressure level was at 60 mm Hg.
          (After BAŞAR et al., 1968)

$2 \cdot 10^3$ Hz in Fig. 6.2.)

        3- f=0.09 Hz. The decreasing portion of the output

signal has distortions similar to the distortions seen in

Fig. 6.2 of the model electronic circuit (curves for 20 Hz

and 200 Hz).

        4- f=0.06 Hz. The distortion of the output has reached

a maximum. The response has a full saturation or the peak

of the output sinusoid is fully clipped. (Compare the curve

for 2 Hz in Fig. 6.2.)

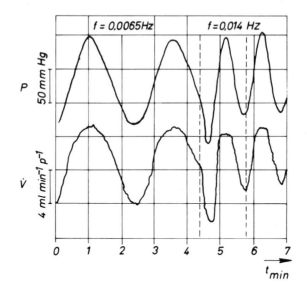

Fig. 6.4B For explanations see the legend of Fig. 6.4A.

5- f=0.0065 Hz. The output wave has nearly a pure
sinusoidal form. (See Fig. 6.4B; compare also the curve for
0.05 Hz in Fig. 6.2.)

Fig. 6.5 shows the input-output relations (volume
current $\dot{V}$ against input pressure P) of the artificially
perfused and isolated rat kidney to which papaverine is
applied. In other words, the circulatory system of the
kidney is reduced to its passive (physical) form. The
ability of the vascular bed to achieve an active vascular
resistance is abolished (see section 3.3). The *actuator*
of the biological system is out of action. This operation

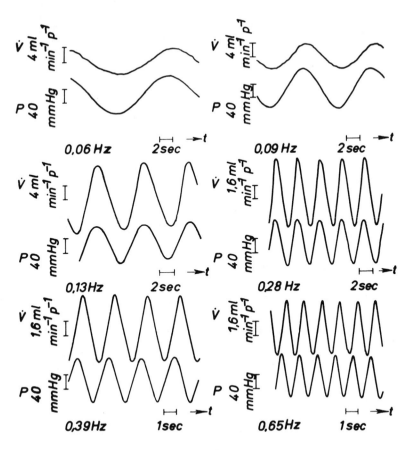

Fig. 6.5 Response patterns (flow, V̇) of the isolated and
         perfused rat kidney to sinusoidally modulated
         input signals (pressure, P) of various frequencies.
         The perfusion medium contained papaverine. (After
         BAŞAR et al., 1968)

is schematically shown in Fig. 6.3B.

As we see the output V̇ has pure sinusoidal shapes in

all frequencies between 0.06 Hz and 0.65 Hz. (In frequency

ranges f > 0.65 Hz and f < 0.06 Hz the output waves also have

sinusoidal shapes.) In this illustration we show only fre-

quency ranges where non-papaverinized kidneys had strong

nonlinear behavior as in Figs. 6.4A and B. In comparing the

curves of Fig. 6.4 and 6.5, one immediately recognizes that

the nonlinearities of the kidney circulatory system are not

due to the physical-hydrodynamic (passive) properties of

the system, but that they are rather due to the active bio-

logical procedures.

Considerations on the Model Circuit

The great similarity between output waveforms of the

electronic circuit of Fig. 6.1 and of the biological system

studied (Fig. 6.3) leads us to consider and compare the

mechanisms giving rise to nonlinear behavior in both systems.

Let us first study the electronic circuit and the causes

of nonlinearities encountered in this system.

An equivalent circuit to that of Fig. 6.1A is re-

presented in Fig. 6.1B for simplicity. The transistor T

is replaced in the equivalent circuit with two diodes D_1

and D_2, which represent the two nonlinear channels to the

output provided by the junctions of the transistor.

The shape of the output signal depends on the

relationship of the input signal, $v_i(t)$, and of the signal

at point B. Fig. 6.6 illustrates the signals $v_i(t)$ (input),

$v_c(t)$ (output) and $v_b(t)$ (voltage at the base of the

transistor T) at different input frequencies. The output
$v_c(t)$ depends on the relationship of $v_i(t)$ and $v_b(t)$. The
relationship between these voltages is represented
graphically in this illustration.

Table 6.1 is given below, showing the impedance
values of all the capacitors in the circuit for different
frequencies. This table should be referred to in order to
understand the following explanation for the development
of various output patterns given in Fig. 6.2.

FREQUENCY (Hz)

		$5 \cdot 10^{-2}$	20	200	$2 \cdot 10^3$	$2 \cdot 10^5$
CAPACITANCE	$C1 = 0.6 \ \mu F$	∞	$13.3 \ K\Omega$	$1.3 \ K\Omega$	$133 \ \Omega$	0
	$C2 = 30 \ \mu F$	∞	$265 \ \Omega$	0	0	0
	$C3 = 10^{-3} \ \mu F$	∞	∞	∞	$80 \ K\Omega$	$800 \ \Omega$
	$C4 = 10^{-2} \ \mu F$	∞	∞	$80 \ K\Omega$	$8 \ K\Omega$	$80 \ \Omega$

TABLE 6.1

We will give this explanation referring to Fig.
6.6(A-E), where the equivalent circuits and the graphical
representations of the development of various output patterns are provided for different frequencies. The variable resistors of the diodes D_1 and D_2 are shown by r.

(A)

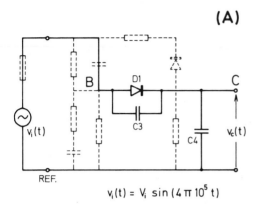

$$v_i(t) = V_i \sin(4\pi\, 10^5\, t)$$

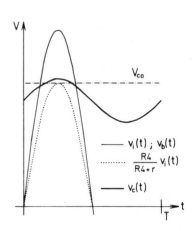

(B)

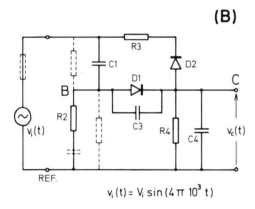

$$v_i(t) = V_i \sin(4\pi\, 10^3\, t)$$

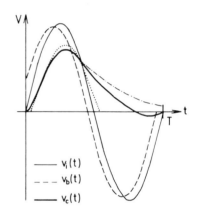

(C)

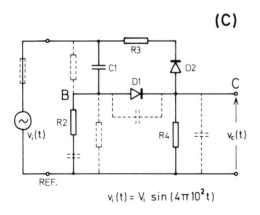

$$v_i(t) = V_i \sin(4\pi\, 10^2\, t)$$

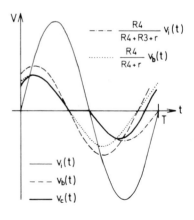

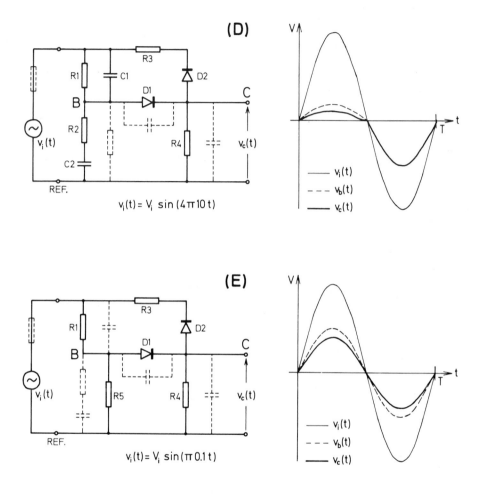

Fig. 6.6(A-E) The equivalent circuits of the model circuit
              given in Fig. 6.1 and the development of the
              output voltage patterns for frequencies of,
              200 KHz, (A); 2 KHz, (B); 200 Hz, (C);
              20 Hz, (D); 0.05 Hz, (E). (A), (B) and (C)
              are illustrated in page 188.

1- For input frequencies of $2 \cdot 10^5$ Hz and above, the effects of all the resistors and capacitors except C_3 and C_4 can be neglected (see Table 6.1). Hence, the equivalent circuit in Fig. 6.6A is obtained. The output waveform is the replication of the input signal without any phase difference.

2- For $2 \cdot 10^3$ Hz, the resistors R_i, R_1, R_5 and the capacitor C_2 can be omitted (see Table 6.1). The equivalent circuit can be regarded as a series diode detector (with D_1) with a negligible contribution through D_2. The phase difference between v_i and v_c is due to the RC-couples formed by R_2, C_1 and R_4, C_3, C_4.

3- For $2 \cdot 10^2$ Hz, the resistors R_i, R_1, R_5 and all the capacitors except C_1 are to be omitted according to Table 6.1. There is a phase difference between v_i and v_b due to the R_2C_1-couple. The positive half of the output signal follows the signal at point B (v_b) and the negative half follows the input signal v_i. Therefore, a distortion takes place during the transition from the positive to the negative half (decreasing phase of the cycle).

4- For 20 Hz, the resistors R_i, R_5 and the capacitors C_3, C_4 have practically no effect. The positive half of the output, which comes from v_b through D_1, is very much attenuated (clipped). However, the attenuation for the negative

half coming from v_i through D_2 is not severe enough to pro-

duce a clipping effect. Therefore, the output waveform looks

like a half-wave rectified sine wave.

5- For frequencies of 0.05 Hz and below, the resis-

tor R_i and all the capacitors can be omitted (see Table 6.1).

Therefore, there is no RC-couple in the equivalent circuit

to produce a phase difference between the input signal v_i

and the signal at point B (v_b). The output waveform is a

replication of the input signal without any phase difference,

as for frequencies above $2 \cdot 10^5$ Hz .

The *frequency-dependent nonlinear* behavior of the

circuit described above can be attributed to two interacting

mechanisms. One of these mechanisms is responsible for

frequency dependency and the other for *nonlinearity*. In

this circuit, these two mechanisms are represented respec-

tively by:

a) *the RC-couples,* which for different input fre-

quencies maintain different phase shifts and different

attenuations for the voltages at the base and collector

terminals of the transistor T,

b) *the transistor,* which provides different junction

resistances for different amplitudes and polarities of the

voltages between its terminals.

When a sinusoidal signal is applied to the input of
this circuit, the transistor T receives two sinusoidal signals, *with a frequency-dependent phase difference* between
them due to the RC-couples, through its collector and base
terminals.

The transistor provides two channels for the transmission of these two signals to the output. It also ar-
ranges the functional relationships of these channels according to relative amplitudes and polarities of the instant
voltages of the two signals.

As a result of these two signals reaching the output through the two channels, different waveforms for different input frequencies are obtained from the output (see
Fig. 6.2). In other words, there are two factors which are
responsible for the fact that the output signal waveform
changes with the input frequency, indicating the frequency-
dependent nonlinear behavior of this circuit. These factors
are the following:

a) two signals with a frequency-dependent phase difference resulting from the circuit elements which can provide a time constant (RC-couples),

b) at least two nonlinear channels for these two signals (the transistor, T).

When there is no time constant (e.g., if all the capacitors are removed), the circuit is still nonlinear but is no longer frequency-dependent (static nonlinearity, see section 6.2). In this case, all the output waveforms, which are obtained for sinusoidal inputs of different frequencies, have the same nonlinear waveform. Accordingly we may describe the static nonlinearities as a special case of our model circuit (the circuit without capacitors).

Conversely, when the transistor is removed (by either short- or open-circuiting), the circuit is still frequency-dependent but is no longer nonlinear.

Therefore, both factors are necessary for a system having *frequency-dependent nonlinear behavior*. Papaverine removes both of these factors in the kidney.

Let us now consider the results of the experiments on the kidney: in the higher frequency range of about 0.8-1 Hz the output (flow) patterns of the perfused kidney have almost sinusoidal shapes. In this frequency range the kidney behaves as a low-pass filter, as we have seen in section 4.8. The form of the input signal is replicated from the kidney vasculature with a phase delay. This point

is supported with the results of papaverine perfusion ex-

periments where the flow pattern responds with sinusoidal

shapes to all the input frequencies. In higher frequencies

(0.13-0.4 Hz) the flow pattern is distorted. The decreasing

part of the output curve is less steep than the increasing

part of the curve. This distortion is absent in the response

of the kidney with paralyzed vasculature (papaverinized

kidney). This fact has the immediate consequence that the

active increase of tension in vascular smooth muscle occurs

with a time delay and that the output pattern is distorted

only in the decreasing part of the sine function. In fact,

in lower frequencies (around 0.06 Hz) the distortions in

the output waveforms are seen in an earlier stage and the

response has a clipped sine wave form. This clipping effect

is due to the fact that at frequencies around 0.06 Hz the

passive increase of flow resulting from the increase of

pressure (input sine wave) is so slow that it is compensated

by the already increased vasculature tension (i.e. decreased

vessel diameter). This compensation can occur only when the

phase angle of the output function has positive values

(approximately 90°) against the input function (see also

the phase characteristics of Fig. 4.17 in section 4.6).

In the lowest frequency range (f<0.006 Hz), where the phase
angle has values around 0°, the output function has again a
sinusoidal waveform.

We have markedly pointed out here that the
output waveforms of the studied biological system and of
the simulation circuit show a strong resemblance. However,
this resemblance of the output waveforms of both systems
is certainly not due to the fact that the experimenter
finds all of the functional correlates of the capacitors,
resistors or transistor of the electronic circuit in the
biological system. But the investigators of nonlinearities
may find the same basic phenomenon and concept in both
systems: the interaction of the attenuated input function
with the active changes in the excited system. The interaction between the passive and the active increases of
vasculature tension in the kidney corresponds in our electronic circuit to the interaction of attenuated input
function $v_i(t)$ with the active part of the circuit con-
sisting of the transistor T, which is timed by means of
the RC-couples.

In concluding the considerations on time-dependent
nonlinearities, we want to emphasize that the model circuit
presented in this section (Fig. 6.1) is valid only for the

circulatory system of the kidney. Only the concept which is developed by building such a model circuit can be useful to the investigator of nonlinear problems arising in biological systems. The phase relations between the two interacting signals can certainly be different in other time-dependent nonlinear biological systems; there the outputs will have waveforms with different symmetries (see for example, KUIPER and LEUTSCHER-HAZELHOFF, 1965). The investigator should build his own model or think only in terms of phase relationships. We should also add that the frequency range which we have chosen is an adequate range for the realization of electronic systems.

6.4 NONLINEARITIES SEEN WHEN THE STUDIED SYSTEM HAS INTRINSIC OSCILLATIONS

The concept of nonlinearity in biological systems related to the problem of relative coordination of *separate rhythms* of biological systems was first recognized and analyzed by VON HOLST (1939). VON HOLST studied the interaction of two oscillating biological systems or subsystems with separate rhythms in a very ingenious way. The interaction of rhythms is the result of two different processes: *superposition* and *magnet* effects. The superposition process is regarded as resulting from the superposition of two rhythms. The magnet effect is due to the fact that one rhythm tends to pull the other into its frequency. The combined result of the two processes leads to complicated forms of periodicity; nonlinear interaction patterns are obtained in such oscillating systems. In order to demonstrate the magnet effect, VON HOLST (1939) constructed a hydrodynamic model (a pendulum oscillating in an oscillating water container), in order to predict the effects of relative coordination in the central nervous system, in locomotion problems and movements of fishes. Although VON HOLST's (1939) first demonstrations of these kinds of nonlinear interactions were based on extremely interesting ideas, there was a lack of mathematical generalization in his work. Therefore many investigators may find his ideas difficult to understand, especially in their application to various biological phenomena. This will be the main problem in this section, and our solution to this problem will form the main topic.

In the experiments described in the last section, it was seen that the existence of two separate rhythms is not always necessary to explain certain kinds of nonlinear interactions. Here we describe some further experiments on nonlinear interactions, using a self-oscillating

electronic circuit constructed specially for the purpose of
drawing deductions about neurological systems' nonlinear
behavior. A different model is described by BAŞAR (1972)
in a study of the highly complicated system of the brain;
study of that model yielded insights on the multiplicative
interactions of spontaneous activity with stimulating signals. We do not presume that the model-experiments which
we present here will surpass the thoughts and concepts of
VON HOLST (1939); however, the form in which we discuss
our experiments will allow for the following important
extensions of view beyond VON HOLST's (1939) "Gedankens"
(concepts) to be made:

1- We will describe the experiments in terms of and
from the viewpoint of systems theory. This will allow the
investigator to apply the "Gedankengang" (the way of thinking)
to various biological problems.

2- We will use a generalizable electronic circuit,
which permits performance of a larger number of extended
experiments which could not have been accomplished with a
hydrodynamic or mechanical model.

3- The experiments will have -due to the model circuit
chosen- a probabilistic nature. This fact is especially

important for the investigator about to start experiments
(or Gedankenexperiments) for the study of the nervous system, particularly the brain: the random nature of the brain
signals makes this kind of model necessary. In the hydrodynamic model of VON HOLST (1939) the probabilistic nature
is missing.

The reader who would seriously consider this section
should also have a general idea of the brain rhythmic and
evoked activities as explained in Chapter 7. Some applications of the principles derived in this section can also be
found in the study of smooth muscle mechanical spontaneous
oscillations presented in Chapter 5.

Considerations on the Model Circuit

Fig. 6.7A shows a relaxation oscillator with a discharge tube. The capacitor C is charged by the supply
voltage V_s through the resistor R. The voltage across C
increases with time until it reaches the ignition threshold
of the discharge tube. At that instant, the capacitor discharges over the tube, giving a short flash, and $v_o(t)$ drops
to zero. After this short discharge time, the capacitor is
ready again to be charged by the supply voltage. This cycle
is repeated with a frequency dependent on the time constant

(A)

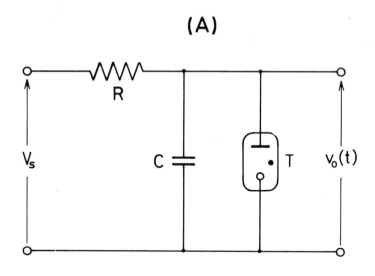

(B)

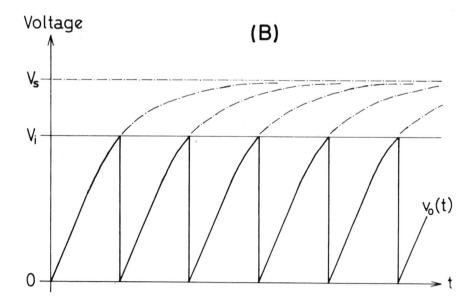

Fig. 6.7 (A): The model circuit with a discharge tube-
          relaxation oscillator.
       (B): Development of free-running oscillations
          at the output of the above circuit.

RC, the supply voltage V_s, and the ignition voltage of the discharge tube. Once these parameters are fixed, the circuit provides a continuous oscillation of a given frequency. Development of such a free-running oscillation is shown in Fig. 6.7B.

If a sinusoidal voltage is inserted into the circuit, as is done in Fig. 6.8, the internal oscillation of the circuit is no longer free, since it is affected by the inserted sinusoidal voltage, v_e. This influence of the external source upon the internal oscillation is graphically demonstrated in Fig. 6.8B. When the discharge tube is not conducting, the voltage across the capacitor is developed regardless of $v_e(t)$. Therefore, the voltage across the tube, $v_t(t)$, which is equal to $v_o(t)-v_e(t)$, gradually increases until it reaches the ignition voltage of the discharge tube, V_i. At this instant, the tube is ignited and is short-circuited for a short time, allowing the capacitor to discharge. Thus, the ignition time depends not only on the voltage developed across the capacitor, but also on the externally applied voltage, $v_e(t)$. The form and significance of this influence of the external voltage on the output is a function of the following two factors:

1- relative frequency disposition

2- relative magnitudes

of the two interacting rhythms (forcing and intrinsic signals).

In general, one of the interacting rhythms tries to pull the other to its frequency. This phenomenon is a kind of magnet effect which was described by VON HOLST (1939). Nevertheless, the magnet effect can also be observed under certain conditions where one of the rhythms tries to pull the other to one of its harmonic frequencies. (See also sections 5.6 and 5.9 on smooth muscles.) Instead of the term "to pull", we will use the term "to force". Therefore, one rhythm forces the other one to a definite frequency.

This effect is more pronounced when the frequency of one interacting rhythm (or one of its harmonic frequencies) is very close to that of the other. Furthermore, the significance of the magnet effect is enhanced with increasing magnitude of the forcing rhythm relative to that of the forced one. That is to say, a greater frequency difference between the two rhythms requires a higher magnitude of the forcing rhythm in order to elicit the magnet effect. Depending on these two factors, namely, the frequency difference between and the relative magnitudes of two rhythms,

(A)

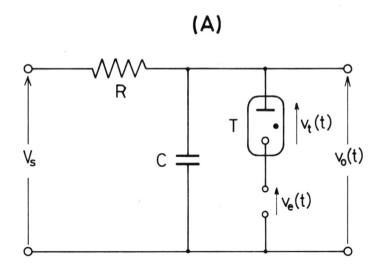

(B)

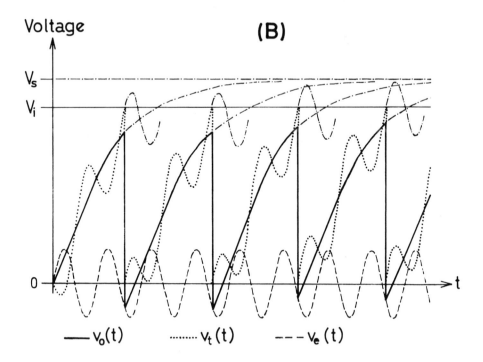

Fig. 6.8 (A): The model circuit which consists of a dis-
            charge tube-relaxation oscillator with an
            inserted control voltage, v_e.
       (B): The development of controlled relaxation os-
            cillations at the output of the above circuit.

a variety of nonlinear interaction types can be observed at
the output of the circuit given in Fig. 6.8A. Some of these
types are as follows:

a) Great frequency difference and/or small magnitude
of the forcing rhythm. No magnet effect takes place, and
the two rhythms continue to have their original frequencies
independent from each other. Consequently, a free-running
oscillation continues at the output (Fig. 6.9A).

b) Small frequency difference and/or sufficiently
large magnitude of the forcing rhythm. A complete locking
of the output with the forcing rhythm occurs. The frequency
of the relaxation oscillations is entrained to that of the
forcing rhythm, although the former would have kept going
at its determined frequency in the absence of any inter-
ference from the latter (Fig. 6.9D).

c) Considerable frequency difference and a moderate
magnitude of the forcing rhythm. A complete captivation of
the relaxation oscillations by the forcing rhythm does not
occur in this state. Instead, an unstable locking is observed. In other words, the relaxation oscillation is locked
with the forcing rhythm for some time, the length of which
depends on the magnitude of the forcing rhythm, and then it
runs independently for a short time until it is forced to

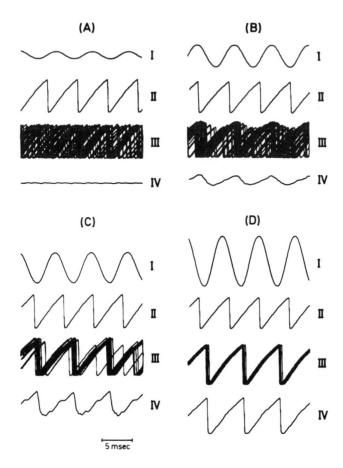

Fig. 6.9 A demonstration with the help of the model circuit
given in Fig. 6.8A of how the significance of the
magnet effect depends on the magnitude of the
forcing rhythm. The frequencies of the free-running
relaxation oscillation and the forcing rhythm are
200 Hz and 167 Hz, respectively.
I   : The forcing signal
II : The relaxation oscillation before the forcing
      signal is applied
III: A number of superimposed randomly selected
      output voltage epochs recorded in phase with
      the forcing signal
IV : The average of 256 epochs of the output volt-
      age, recorded in phase with the forcing sig-
      nal
Note that the amplitude of the average output is
increased in steps from (A) through (D) with the
increasing amplitude of the forcing signal.

interaction again. This aspect of the phenomenon involves

a probabilistic viewpoint. The probability of the discharge

tube firing is not uniformly distributed in time, but it is

maximum near the minima of the forcing oscillation. This

fact is graphically shown in Fig. 6.10. The time lag τ

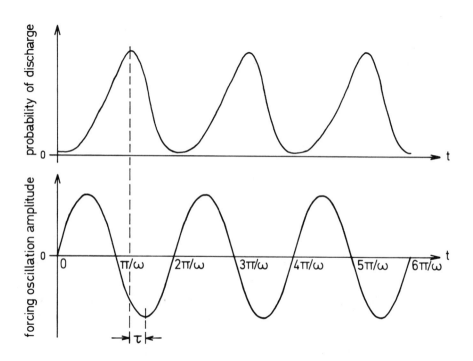

Fig. 6.10 The phasic relationship of the discharge probabi-
          lity of the tube with the sinusoidal forcing sig-
          nal in the model circuit of Fig. 6.8A.

changes with the relative magnitude of the forcing rhythm.

When this magnitude is high enough, a complete captivation

of the relaxation oscillations occurs and the firing pro-

bability reaches 1 for a specific τ. The case of unstable locking is demonstrated by Fig. 6.9B and C. The sequential

inspection of Fig. 6.9(A-D) shows how the probability of firing

at a specific phase gradually decreases (declining of the

captivation) with degrading magnitude of the forcing rhythm.

Another aspect of this state of unstable oscillations is

observed as the beating of two frequencies at the output

forming an amplitude-modulation-like pattern (Fig. 6.11).

The beating frequency is approximately equal to the fre-

quency difference of the two rhythms.

d) The frequency of the relaxation oscillation is

around the harmonic frequencies of the forcing rhythm and

sufficiently large magnitude of the latter. When these

conditions hold, a strict locking is also observed with

some patterns showing a phenomenon known as doubling or

tripling effect, depending upon whether the frequency

of the relaxation oscillation is around that of the first

or the second harmonic of the forcing rhythm, respectively.

These types of patterns obtained from the circuit of Fig.

6.8A are given in Fig. 6.12A and B. When the frequency

of the ongoing rhythm (relaxation oscillation) has some

value in between, a complete captivation can still be

observed. But in this case a higher magnitude of forcing

rhythm is required, and some cycles of the forcing rhythm

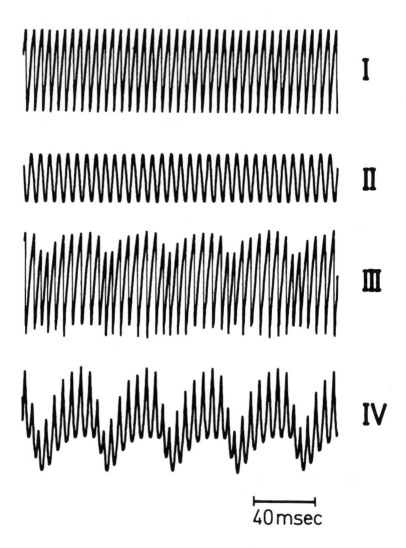

Fig. 6.11 The amplitude modulation-like pattern resulting
         from the beating phenomenon in the model circuit
         of Fig. 6.8A.
         I : The relaxation oscillation without the forc-
              ing signal (f=165 Hz)
         II : The forcing signal (f=190 Hz)
         III: The modulation pattern recorded from the
              output
         IV : Low-pass filtered output pattern with a
              beating of 25 Hz corresponding to the fre-
              quency difference between the relaxation os-
              cillation and the forcing signal (beating
              frequency: 190-165=25 Hz)

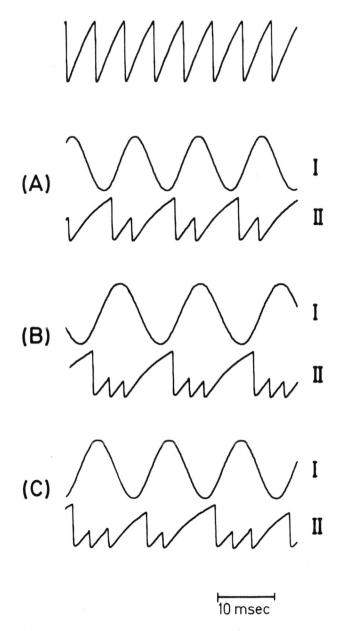

(A)   I
        II

(B)   I
        II

(C)   I
        II

10 msec

Fig. 6.12 The output patterns (II of each set) of the model
          circuit in Fig. 6.8A showing doubling and tripling
          effects. The curve at the top is the relaxa-
          tion oscillation before the forcing signal is ap-
          plied (f=200 Hz). For the patterns (A), (B) and
          (C), the frequency of the forcing signal (I of
          each set) is 90 Hz, 72 Hz and 80 Hz respectively.

correspond to double peaking of the ongoing oscillation,
whereas others correspond to triple peaking (Fig. 6.12C).
A magnet effect occurs not only around the two or three folds
of the forcing frequency, but around its higher harmonics,
as well. If, on the contrary, the frequency of the relaxation oscillation is around the sub-harmonics of the forcing
rhythm with sufficiently large magnitude of the latter, the
output also shows a complete locking. This case is demonstrated in Fig. 6.13.

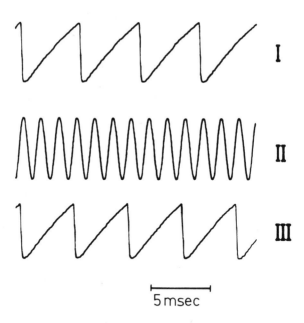

                        5 msec

Fig. 6.13 The magnet effect seen in the model circuit of Fig.
          6.8A for the sub-harmonics of the forcing rhythm.
          I   : The relaxation oscillation before the forcing
                signal is applied (f=200 Hz)
          II : The forcing signal (f=670 Hz)
          III : The output voltage of the model circuit which
                shows a complete phase-locking with the third
                sub-harmonic of the forcing signal (f=223 Hz)

6.5 CORRELATION OF THE MODEL-CIRCUIT WITH THE SPON-
TANEOUS AND FORCED OSCILLATIONS IN THE BRAIN

Now, let us correlate the above explained nonlinear effects and their consequences with the interactions between biological rhythms. As an example, we can take the electrical rhythms of the brain, keeping in mind, though, that the brain is much more complex than the model circuit given above!

Without any peripheral stimulation, the brain has intrinsic spontaneous activity corresponding to the relaxation oscillation of the above model circuit. "Neurons onto which different sensory messages can converge are often, in awake animals, in a state of quasi-permanent *repetitive firing,* a consequence of sustained depolarization due to an incessant random bombardment by afferent impulses coming from everywhere; this is a property of major importance" (FESSARD, 1961). When the brain is stimulated peripherally, for instance, by means of an acoustic stimulus, this stimulus is transduced in lower structures of the auditory pathway to an electrical signal, and an additional electrical activity is evoked at the brain output which is called the "evoked potential" (see section 7.1). This evoked activity should not be considered to be an electrical variation which undergoes no interaction with the ongoing (spontaneous) activity. (Unfortunately, this error is often made by investigators.) These two activities do undergo an interaction, the form and significance of which depend on their frequencies and relative magnitudes (see section 7.12).

A Gedankenexperiment (Experiment of Thought)

Let us suppose that the brain is stimulated by a peripheral sinusoidal stimulus with a frequency around the frequency of its spontaneous activity. Furthermore, let us assume that the stimulus amplitude is sufficiently high to create an evoked activity with adequate magnitude. The frequency of the evoked activity is to be equal to that of the stimulation signal. Under these conditions, the evoked oscillation (corresponding to the external voltage inserted into the model circuit given above) tries to force the spontaneous activity exactly to its frequency, and a phase- (or time-) locking is maintained due to the so-called magnet effect. When this strictly phase-locked (with the sinusoidal stimulation) activity undergoes an averaging process, the result is the summation of phase-locked periodical variations. The result is a high-amplitude variation with the stimulus frequency, as shown in Fig. 6.9D. If the amplitude of the evoked activity is not high or if the fre-

quencies of the evoked and the spontaneous activities are
not close enough, an unstable magnet effect occurs (or it
does not occur at all) as in Fig. 6.9A and B. In this case,
consequently, the averaged output is very small in amplitude.
In other words, if a spontaneous activity with a frequency
around the frequency of the stimulus is already going on in
the brain, the average output amplitude is high; otherwise
it is small or practically zero. This is a probabilistic
approach to the explanation of resonance phenomenon observed at the brain output due to sinusoidally modulated
peripheral stimuli. The experimental fact that the closer
the frequencies of the spontaneous activity and of the
stimulus the higher the amplitude of the averaged output is
in agreement with the above reasoning.

When the stimulus frequency is around half of the
spontaneous frequency, again a phase-locking occurs; but
this time a doubling effect is elicited accompanying the
resonance. For the cases considered above, there is only
one spontaneous frequency. In fact, more than one ongoing
activity (i.e. more than one spontaneous frequency) does
exist in the spontaneous activity of the brain. Therefore,
the resonance, which is identified by an increase in the
output amplitude around a specific stimulus frequency, is

generally accompanied by doubling or tripling effects (or the response wave has a periodicity corresponding to a non-integer multiple of the input frequency, for example, 2.5). This is due to the magnet effect which occurs at the first or the second harmonic frequencies of the evoked activity as in Fig. 6.12C. Fig. 6.14 shows the responses of the acoustical cortex of the cat to different stimulation frequencies. One should see the resemblances of these curves with the results of the model experiment given in Fig. 6.12.

Some authors describe the doubling effect as a consequence of the responses of "on and off" neurons (CLYNES et al., 1964; SPEKREIJSE, 1966). This explanation certainly has a basic reality. However, the occurence of a number of waves in the response cannot be explained with only "on and off" responses or rectification: firstly, the response functions do not always show a doubling effect regardless of the input frequency. Secondly, there is not only the doubling effect; one cycle of the output function often contains more than two waves (and sometimes less than two waves). These are the major objections showing that the on-off effect alone does not explain the complexity of the waveforms seen at the brain output.

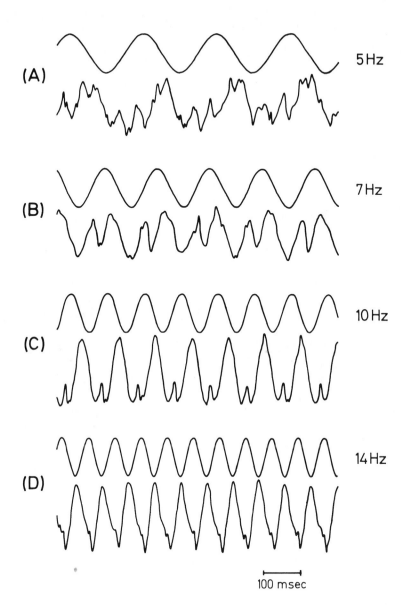

5 Hz

(A)

7 Hz

(B)

10 Hz

(C)

14 Hz

(D)

100 msec

Fig. 6.14 The evoked potential patterns recorded from the cat auditory cortex in response to sinusoidally modulated acoustical stimulation with different modulation frequencies. The upper curve shows the stimulus and the lower one is the average of 128 responses for each set. (Unpublished observations, UNGAN and BAŞAR)

The so-called magnet effect is another and more adequate explanation for doubling or tripling phenomena seen at the brain output. The peripheral mechanisms cannot be the only reason for these phenomena. The following example will support this argument.

The evoked potential patterns given in Fig. 6.14 were recorded from the cat auditory cortex in response to sinusoidally modulated tones. Before the stimulation was applied, the cortical EEG showed a spontaneous alpha activity of around 13-16 Hz. With a modulation frequency of 5 Hz, a tripling effect was seen in the average evoked potential (Fig. 6.14A). It showed that the 5 Hz-modulated stimulation signal forced and phase-locked the spontaneous activity to 15 Hz (second harmonic). Therefore, a pattern with a doubling effect was to be expected for a 7 Hz-modulated stimulation signal. The evoked potential obtained for a modulation signal of 7 Hz supported this prediction (Fig. 6.14B). A 10 Hz-modulated signal evoked a potential with less distinct doubling (Fig. 6.14C). For 14 Hz-modulated stimulation, the evoked potential was practically sinusoidal, with minor higher frequency waves (Fig. 6.14D). In this last case, the stimulation signal forced and phase-locked the spontaneous alpha activity strictly to 14 Hz, although the spontaneous activity would have kept its original frequency changing between 13 Hz and 16 Hz, with no correlation regarding its time history.

The magnet effect is also observed for spontaneous frequencies around the higher harmonics of the stimulation signal. Hence, a phase locking (strict or partial) for spontaneous activities having approximately these frequencies should also be expected. As a matter of fact, some high frequency variations are always measured superimposed on the averaged brain output due to the magnet effect at higher harmonic frequencies (UNGAN and BAŞAR, unpublished observations).

Another phenomenon, which is observed as slow oscillations at the brain output when the brain is peripherally stimulated by a sinusoidally modulated sound, can also be explained with the help of the model circuit presented in Fig. 6.8A. In Fig. 6.15, the result of such an experiment on the cat brain is given. One can easily see a very slow oscillation with a period of approximately 1 sec, besides the evoked activity with a frequency of 15 Hz following the stimulation signal. During this experiment, the EEG recorded from the visual cortex of the cat showed a spontaneous activity of around 16 Hz without any stimulation.

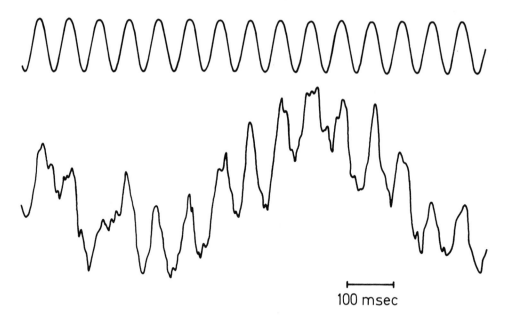

Fig. 6.15 The evoked potential pattern (average of 256
         sweeps) recorded from the cat visual cortex (low-
         er curve) in response to sinusoidally modulated
         optical stimulation (upper curve). (Unpublished
         observations, UNGAN and BAŞAR)

The stimulation signal consisted of a 15 Hz-modulated light.

The 1 Hz-oscillation seen in this figure is a result of

the beating of two rhythms; these are the evoked and the

spontaneous activities with a frequency difference of 1 Hz.

One can see the great resemblance in the patterns presented

in Fig. 6.15 (the brain output) and in Fig. 6.11 (the out-

put of the model circuit). Therefore, the amplitude-

modulation-like patterns observed at the brain output can

be explained in the same way as is followed for the explanation

of beating patterns obtained at the output of the model
circuit for unstable locking of the relaxation oscillations.

In the light of the above evidence, the spontaneous
activity of the brain should not be considered just as
random noise which has no effect on the averaged evoked
activity! As a matter of fact, three reasons can be cited
to explain why different evoked potentials are obtained in
waking and sleep stages for various brain structures. (At
this point the reader should read carefully the resonance
phenomena described in section 7.12.) These are:

1- in different stages, mechanisms with different
selectivities are responsible for evoked activities (sections
7.7-7.9);

2- brain centers have different spontaneous activities in different waking and sleep stages as far as their
frequencies and magnitudes are concerned (section 7.5);

3- different brain structures have different selectivities and different spontaneous activities (sections 7.5
and 7.7-7.9).

The second and third reasons involve the interaction
between the evoked and spontaneous activities.

Until now, we have considered the influence of a
peripheral *sinusoidal steady stimulation* upon the spontaneous
brain activity and the consequences of this interaction on
the evoked response pattern. Now, let us consider the effect
of a *transient stimulus* (such as a click or a step function)
on the ongoing activity. When such a transient stimulation
is applied peripherally, a damped oscillatory disturbance
is observed in the electrical activity of the brain, provided that the stimulus magnitude is adequate. This damped
oscillation affects the spontaneous activity as does a
sinusoidal stimulation. The significance and the form of
the interaction between this oscillatory evoked activity
and the ongoing activity, which takes place until the disturbance dies away with time (decays because of the damping),
depends mainly on three factors:

1- frequency disposition of the spontaneous and
the transient evoked activities,

2- significance of the evoked activity's magnitude
relative to the amplitude of the spontaneous activity, and

3- damping factor (decay rate) of the transient
evoked activity.

The sharpness of the evoked variation might be cited

as a fourth factor, but it is not independent of the frequency and the magnitude of the evoked activity. Concerning
the third factor, the phase- (or time-) locking of the
spontaneous activity with the evoked disturbance is more
pronounced right after the transient stimulus, and it
loosens with time. This is because of the fact that the
ongoing activity is also affected by (and partly is a result
of) other stimuli coming via various afferent connections
and uncorrelated with the presented stimulus. However, a
a more prolonged locking should be expected with an evoked
activity having a low damping factor, which corresponds to
a low decay rate.

It should also be pointed out here that even without
any peripheral disturbance, the *components of the spontaneous
activity in different frequency bands also affect each other.*
Therefore, various types of such nonlinear interactions between these components should be expected as well.

Resonance and Time-Locking Phenomena

When the reader studies Chapter 7 on rhythmical and
evoked potentials of the brain, he will encounter the systems theoretical and probabilistic implications which can
also be immediately predicted from study of the model given
in Fig. 6.8A. The weak and strong resonance phenomena of

brain potentials (described in section 7.12), especially, can be better understood through careful consideration of a model similar to the one presented. We would like to direct the attention of the reader to the strong interactions described in section 7.12, where one can easily see that the resonance phenomena observed in higher frequency ranges are strong resonance phenomena. This is because the spontaneous activities in higher frequencies generally have smaller magnitudes and, therefore, can be regularized and time-locked more effectively by the input signals (forcing signals). For example, in the cat inferior colliculus, where the spontaneous activities around 80 Hz or 180 Hz have less intense magnitudes compared to the activities of lower frequencies (as shown by the power spectrum), strong resonances around these high frequencies are observed through the amplitude characteristics. Conversely, during slow wave sleep (SWS), where large spontaneous delta waves are recorded in various brain nuclei, the resulting resonances in this low frequency range are not as significant as in high frequency bands.

We see a similar effect in studying the forced oscillations of smooth muscles: even though the power spectral density function of the smooth muscle intrinsic oscillations depicts relatively small maxima around 0.1 Hz, the spectrum of the forced oscillations (amplitude characteristics shown in Fig. 5.12) in the same frequency range reveals very

large and comparable responses to those of the Minute-

Rhythm, around 0.02 Hz. The increase of amplitudes of forced

oscillations (resonance) is always important when the ampli-

tudes of the intrinsic oscillations are small in comparison

to the forcing oscillator or forcing rhythm. These con-

siderations will be reviewed further in the concluding

chapter (Chapter 8).

A study of the relationships between the responses

to photic stimulation with various flash rates and the fre-

quency of the resting occipital EEG was made by BARLOW

(1962). A relaxation oscillator with an entraining signal

was first used as a model in his study, but only for the

demonstration of the phasic relationship between the relax-

ation oscillation and the entraining signal. The results of

the experiments were analyzed mainly in terms of response

latencies and phase shifts in the time domain. Therefore,

in the study mentioned, it was concluded that there was

only minimal and indirect evidence to indicate a true

entrainment of the spontaneous activity by the stimulation.

Despite the close resemblance between the cortical response

patterns given by BARLOW (1962) and those presented in this

chapter, only the generation of harmonic components of twice or thrice the flash rate and the slight magnification around specific frequencies (without using the term "resonance") were mentioned in his report, and these phenomena were analyzed from a limited viewpoint.

6.6 LINEAR APPROACH TO THE ANALYSIS OF NONLINEAR BIOLOGICAL SYSTEMS

In previous sections we have seen that different kinds of marked nonlinearities are observed in biological systems. One of the methods, which is used for the evaluation of the frequency characteristics from the transient evoked responses (the TRFC-Method; see section 3.2), can only be considered as a first approach in the study of biological systems, since this method is a linear analysis method. A critical check was performed by means of an electronic model in order to make sure that the TRFC-Method is capable of detecting the intrinsic frequencies of an active nonlinear system:

A typical average evoked potential of the cat auditory cortex is seen in Fig. 6.16A. Application of the TRFC-Method to this transient response gives the amplitude characteristic shown in Fig. 6.17A. This amplitude characteristic has two maxima at approximately 13 Hz and 65 Hz. Starting with these two frequency values, and also taking

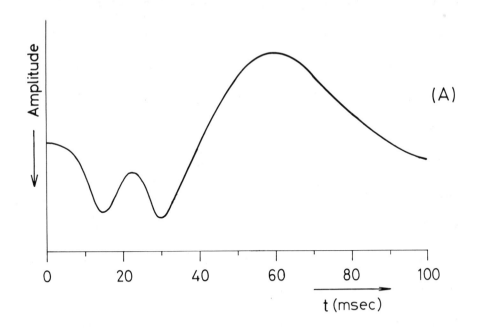

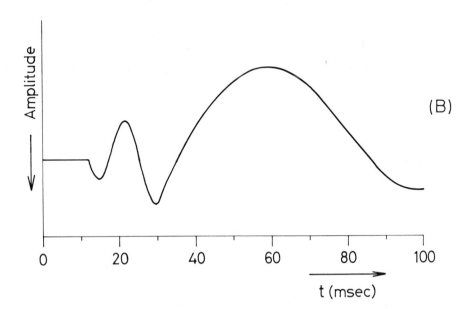

Fig. 6.16 (A): A typical auditory cortical average evoked
              potential of the cat brain.
        (B): Its simulation by means of the electronic
              model in Fig. 6.17B. (After UNGAN, 1974)

a suitable time delay into account, the model circuit of
Fig. 6.17B is then set up in order to simulate the step
response of the auditory cortex. The step response of this
model is given in Fig. 6.16B for comparison. The delay
time and the DC offset of the function generators (FG1 and
FG2) are adjusted to maintain a resemblance between the
actual auditory cortical response and the model step response. (This is done just for the sake of appearance and
has no influence upon the internal frequencies of the model
system.) The correspondence between the intrinsic frequencies of this model and the maxima of the amplitude characteristic is obvious. Detailed critical analyses with supplementary models are given by UNGAN (1974).

In Chapter 4 we obtained the amplitude characteris-
tics of the isolated rat kidneys using the TRFC-Method.
Using sinusoidal input functions instead, the amplitude
characteristics obtained gave basically similar results.
For comparison, the reader is referred to the literature
(BAŞAR et al., 1968; BAŞAR and WEISS, 1968).

Further examples demonstrating the validity of a
linear approach to nonlinear biological systems are given
in sections 7.9 and 7.19.

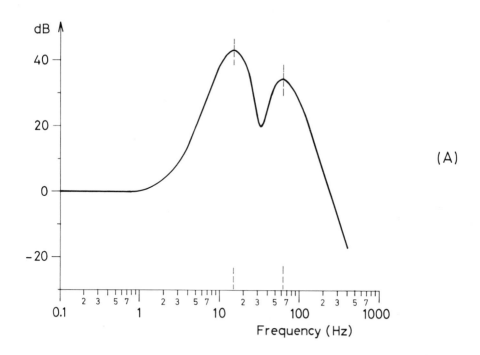

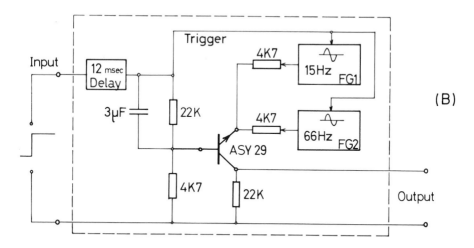

Fig. 6.17 (A): The amplitude characteristic computed from
               the average evoked potential in Fig. 6.16A.
         (B): The model circuit with internal sources (FG1
               and FG2) tuned to the frequencies of the two
               maxima of the above amplitude characteristic.
               (After UNGAN, 1974)

6.7 CONCLUDING REMARKS

We would like to draw the attention of the reader
to the following point in particular: by exciting the model
circuit of Fig. 6.1 (the circuit which gives the interaction
of the input with the phase-shifted signal) and the model
circuit of Fig. 6.8 (the self-oscillating system which is
influenced by an external signal), the investigator obtains
remarkable output patterns showing effects such as clipping,
doubling, tripling, etc. It is certainly to be expected
that the Fourier analysis of such responses will show the
presence of harmonics. The investigator should not search
for the origin of these harmonics in entirely separate
mechanisms. (In the brain, for instance, the harmonics
in the electrical activity are not necessarily to be considered as the result of separate neural groups.) However,
the investigator can certainly have a more profound understanding of the generation of various patterns of output
from biological systems through the use of model circuits
as described.

We have chosen an electronic model circuit in order
to describe the general phenomena which can arise from the
nonlinear interaction of two coupled oscillatory systems.
This is easy. However, besides the hydrodynamic model

of VON HOLST (1939), which is more difficult to understand,
one can choose examples with coupled pendulums (FEYNMAN et al.,
1963) or with alternators (WIENER, 1958). Although experi-
menting with pendulums or alternators is not easy, investigators well-trained in theory can play with mathematical
differential equations in order to establish the same basic
findings which we obtained with the help of our electronic
model. However, the *relaxation oscillator* which we presented
still has an advantage in its *probabilistic nature,* and this
is not a small advantage. Remember, the brain potentials
and many other biological phenomena have a probabilistic
nature, similar to quantum mechanics.

REFERENCES

Barlow, J.S.: The relationship among "photic driving" re-
sponses to single flashes, and the resting EEG. Quarterly
Progress Report 64, Res. Lab. Electronics, M.I.T.
Massachusetts (1962).

Başar, E.: Remarks on mathematical signal processing by the
brain during rhythmic neurophysiological stimulation.
Int. J. Neuroscience 4, 71-76 (1972).

Başar, E., H. Tischner, and Ch. Weiss: Untersuchungen zur
Dynamik druckinduzierter Änderungen des Strömungswider-
standes der autoregulierenden isolierten Rattenniere.
Pflüg. Arch. Ges. Physiol. 299, 191 (1968).

Başar, E., and Ch. Weiss: Analyse des Frequenzganges druckinduzierter Änderungen des Strömungswiderstandes isolierten
Rattennieren. Pflüg. Arch. 304, 121-125 (1968).

Borg, E.: Nonlinear dynamic properties of a somatomotor
reflex system. A model study. Acta Physiol. Scand. 87,
15-26 (1973).

Clynes, M.: Unidirectional rate sensitivity: A Biocybernetic
law of reflex and humoral systems as physiologic channels
of control and communication. Ann. N.Y. Acad. Sci. 92,
946-969 (1961).

Clynes, M.: The non-linear biological dynamics of unidirectional rate sensitivity illustrated by analog computer
analysis, pupillary reflex to light and sound, and heart
rate behavior. Ann. N.Y. Acad. Sci. 98, 806-845 (1962).

Clynes, M., M. Kohn, and K. Lifshitz: Dynamics and spatial
behavior of light evoked potentials, their modification
under hypnosis, and on-line correlation in relation to
rhythmic components. Ann. N.Y. Acad. Sci. 112, 468-508
(1964).

Fessard, A.: The role of neuronal networks in sensory
communication within the brain. In, W.A. Rosenblith
(Ed.): Sensory Communication. M.I.T. Press, Massachusetts
(1961).

Feynman, R.P., R.B. Leighton, and M. Sands: The Feynman
    Lectures on Physics. Volume I, Addison-Wesley Publishing
    Company Reading, Massachusetts (1963).

Kuiper, J.W., and J.T. Leutscher-Hazelhoff: Linear and non-
    linear responses from the compound eye of Calliphora
    Erythrocephala. In, Cold Spring Harbor Symposia on
    Quantitative Biology, Volume XXX, Sensory Receptors.
    Cold Spring Harbor Lab. of Quantitative Biol., New York
    (1965).

Spekreijse, H.: Analysis of EEG responses in man, evoked by
    sine wave modulated light. Thesis. Univ of Amsterdam
    (1966).

Spekreijse, H., and H. Oosting: Linearizing: A method for
    analysing and synthesizing nonlinear systems. Kybernetik
    7, 22-31 (1970).

Truxal, J.G.: Automatic Feedback Control System Synthesis.
    McGrauw-Hill, New York (1955).

Ungan, P.: Systems theoretical analysis of potentials evoked
    in the cat auditory cortex. Thesis, Hacettepe Univ.,
    Ankara (1974).

van der Tweel, L.H., and H.F.E. Verduyn Lunel: Human visual
    responses to sinusoidally modulated light. Electroenceph.
    Clin. Neurophysiol. 18, 587-598 (1965).

von Holst, E.: Die relative Koordination als Phänomen und als
    Methode Zentralnervöser Funktionsanalyse. Ergebn. Physiol.
    42, 228-306 (1939).

Wiener, N.: Nonlinear Problems in Random Theory. The Technology
    Press of MIT and John Wiley and Sons, Chapman and Hall,
    London (1958).

Chapter 7

Electrical Signals from the Brain

A. INTRODUCTORY REMARKS AND METHODS

7.1 ELECTRICAL ACTIVITY OF THE BRAIN: SPONTANEOUS

ACTIVITY (EEG) AND EVOKED POTENTIALS (EPs)

It has been known for a long time that the brain emits
some electrical signals. This spontaneous electrical activity
was first observed by CATON (1875) as early as 1875. Following
technological advances, which provided low-noise, high-gain
amplifiers and suitable recording techniques, it became possible to obtain some reliable tracings of the activities
emitted by the brain. These tracings, which are recorded
either superficially or through surgically implanted deep
electrodes, are called the electroencephalogram (EEG). The
periodicities of EEG, recorded from different nuclei of the

brain (or from the various locations on the skull by means of surface electrodes) under different behavioral or pathological conditions and in different sleep stages, have been categorized according to their frequencies and magnitudes (BRAZIER, 1968). Consequently, some frequency bands, such as *delta* (0.5-3 Hz), *theta* (3-8 Hz), *alpha* (8-13 Hz), *beta* (13-35 Hz), have been assumed conventionally in order to identify the various types of EEG patterns.

The study of brain potentials and their rhythms is one of the most complicated tasks that has ever been proposed to physiologists. Brain potentials and their rhythms are the net result of a conjunction of many heterogenous factors-physical conditions, anatomical organization, statistical effects and differential properties of the neuron segments-implicated in different ways (FESSARD, 1959).

The spontaneous electrical activity of the brain (EEG) can be influenced by direct or peripheral deterministic stimulation (electrical, optical, acoustical, etc., whichever is adequate). Such an induced change in the brain electrical activity is called Evoked Potential (EP). If the EPs obtained in response to identical succesive stimuli are averaged, the resultant variation is called Averaged Evoked Potential (AEP). UNGAN (1974) describes the AEPs as follows:

> "These are reasonably purified gross responses
> of large neuronal populations in the central
> nervous system and are obtained by averaging
> the brain potentials evoked by identical suc-
> cessive stimuli. The stimulation used must be
> a deterministic signal in order to interpret
> the obtained AEP."

CHANG (1959) defines the brain evoked potentials in

similar, but more physiological terms:

> "By an evoked potential is meant the detectable
> electrical change of any part of the brain in
> response to deliberate stimulation of a periph-
> eral sense organ, a sensory nerve, a point of
> sensory pathway or any related structure of
> the sensory system."

Although observations of evoked potentials have most

frequently been made in the sensory system, potentials pro-

duced by other means, such as by direct electrical stimu-

lation of the neuron, fall into the same category. The

brain evoked potentials are described as potentials recorded

in various structures of the brain and also on the human

scalp. Evoked potentials differ from the so-called spontane-

ous electrical changes in many respects, notably the fol-

lowing:

> " a) It bears definite temporal relationship to
> the onset of the stimulus. In other words, it
> has definite latent period determined by the
> conduction distance between the point of stimu-
> lation and the point of recording.
>   b) It has a definite pattern of response
> characteristic of a specific system which is
> more or less predictable under similar condi-
> tions." (CHANG, 1959)

From the systems theory point of view the study of evoked potentials is nothing else than the application of deterministic input signals to a black box showing intrinsic activity (sometimes regular and sometimes irregular intrinsic activity). The black box concept introduced in section 3.1 (see also Fig. 3.1) holds also here with all the implications. The basic difference between the black boxes studied in previous chapters and the brain, which will be the subject in this chapter, is the highly complicated structure and highly *nonstationary* behavior of this organ. However, in the present chapter, we will try to reduce the nonstationarity of brain signals using some specific methods, as we have mentioned in section 3.4, and also try to use the very complicated character of the brain areas under study, in order to eliminate difficulties coming from heterogeneous responses and *"discrepent appearing"* data revealed in brain research.

In other words, we will try to demonstrate that the brain too, despite its indeterministic way of functioning, nonstationary character and considerably high anatomical complexity, can be analyzed with tools of systems theory and that it can be reduced to a more understandable system after application of the "Biological Systems Analysis

Program" of Chapter 3. But before doing this, we will raise some difficulties related to systems analysis of the brain. We emphasize these difficulties, as we have done in previous chapters in the cases of less complicated biological mechanisms.

7.2 BASIC DIFFICULTIES FOR SYSTEMS ANALYSIS OF BRAIN SIGNALS

The reader should recall the brief classification of systems, in general, as we have given in Chapter 3. What is the place of the brain in this classification? We have already tried to point out in the systems theory configuration difficulties arising from systems analysis of the brain (BAŞAR, 1972a; BAŞAR, 1972b; BAŞAR, 1974; BAŞAR and ÖZESMİ, 1972; ÖZESMİ and BAŞAR, 1974). UNGAN (1974) has, in his study on systems analysis of cortex potentials, treated our questions and points in a more systematic manner, as follows:

"The brain is a time varying system. Because, it is very well known that there are a number of behavioral states such as *alertness*, *waking*, *drowsiness*, etc. *Sleep* is also subdivided into stages like *Spindle Sleep* (SS-Stage), *Slow Wave Sleep* (SWS) and *Rapid Eye Movements* (REM) sleep. Such a classification is, of course, not yet fully objective and has its basis on behavioral criteria. However, it is conventionaly used for the time being".

Its spontaneous activity shows that the brain is

not a causal system. This activity has its origin at the
neuronal level, and neurons do have some elements which provide the energy required for their electrical activity.
Therefore, the brain is an active system. The nonlinearity
is also a very important consequence of this fact.

A system which is lumped, time invariant, linear,
causal and passive is the simplest case of the systems
theory. Any deviation from these conditions makes the analysis more complicated.

The deviations from the simplest case create some
difficulties during the brain experiments and some compli-
cations for interpretation. We attempt to avoid these inherent difficulties as follows (UNGAN, 1974):

"i) Measurements are confined to a period short enough
to assume that the type of the brain activity has not
changed. Therefore, the brain is considered in different
behavioral states, the experiments being made and evaluated
for one state at a time.

ii) Identical inputs (stimulations) are applied successively with an inter-stimulus interval which is long
enough to maintain a stationary state for the next excitation. The responses to these stimuli are averaged. Hence,
any random noise and the variations of the EEG which are

not time locked with the stimulus are eliminated as the number of successive stimuli is maintained large enough. The average evoked potentials (AEPs) obtained by this procedure can be assumed to be the responses of a causal system.

iii) The fact that the brain is an active system does not cause any difficulty in the systems theoretical analysis directed to the frequency bands of signal transmission. This nature of the brain, however, should be considered for its system synthesis and modelling.

iv) The last (but not least) difficulty is the brain's nonlinear character. Generally, such behavior is avoided as much as possible in technical systems and design engineering, apart from the nonlinearities deliberately introduced for some control systems. But in biological systems, the phenomena created by nonlinear behaviors must be taken into account as keys which give an insight to the system, rather than trying to eliminate them. This fact is pointed out by BORG (1973) and in our earlier studies (BAŞAR, 1972a). In his study, for instance, the nonlinearities are suggested to be important in biological systems as factors which improve the stability of the system without decreasing its band width. However, before a detailed analysis the nonlinearity of the system can be ignored, and the system can be assumed to be linear as the first approach as is done in this work. Some theoretical considerations on the application of linear analysis to neuronal masses are discussed by FREEMAN (1972a)." The reader should also see Chapter 6.

In section 7.21 we will see that nonlinearities do not present an important handicap for understanding of signal transmission in the brain.

7.3 SOME ADDITIONAL COMPUTATIONAL METHODS

a) *Experimental Setup*

In this chapter, too, we will apply the program of section 3.2. However, some methods which ensure a better stationarity of the system will be explained in this section.

The experimental setup shown in Fig. 7.1 allows for the measurement of the spontaneous activity of the brain, the evaluation of power spectra, account of evoked potentials (EPs) and storage of all measured data, as well as for the evaluation of selectively averaged evoked potentials at the end of the experiments. Also the ideal filtering method (described in section 3.2) and the Wiener filter method (described in this section) can be applied after long experimental sessions, using the stored recordings.

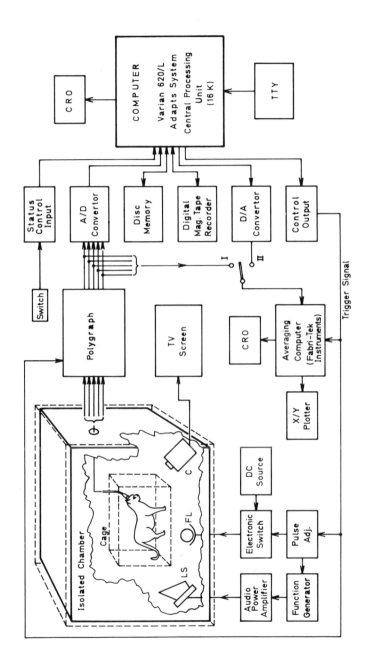

Fig. 7.1 The experimental setup used for the simultaneous recording of the spontaneous brain activity and evoked potentials as well as the storage of all measured data. The evaluation of selectively averaged evoked potentials (SAEPs) and the appli- cation of computational methods of TRFC, ideal filtering and Wiener filtering are carried out by means of this setup.

The electrical activity of the cat brain is pre-
amplified and recorded with the help of the Schwarzer
Encephysioscript EEG machine. The movements and the different waking and sleep stages of the cat are monitored
using a closed circuit television scope. The cat is able
to move freely in a comfortable cage placed in a fully
soundproof and electrically isolated echofree room. The
stimulation signals (acoustic or optic stimuli) are timed
and triggered with the Varian 620/L computer, which is the
most important device for control and evaluation in the
experimental setup. The computer triggers either an optic
stimulator system or the function generator, depending on
the nature of experiments. When triggered, the function
generator (Data Pulse 410) elicits sound signals over a
power amplifier and a loudspeaker. When a stimulation
signal is produced, single (non-averaged) evoked potentials
are recorded simultaneously from different brain nuclei and
fed to the analog inputs of the Varian computer, where they
are digitized and stored immediately in the magnetic tape
controlled by the computer. The second computer (Fabri-Tek
Instrument-Computer FT-1072) is used to monitor the AEPs
which are also obtained conventionally on-line. The non-
selective AEPs obtained with the FT-1072 computer are used

only for monitoring purposes during the recording sessions. The FT-1072 computer serves also for the monitoring of all results obtained with the Varian computer and to drive the X/Y Recorder (HP-7005 B) to plot all the evaluated data (selective AEPs, power spectra, frequency characteristics, filtered AEPs).

The advantages of this experimental setup are that it enables the experimenter to evaluate the recorded electrical signals of the brain after long recording sessions and also to apply diverse computational methods successively after the experiments have finished. These methods will be described in this section.

The disc-memory of the Varian computer shown in Fig. 7.1 allows the segmentation of complicated and long computation problems. It helps to increase the effective core memory and provides the possibility of increasing the number of simultaneously applied methods. The computation time is shortened and subsequently more data can be stored and evaluated.

b) *Selective Averaging*

Since the spontaneous activity of the brain has a nonstationary character, the conventional averaging method is not the ideal method for the investigator interested

in analyzing evoked responses in brain states during almost
invariable experimental conditions. In order to eliminate
the disadvantages of the conventional averaging method,
which are due to the nonstationarity of EEG, we have used
a selective averaging method. (For information on the conventional averaging method the reader is referred to literature: BRAZIER and WALTER, 1972; MATOUŠEK, 1973.) The
method presented permits the experimenter to select single
EPs after the experiments and to eliminate perturbations
and stage changes which could occur during the recording
of evoked potentials. The experimental and computational
procedures to obtain selectively averaged evoked potentials
are carried out with the help of the experimental setup
shown in Fig. 7.1. The procedures for the selectively averaged evoked potentials (SAEPs) are as follows:

The cat is placed in a cage in a soundproof and
echofree isolated room and can be freely moving, resting
or sleeping. The movements are monitored on the scope of
a closed circuit television in the laboratory where the
EEG machine, the computer and all the necessary instruments
are located. The stimulation signals are produced using a
function generator and power amplifier. The Varian computer
triggers the function generator, and simultaneously,

the brain potentials are amplified with the help of the EEG machine. The electrical activity from various brain nuclei are recorded simultaneously and continually by the EEG machine. The potentials evoked following each stimulus (which has a duration of 3 seconds and is applied at intervals of 16 seconds) are digitized by the Varian computer and are stored successively on magnetic tapes driven and controlled by the same computer. The movements of the cat and the transitions from one brain stage to another are marked on the EEG recordings and also in the experimenter's book.

After the recording session, the duration of which depends on the condition of the cat and on the experimental needs, the data processing for the evaluation of selectively averaged evoked potentials commences. The individual sweeps or EPs are averaged, taking into account the following criteria:

1) the EPs, where a movement artifact is observed and
2) the EPs, during which a transition from one stage to another is observed, are discarded.

An average of EPs is evaluated only where a homogeneous stage is recorded in the cortical EEG recordings.

For example, when a selectively averaged evoked potential
in the waking stage is evaluated, none of the recorded
epochs which could contain a deviation from the waking
stage (e.g., a single 12-14 Hz spindle) can be considered.
During studies which we will present in the next sections,
7.5, 7.6 and 7.7, we mainly selected three types of EPs:
The potentials evoked during waking stage, spindle sleep
stage and slow wave sleep stage. The criteria for the
selection of EPs are described in following sections where
waking and sleep stages are handled separately.

The procedure for selective averaging is shown
below schematically.

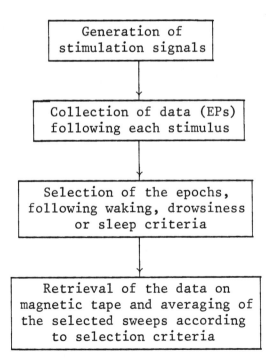

c) Power Spectra after Welch

In order to obtain the most descriptive, smooth power spectra, purified from insignificant minor peakings, we use a method proposed by WELCH (1967). This method consists of the followings steps, which are accomplished by means of the computer.

1) A rather long period of EEG is sampled with a sampling interval adequate for the highest frequency interested, and this data block, which presumably represents a typical stage of a given EEG pattern, is recorded on magnetic tape during the measurements.

2) This record is retrieved after the measurements and is sectioned in time into N overlapped segments. The length of segments (or the number of segmentations) are determined according to the frequency resolution required.

3) A data window, W(t), of the following form is applied to each segment:

$$W(t) = 1-t^2 \qquad (-1 \leq t \leq +1)$$

4) Windowed segments are Fourier transformed using a FFT algorithm, and N modified periodograms are obtained.

5) Power spectrum estimate of the EEG record is obtained by averaging these modified periodograms.

d) *TRFC-Method*

See section 3.2.

e) *Theoretical Isolation Method*

See section 3.2.

f) *A Posteriori Wiener Filtering*

A posteriori Wiener filtering of evoked potentials was first proposed by WALTER (1969) and applied by NOGAWA et al. (1973). We included the Wiener filtering method in our computational program in order to compare this method with the selective averaging method presented in the sub-section 7.3 (b).

The Wiener filter procedures are as follows: after recording M individual epochs of evoked potentials, the Wiener filtering is applied by the following formula:

$$\bar{Y}(j\omega) = \frac{1}{M-1} \left[\frac{M\,|\bar{X}(j\omega)|^2}{\bar{S}(\omega)} - 1 \right] \bar{X}(j\omega)$$

where, $\bar{X}(j\omega)$: average of the Fourier transforms of all the epochs (i.e. the Fourier transform of the conventional AEP),

$\bar{S}(\omega)$: average of the power spectra of all the epochs (i.e. average of $|X(j\omega)|^2$),

$\bar{Y}(j\omega)$: Fourier transformed estimate of the Wiener
        filtered AEP,
   ω : $2\pi f$ (f is the frequency).

The inverse Fourier transform of $\bar{Y}(j\omega)$ gives the
estimate of Wiener filtered AEP in the time domain. Fourier
transforms are carried out by a FFT algorithm. NOGAWA et
al. (1973) first applied this method for estimating
human visual evoked potentials.

During our studies we also applied the Wiener filtering
method in order to estimate the evoked potentials of diverse
brain nuclei. However, as the discussion of results
(section 7.7) will show, the selective averaging method
is much easier to apply and more reliable. Therefore the
estimation of evoked potentials which will be presented
in the coming sections (7.5 and 7.7) was performed with the
help of the selective averaging method rather than the
Wiener filtering method.

7.4 SHORT REVIEW OF THE ANATOMY AND PHYSIOLOGY OF
SOME PATHWAYS OR SUBSYSTEMS OF THE BRAIN

a) *Major Auditory Pathways*

Fig. 7.2 illustrates the major auditory pathways
and some of the related nuclei. Nerve fibers from the
spinal ganglion of the organ of Corti enter the dorsal and

ventral cochlear nuclei located in the upper part of the
medulla. The second order neurons of the dorsal cochlear
nucleus cross to the *superior olive* of the opposite side,
where many terminate.

Third order neurons send their axons via the lateral
lemniscus to the *inferior colliculus*, where some cross to
the opposite side. (Some terminate at a lower level in the
nucleus of *the lateral lemniscus*.) A few fibers cross from
the nucleus of the lateral lemniscus through the commissure
of Probst to the contralateral nucleus, and still other
fibers cross through the inferior collicular commissure
from one inferior colliculus to the other. From the inferior
colliculus, the pathway then passes through the peduncle of
the inferior colliculus to the *medial geniculate nucleus*
where all the fibers synapse. From here, the auditory tract
spreads by way of the auditory radiation to the *auditory
cortex* (GUYTON, 1971; BRAZIER, 1968).

Several points of importance in relation to the
auditory pathway should be noted. Collaterals from the main
auditory pathway pass into the brain stem reticular formation.
Direct connections between the inferior colliculus and
the auditory cortex are also established. Several important
pathways also exist from the auditory system into the

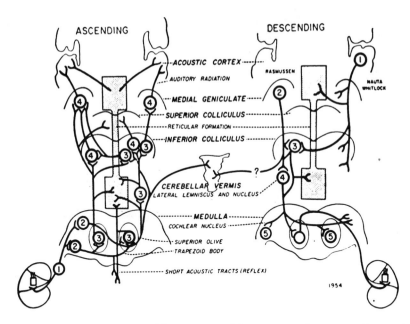

Fig. 7.2 On left : The afferent auditory pathways. Second,
                    third and fourth order neurons are
                    indicated by numerals.
          On right : The descending pathways of the auditory
                    system.
                    (After GALAMBOS, 1956)

cerebellum: (1) directly from the cochlear nuclei, (2) from

the inferior colliculi, (3) from the reticular formation,

and (4) from the cerebral auditory areas. Moreover, we should

indicate that interconnections between the thalamus and the

limbic system also exist (POWELL, 1973) (Fig. 7.4).

    Fig. 7.3 represents the afferent auditory pathways

of Fig. 7.2 with systems theory convention. The input of

the system is the ear. Different outputs can be defined or

chosen. When the investigator locates his electrodes in

the cortex, the output will be measured in the cortex; if

he locates the electrodes in the medial geniculate nucleus
the output signal will be the potential changes in the
medial geniculate nucleus. The reader should be aware of
the fact that the auditory pathway of the brain is an
extremely complicated system, especially compared with the
vascular systems described in Chapter 4 (Figs. 4.3, 4.4, 4.5).
Signal transport through the auditory pathway occurs, as
this schema illustrates, in the major brain centers, such
as the midbrain, brain stem, reticular formation, thalamus,
cerebellum, cortex, etc. In other words, the whole brain
is involved with the signal transmission of signals elicited
by auditory stimulation. Therefore, it should be expected
that the transfer function of signal transmission through
the auditory pathway must be very complicated.

It would be very difficult (or almost impossible)
to consider the auditory pathway as a fully isolated system
in the brain. Although the hippocampus is not an auditory
nucleus, it has direct connections with some nuclei of the
thalamus (Fig. 7.4). On the other hand, all these nuclei
are interconnected through the reticular formation.
Therefore, in measuring outputs from the auditory pathway,
one can never exclude influences of the limbic system
nuclei nor the influence of the visual pathway (collaterals

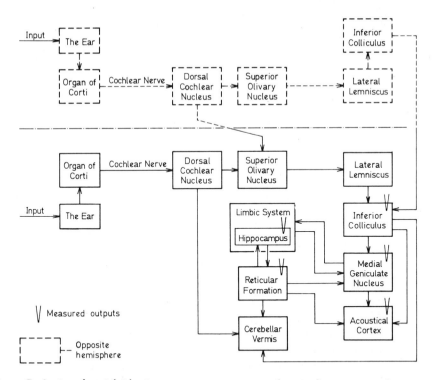

Fig. 7.3 A simplified systems theoretical illustration of the afferent auditory pathways and some related nuclei. Note that only the cross connections from one hemisphere to the other are presented. (After BAŞAR et al., 1975b)

between superior and inferior colluculi). Similarly, measurements in different parts of the cortex can not be considered as outputs of morphologically or functionally isolated structures, since various cortical areas are inter-connected through association areas (for example, the acoustical and motor cortices). (See THOMPSON, 1967).

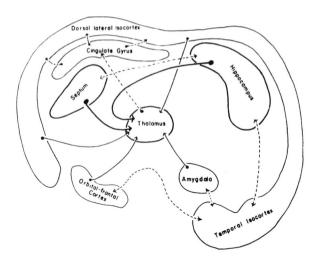

Fig. 7.4 Thalamic emphasis of limbic connections. The solid
lines, especially the darker ones from septum and
hippocampus, emphasize the main point of this
evaluation of selected limbic projections. The
light lines, especially the broken ones, are
based on the work of other investigators. (After
POWELL, 1973)

b) *The Hippocampus and The Limbic System*

The hippocampus is a rather large nuclear mass lying

in the depths of the cerebrum, shaped grossly like a long

curved tube bordering the floor of the lateral ventricle.

Like the amygdala it is a large nucleus structure, forming

a portion of the limbic system, whose functions are unknown.

The gross electrical activity recorded from the hippocampus

in infraprimate mammals exhibits a characteristic slow

(4 to 7 Hz) "theta" rhythm. There has been considerable

speculation about possible hippocampal function, but there

is a lack of solid evidence. The hippocampus has been

implicated in *emotion, visceral activity, immediate memory*

and as a part of a behavior supressor system. The discussion

of the hippocampal function is not in the scope of this

book. However, we will briefly discuss the fundamental

hypothetical hippocampal functions in order to draw the

attention of the reader who does not have an extended back-

ground in functional neurophysiology to the fact that the

hippocampus should have quite a different function from the

nuclei of the auditory pathway mentioned in the previous

section.

THOMPSON (1967), described some of the anatomical

interconnections as follows:

> "{Fig. 7.5} illustrates some of the better known
> anatomical interconnections among limbic struc-
> tures (KAPPERS et al., 1963; NAUTA, 1958; NAUTA,
> 1962; PRIBRAM and KRUGER, 1954; BRADY, 1961;
> BRADY, 1962). The olfactory bulb projects
> directly to the olfactory tubercle, prepyriform
> cortex, and a portion of the amygdaloid nucleus.
> The olfactory tubercle in turn projects to the
> *septal area*. The prepyriform and periamygdaloid
> cortical areas (lying on the base of the
> cerebral hemisphere) also receive projections
> from the diffuse thalamic system. The *entorhinal
> area*, lying just posterior to the periamygdaloid
> region, receives connections from the diffuse
> thalamic system and temporal neocortex, and
> projects to the *hippocampus*. This latter struc-
> ture, embedded in the temporal lobe, also
> receives fibers from the *presubiculum* and from
> the *septal area*. All of its output is carried
> by a fiber bundle called the *fornix*. This pro-
> jects to the septal area, several regions of

the *hypothalamus*, the diffuse thalamic system,
and the central gray of the midbrain. The
presubiculum, all of whose output goes to the
hippocampus, receives input from the cingulate
gyrus and from the diffuse thalamic system.
The *cingulate gyrus* in turn receives projections
from the anterior thalamic nuclei and diffuse
thalamic system. It projects to the presubiculum,
several thalamic regions, the hypothalamus and
several regions of the brain. The *amygdala*,
lying near the base of the cerebrum, receives
input from the olfactory bulb and the basal
temporal neocortex and sends fibers to the
septal area and the hypothalamus. The septal
area receives fibes from the hippocampus and
amygdala, and connects to the thalamus,
hippocampus, and brain stem. The reticular
formation finally, projects to the diffuse
thalamic systems, the hypothalamus and the
cerebral cortex, and receives projections from
a variety of systems.

Perhaps, the most significant generalizations
to be made about all these structures are: one,
they are all relatively directly interconnected
with one another, and two, they all seem to be
involved in one way or another with emotional
aspects of behavior (some authorities feel that
the hippocampus is an exception to this rule)."

ALTMAN et al. (1973) summarizes only the well-

established relations of the hippocampus as follows:

"(1) reciprocal connections with the septum,
 (2) afferents from the entorhinal cortex, and
 (3) efferents to the anterior thalamus, directly
and by way of the mammillary body. Connections
with other structures are hypothetical and, at
best, indirect ones. Thus, the outstanding
feature of the hippocampus is that, except for
sparse projection to some hypothalamic (other
than mammillary) and tegmental nuclei, it has
direct connections with neither primary sensory relay and projection areas nor with major
visceral or somatic motor structures."

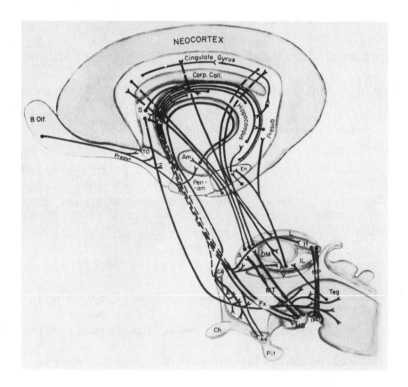

Fig. 7.5 Schematic diagram of the principal anatomical relationships between the allocortex, the jucta-
allocortex, and the several subcortical structures
considered in the present treatment of the limbic
system. The brain-stem portions of the system have
been schematically displaced from the hilus of the
hemisphere and represented in the lower half of the
illustration in order to facilitate visualization
of the numerous anatomical interconnections involving
these structures. Abbreviations: A, anterior nucleus
of the thalamus; Am, amygdaloid complex; Ar, arcuate
nucleus; B.Olf, olfactory bulb; CA, anterior commissure; Ch, optic chiasm; Corp. Call, corpus callosum;
DM, medial dorsal nucleus of the thalamus; En,
entorhinal area; Fx, fornix; H, habenular complex;
HP, habenulo-interpeduncular tract; IL, intralaminar
thalamic nuclei; IP, interpeduncular nucleus; L,
lateral thalamic nucleus; MB, mammillary body; MT,
mammillothalamic tract; Periam, periamygdaloid
cortex; Pit, Pituitary; Pepyr, prepyriform cortex;
Presub, presubiculum; S, septal region; Teg, midbrain tegmentum; TO, olfactory tubercle; V, ventral
nucleus of the thalamus. (After BRADY, 1961)

Fig. 7.6A shows the schematic diagram of the hippocampal formation, and Fig. 7.6B sumarizes schematically the interrelationships of the hippocampus.

c) Reticular Formation

In the scope of this book it is not possible to try to describe perfectly the anatomical and functional organization of the reticular formation, which is a complicated polysensory structure of the brain-stem. In the coming sections (sections 7.5, 7.6, 7.7 and 7.8) we will describe experiments on dynamics of reticular formation rhythmic and evoked potentials. Therefore, we will mention here briefly some important anatomical and physiological features of the brain-stem reticular formation. (The reader is referred to excellent reviews on the reticular formation: BRAZIER, 1968; HERNANDEZ-PEON, 1961; GROSSMAN, 1967; THOMPSON, 1967; MONNIER, 1968; MORUZZI, 1972; VALDMAN, 1967.)

BRAZIER (1968) summarizes some of the anatomical and functional features of the reticular formation as follows:

"In the brain stem, among the long ascending
and descending fibre tracts that pass through
it, lie many nuclei, the nuclei for the cranial
nerves being the most prominent. But in addition to the latter there is a central network

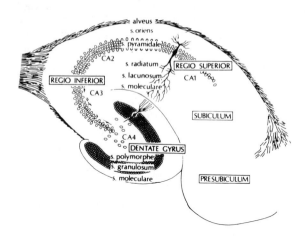

Fig. 7.6A Schematic diagram of the hippocampal formation.
        The layers of the dentate gyrus and Ammon's horn
        (CA1-4) are indicated together with a drawing of a
        granule cell and a pyramidal cell. (After ALTMAN
        et al., 1973)

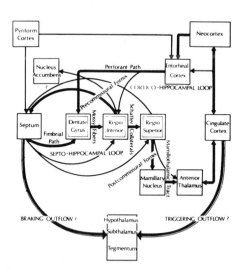

Fig. 7.6B Schematic diagram of the interconnections of the
        hippocampus. Components of the hippocampus are
        indicated by double-lined boxes in the center.
        (After ALTMAN et al., 1973)

of neural tissue containing cells which give
rise to longitudinal fibres of considerable
length, running both rostrally and caudally
{Fig. 7.7A}. Branching collaterals from the
axons together with prolific dendritic rami-
fications from the cell bodies, mostly at
right angles to the longitudinal axis, form
what HERRICK described as *a web of tissue*.
And because of its net-like structure this
crowded mesh is known as the reticular
formation of the brain stem.

The reticular formation extends through the
central core of the bulb, pons and mid-brain,
resembling in some ways a rostral continuation
of the grey matter that extends throughout
the spinal cord. Functionally, and to a certain
degree topographically, two main influences
may be differentiated at the level of the brain
stem: a descending system, modulating spinal
activity by inhibitory and facilitatory influence over the hypothalamus, thalamus, the
neocortex, and the older rhinencephalic stuc-
tures."

The reticular function is mostly involved in the

control of sleep and waking. Although we do not mention

here all the functions attributed to the reticular formation,

we will emphasize a working hypothesis which is formulated

by HERNÁNDEZ-PEÓN (1961) as follows:

"1) The brain stem reticular system is a region
where impulses of all sensory modalities converge. It is reached by impulses from the lower
segments of the specific afferent paths as well
as by those arising from the cortical receiving
areas.

 2) The same central region is able to decrease
or increase the excitability of most sensory

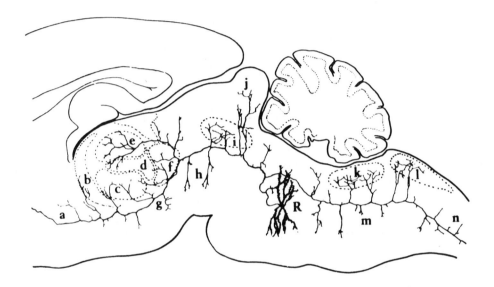

Fig. 7.7A A sagittal section of two-day rat showing a single
          large reticular neurone of the nucleus gigantocel-
          lularis of the medulla. The large cell emits an
          axon which bifurcates into caudal and rostralrun-
          ning segments. The caudal segment projects upon
          spinal proprioneurones and motor neurones. The
          rostral segment extends into both dorsal and ventral
          subthalamus. Areas innervated include (a) basal
          forebrain; (b) nucleus reticularis thalami; (c) com-
          missural nuclei of medial thalamus; (d) thalamic
          intralaminar system; (e) dorso-medial nucleus;
          (f) centromedianparafascicular complex; (g) zona
          incerta; (h) mesencephalic tegmentum; (i) nuclei
          of 3rd and 4th cranial nerves; (j) inferior
          colliculus; (k) nucleus of 12th cranial nerve;
          (l) nucleus gracilis; (m) medullary reticular
          formation; (n) ventral half of spinal cord.
          (After BRAZIER, 1968)

neurons, and thus to inhibit or facilitate sensory transmission at all the levels of the specific afferent paths.

 3) The centrifugal control of sensory paths exerted by the reticular system is tonic and selective.

It follows that the core of the brain stem may be looked upon as a form of *high command* which constantly receives and controls all information from the external and internal environment, as well as from other parts of the brain itself. But at a given moment only a limited part of the information reaches this central area, and a large number of informing signals are excluded. The exclusion of afferent impulses from sensory receptors takes place just as they enter the central nervous system. Therefore, the first sensory synapse functions as a valve where sensory filtering occurs.

We might conceive the reticular mechanisms of sensory filtering as formed by a feedback loop with an ascending segment from second-order sensory neurons to the reticular formation and descending limb carrying impulses in the opposite direction. It is not unlikely that both centripetal and centrifugal limbs of the loop contain specific facilitatory and inhibitory fibers with reciprocal neuronal connections, as illustrated in {Fig. 7.7B}. Such an arrangement would prevent over-activation of sensory neurons and, therefore, an excessive bombardment of the brain by afferent impulses. In this way, the dynamic equilibrium operating at the entrance gates of the central nervous system would preserve the delicate and selective mechanisms of sensory integration."

"{Fig. 7.7B} illustrates a working hypothesis according to which three fundamental levels of the central nervous system participate in the amplification, integration, and filtering

of sensory signals. It must be emphasized that
the oversimplified diagram by mo means pretends
to include all the neuronal systems involved
in the regulation and integration of sensory
impulses, nor is it claimed that the postulated
functions are exclusive to the corresponding
levels."

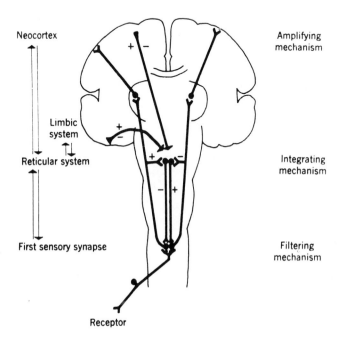

Fig. 7.7B Schematic representation of some of the main
          neuronal circuits involved in the transmission
          and integration of sensory impulses. (After
          HERNÁNDEZ-PEÓN, 1961)

We will also attract the attention of the reader

to Figs. 7.2, 7.5, 7.6 and to the related texts.

d) *The Visual Pathway*

The major afferent pathways of the visual system are

relatively simple (Fig. 7.8) (THOMPSON, 1967).

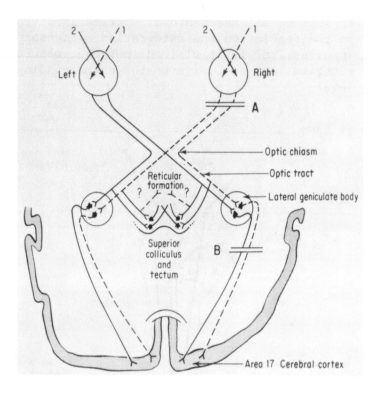

Fig. 7.8 Schematic diagram of the visual system. Section
        at A eliminates input from right eye, but sec-
        tion at B eliminates input from the right half
        of each eye. (Modified from GARDNER, E.,
        FUNDAMENTALS OF NEUROLOGY, SAUNDERS, 1952)

   "In lower vertebrates, such as the frog the
    entire optic nerve from the right retina goes
    to the left side of the brain, and vice versa.
    In higher vertebrates, where some degree of
    binocular vision exists, a portion of each
    optic nerve goes to each side of the brain.
    In man, *optic nerve fibers* from the left half
    of the retina (representing the right half
    of each visual field) project to the left
    lateral geniculate nucleus of the thalamus and
    fibers from the right half of each retina pro-
    ject to the right lateral geniculate nucleus.

The resorting of fibers takes place at the *optic chiasm*, the point at which the two optic nerves come together. Although the retina grows out from the brain embryologically, and the optic nerve fibers are at the very least second-order fibers (receptors–bipolar cells–ganglion cells) convention dictates that the fibers from the retinas to chiasm are called optic nerves and those from chiasm to *CNS* are called optic tracts. The optic tracts synapse in the lateral geniculate body, the thalamic relay nucleus with projections to the visual region of the cerebral cortex. Each lateral geniculate body is typically composed of several layers or regions, three in the cat and six in primates. In the cat the top and bottom layers receive optic tract fibers from the contralateral eye and the middle layer from the ipsilateral eye. In the six-layered primate geniculate body (layers termed 1 to 6 from ventral to dorsal) layers 1, 4, and 6 receive projections from the contralateral eye and layers 2, 3, and 5 from the ipsilateral eye.

Although the projections from the optic tract to the lateral geniculate body to the cerebral cortex constitute the main visual pathways in higher vertebrates, there are several other pathways. Some optic fibers project to the superior colliculus in the midbrain. In lower vertebrates like the frog, which have no cerebral cortex or lateral geniculate body, the superior colliculus is the major receiving area for visual projections. (There are four separate layers of cells in the frog superior colliculus that appear to be differentiated functionally as well as histologically.) A portion of the optic tract fibers also connect to the pretectal area (a region in front of the superior colliculus) in the midbrain. This pathway appears to mediate the pupillary reflex response to light (i.e. contraction of pupils in bright light, MAGOUN and RANSON, 1935). Electrophysiological and anatomical evidence indicates the existence of projections

from the visual system into the midbrain
reticular formation (FRENCH, VERZEANO and
MAGOUN, 1953). Anatomical data suggests that
might be due to a pathway from the superior
colliculus to the reticular formation (BRODAL,
1957). Finally, there appears to be a projection of optic tract fibers to the hypothalamus,
at least in birds, where it is believed to be
involved in the control of reproductive and
migratory behavior (BENOIT, 1962)."

B. DYNAMICS OF RHYTHMIC AND EVOKED POTENTIALS
   IN THE AUDITORY PATHWAY, RETICULAR FORMATION
   AND HIPPOCAMPUS

The measurements of brain potentials which will be described in the following sections were performed using chronically implanted cats. The recording electrodes were located in some nuclei of the auditory pathway: acoustical cortex (gyrus ectosylvian anterior), GEA; medial geniculate nucleus, MG; inferior colliculus, IC; mesencephalic reticular formation, RF; and hippocampus, HI. The electrodes were placed in these nuclei according to the stereotaxic atlas by SNIDER and NIEMER (1961) in the following coordinates: medial geniculate nucleus (Fr.A:3.5, L:9, H:1.5), inferior colliculus (Fr.P:2.5, L:5, H:3.5), mesencephalic reticular formation (Fr.A:3, L:4, H:-1), dorsal hippocampus (Fr.A:3.5, L:6.2, H:8.8). The derivations were against a common reference which consisted of three stainless steel screws in different regions of the skull. A David Kopf 1404 Instrument was used for stereotaxic surgery. During the experiments the cats were freely moving, resting or sleeping in an echo-free and sound-proof room. The stereotaxic implanting techniques and bioelectric recording techniques used are described in an excellent manner by THOMPSON (1967) and THOMPSON and PATTERSON (1973)

The experimental setup and the evaluation of the data for selective averaging, power spectra, frequency characteristics, and theoretical filtering were explained in detail in section 7.3 and in Chapter 3.

The anatomical and functional organization of the brain structures which will be studied in the following sections were explained in the previous section. As we know from section 7.4 (a), the acoustical cortex, the medial geniculate nucleus and the inferior colliculus are primarily involved with the transmission and processing of acoustical information. The reticular formation is a polysensory structure to which a high command and regulatory function of the brain is attributed (see section 7.4 (c). The hippocampus is supposed to be a structure responsible for emotion, alertness, memory, etc. (see section 7.4 (b). In other words, in addition to brain nuclei of a specific system (e.g. auditory pathway), we also study centers involved with more general and diffuse systems (e.g. reticular formation and hippocampus).

The results and their discussion which will be presented in sections 7.5 through 7.15,establish an important base for the understanding of the dynamics of rhythmic and evoked potentials in the studied brain structures. The question to which extent the general implication resulting from this analysis can be further translated to other brain pathways will be treated briefly in part E of this chapter,which describes the dynamics of potentials in the cat visual pathway, and also in the general discussion (see Chapter 8).

7.5 SPONTANEOUS ACTIVITY OF DIFFERENT NUCLEI OF THE BRAIN DURING WAKING AND SLEEP STAGES, CRITERIA FOR THE SELECTION OF EVOKED POTENTIAL EPOCHS

Fig. 7.9A illustrates spontaneous activities of the acoustical cortex (GEA, gyrus ectosylvian anterior), medial geniculate nucleus (MG), inferior colliculus (IC), mesencephalic reticular formation (RF) and the dorsal hippocampus (HI) during the waking stage. We used the same kind of cortical EEG pattern as the sample pattern in selecting the epochs for the evaluation of selectively averaged evoked potentials for the waking stage.

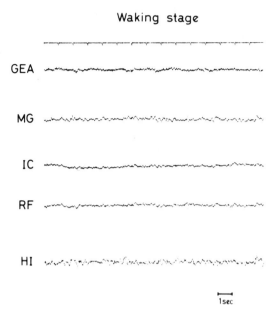

Fig. 7.9A Simultaneously recorded spontaneous activity of
          different brain nuclei during the waking stage.
          (After BAŞAR et al., 1975b)

During spindle sleep stage (SS-Stage) 10-14 Hz high

voltage spindles appear in the cortical EEG recording, as

Fig. 7.9B illustrates. Usually spindles were recorded in

the cortex, however thalamic or hippocampal spindles were

observed in some experiments. For selective averaging of

evoked potentials during the SS-Stage, we selected only

those patterns where spindles were observed in the cortex.

Interspindle intervals were not considered for the selec-

tive averaging. In other words, for the evaluation of

selectively averaged evoked potentials during SS-Stage,

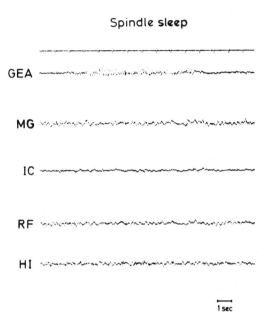

Fig. 7.9B Simultaneously recorded spontaneous activity of
different brain nuclei during the spindle sleep
stage. (After BAŞAR et al., 1975c)

only epochs with cortex spindles were averaged. The inter-

spindle periods were eliminated for the evaluation of

spindle sleep stage EPs and for all the nuclei under study.

The invasion of high voltage slow waves (1-3 Hz) in

the acoustical cortex was accompanied by the occurence of

the same waves in all the nuclei under study (Fig. 7.9C).

We used this kind of period (or epoch) as sample patterns

in selecting the epochs for the evaluation of evoked poten-

Slow wave sleep

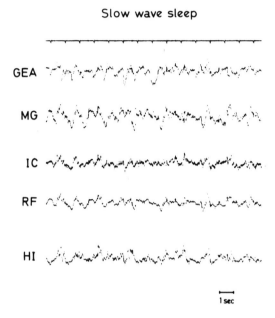

Fig. 7.9C Simultaneously recorded spontaneous activity of
         different brain nuclei during the slow wave sleep
         stage. (After BAŞAR et al., 1975c)

tials during slow wave sleep stage (SWS-Stage). We selec-

ted the EP-epochs for the SWS-Stage only from a recording

period where the state of hypersynchrony shown in Fig. 7.9C

was observed in all the nuclei during a sufficiently long

sleep duration.

7.6 SELECTIVELY AVERAGED TRANSIENT EVOKED POTENTIALS DURING WAKING AND SLEEP STAGES

Figs. 7.10A, B, and C illustrate typical examples of the selectively averaged evoked potentials in all the nuclei under study during waking and sleep stages. The stimulation consisted of auditory step functions in the form of tone bursts of 2000 Hz.

During waking stage transient evoked potentials (selective AEPs or SAEPs) usually depict three different kinds of waves or peaks:

(1) short latency-waves (between 3-12 msec latency) with large slope and slope changes,

(2) middle range latency-waves (20-50 msec),

(3) long latency-waves (80-300 msec) with relatively small slope or slope changes.

The evoked potentials of the reticular formation and of the inferior colliculus have marked short latency-waves, whereas GEA, MG and HI have smaller short latency components.

During the slow wave sleep stage the short latency components of AEPs of all these nuclei (especially of RF and IC) have lower magnitudes. On the contrary 80-100 msec waves (long latency waves) in all these nuclei depict

Waking Stage

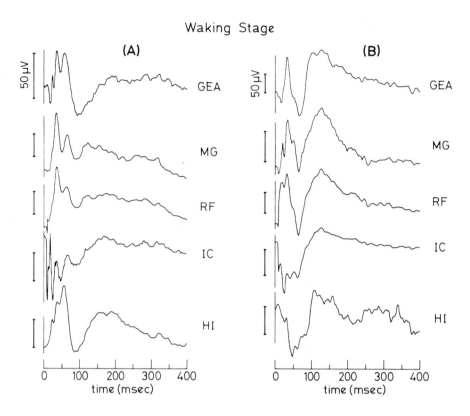

Fig. 7.10A Two typical sets of simultaneously recorded and
          selectively averaged evoked potentials in dif-
          ferent brain nuclei of chronically implanted
          cats, elicited during the waking stage by an
          auditory stimulation in the form of step func-
          tion. Direct computer-plottings. Negativity
          upwards. (After BAŞAR et al., 1975b)

the largest magnitudes.

       As systems theoretical implications in section 7.14

will show, we do not intend to analyze in detail the

latencies and waveforms of the transient responses.

However, we want to emphasize, that the recordings of

Figs. 7.10A, B, C are simultaneously recorded and selectively averaged EPs and that for the reader interested in empirical

findings, the EPs in these illustrations might be interesting

for comparative studies.

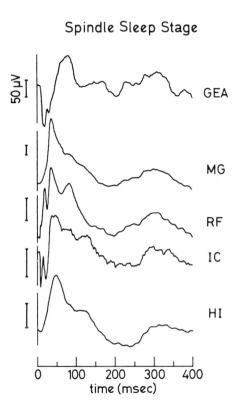

Fig. 7.10B A typical set of simultaneously recorded and
selectively averaged evoked potentials in different brain nuclei of chronically implanted
cats, elicited during the spindle sleep stage
by an auditory stimulation in the form of step
function. Direct computer-plottings. Negativity
upwards. (After BAŞAR et al., 1975c)

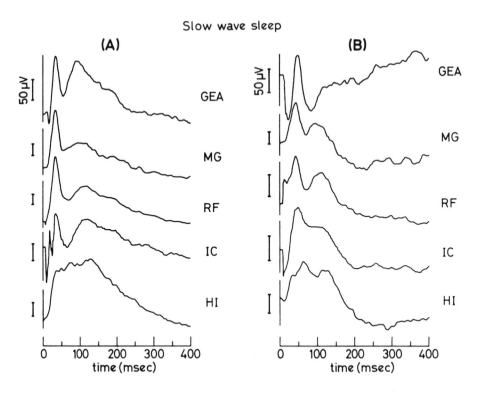

Fig. 7.10C Two typical sets of simultaneously recorded and
          selectively averaged evoked potentials in dif-
          ferent brain nuclei of chronically implanted
          cats, elicited during the slow wave sleep
          stage by an auditory stimulation in the form
          of step function. Direct computer-plottings.
          Negativity upwards. (After BAŞAR et al., 1975c)

The similarity of simultaneously recorded evoked

potentials, especially for waves of middle and long-

latencies is striking. The SAEPs of slow wave sleep

particularly resemble each other. The similarity of long-

latency components is analyzed in detail in section 7.9.

We also want to point out that the short-latency compo-

nents are not existent in all the EPs, and that they

usually have dissimilar time courses.

7.7 AMPLITUDE FREQUENCY CHARACTERISTICS DURING WAKING AND SLEEP STAGES

a) WAKING STAGE

Fig. 7.11 shows typical amplitude frequency characteristics in all the brain nuclei under study. These amplitude frequency characteristics were computed using selectively averaged transient responses similar to those of Fig. 7.10A with the help of the mathematical method (TRFC-Method) presented in section 3.2. Along the abscissa is the input frequency in logarithmic scale, and along the ordinate is the potential amplitude, $|G(j\omega)|$, in relative units and decibels. The curves are normalized in such a way that the amplitude at 0 Hz is equal to 1 (or 20 log 1=0).

As previously reported (BAŞAR, 1974), the study of frequency characteristics of different brain nuclei is nothing else than to consider them as a filter system or a device which eliminates, impedes or activates the transmission of electrical signals. With this train of thought, we will describe these frequency characteristics using the terminology of communication networks and refer to the expression "filtering properties".

Acoustical Cortex (GEA)

Fig. 7.11A presents two typical amplitude characteristics computed from the transient SAEPs of the cat
acoustical cortex (gyrus ectosylvian anterior). Amplitude
maxima in the frequency ranges of 8-15 Hz, 40 Hz and 80 Hz
were most commonly observed (upper curve). The amplitude
maximum in the 8-15 Hz range was sometimes shifted to higher
frequencies of 14-20 Hz, as was observed in 35% of the
curves (lower curve). The maximum around 8-15 Hz (i.e. alpha
frequency range) was the most prominent maximum in almost
all cases.

Medial Geniculate Nucleus (MG)

Amplitude maxima in the frequency ranges of 3-4 Hz
(theta range), 8-15 Hz (alpha range) and around 50 Hz,
characterized the dynamics of the medial geniculate nucleus.
The maximum around 8-15 Hz sometimes had narrow filter
properties with sharp edges. The dominant maximum was either
in the alpha frequency range (75% of the curves) or in the
theta frequency range (25% of the curves). We draw attention
here to the spontaneous activity of the medial geniculate
nucleus during the waking stage, which depicted regular
theta waves as in the case of the hippocampus (Fig. 7.11B).

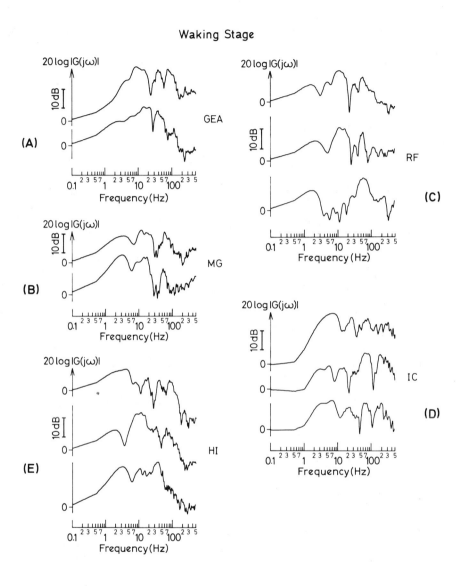

Fig. 7.11 Examples of typical amplitude characteristics of
          different brain nuclei of the cat determined by
          the TRFC—Method and using similar transient evoked
          responses of Fig. 7.10A. Direct computer-plottings.
          Along the abscissa is the input frequency in
          logarithmic scale, along the ordinate the poten-
          tial amplitude, |G(jω)|, in decibels. The curves
          are normalized in such a way that the amplitude
          at 0 Hz is equal to 1 (or 20 log 1=0). (After
          BAŞAR et al., 1975b)

Mesencephalic Reticular Formation (RF)

The most prominent amplitude maxima in the frequency characteristics of the reticular formation were at about 50 Hz and in a frequency range between 100 and 500 Hz. The 50 Hz maximum was the dominant maximum in almost all the curves. A maximum at about 30 Hz was also found to exist in all curves. Amplitude maxima in the alpha frequency range were also recorded. However, the alpha maximum was sometimes missing (30% of the curves) or reduced to a low magnitude (lowest curve) (Fig. 7.11C).

Inferior Colliculus (IC)

Inferior colliculus amplitude characteristics exhibited the most prominent maxima in higher frequency ranges, similar to the characteristics of the reticular formation. Amplitude maxima around 80 Hz and 180 Hz were, in most of the curves (66% of the curves), the maxima with the largest magnitudes. Maxima between 3-8 Hz were seen in all curves, while a maximum around 10-12 Hz was seen only in 40% of the experiments. When the maximum in the alpha frequency range was missing, a maximum in the 20-25 Hz (beta range) was observed (Fig. 7.11D).

Hippocampus (HI)

The hippocampus is a nucleus which shows less consistent dynamic characteristics. The amplitude characteristics may show variable maxima even during the waking stage,
without the cat's going through transition and sleep stages.
Fig. 7.11E illustrates some typical hippocampal amplitude
characteristics during the waking stage. Sometimes the
maximum in the theta frequency range was the most prominent
one (the upper curve and the lowest curve). Dominant amplitude maxima in the alpha, beta and in the 40 Hz frequency
ranges were also observed.

b) SPINDLE SLEEP STAGE

The most common feature of the amplitude characteristics of all the nuclei were the maxima around 4-5 Hz
(theta frequency range). This theta maximum was the dominant
maximum in the characteristics of all the studied nuclei
except the acoustical cortex (GEA) (Fig. 7.12). The 50 Hz
maximum in the reticular formation and the 70 Hz maximum
of the inferior colliculus, which were found to be the
usual dominant maxima during the waking stage, remained
unchanged during the spindle sleep stage. For this transition
stage (spindle sleep stage) we cannot describe all the
maxima of the amplitude characteristics as we could in the

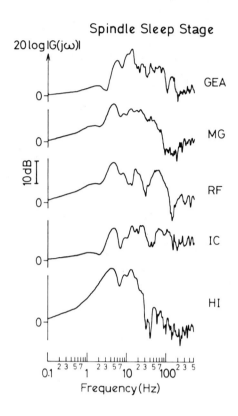

Fig. 7.12 A set of simultaneously obtained amplitude charac-
          teristics of different brain nuclei of the cat
          determined by the TRFC-Method and using the selec-
          tively averaged transient responses of Fig. 7.10B.
          Direct computer-plottings. Along the abscissa is
          the input frequency in logarithmic scale, along
          the ordinate the potential amplitude, $|G(j\omega)|$, in
          decibels. The curves are normalized in such a way
          that the amplitude at 0 Hz is equal to 1 (or
          20 log 1=0). (After BAŞAR et al., 1975c)

case of waking stage and slow wave sleep stage. This is due

to the fact that we do not have sufficient experiments with

pure cortex spindles. (We were only able to *complete* six

experiments using the method of selective averaging.) The

appearance of the cortex spindles was often accompanied by

Spindle Sleep Stage
(mean value curves)

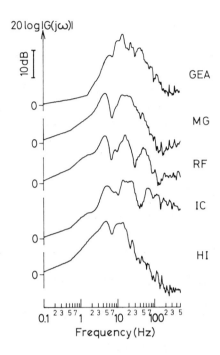

Fig. 7.13 Mean value curves of simultaneous amplitude characteristics of different brain nuclei of the cat
obtained from six experiments with auditory stimulation during the spindle sleep stage. Direct
computer-plottings. Along the abscissa is the
input frequency in logarithmic scale, along the
ordinate the mean value potential amplitude,
$|G(j\omega)|$, in decibels. The curves are normalized
in such a way that the amplitude at 0 Hz is equal
to 1 (or 20 log 1=0). (After BAŞAR et al., 1975c)

large amplitude slow waves. We did not selectively average

potentials evoked in this stage (called by some authors

LSWS or Light Slow Wave Sleep). The dominant theta maximum

in subcortical structures and the dominant maximum around

14 Hz of the acoustical cortex can, *in any event*, be

described as the constant and important finding. Fig. 7.13 presents the mean value curves of amplitude characteristics from six experiments performed during spindle sleep stage. As mentioned in the experiments on waking stage, the averaged curves from different cats and different experiments can only give *information to a decreased degree*. However, the existence of dominant maxima in the theta frequency range, the dominant alpha maximum in the cortex and the reticular 50 Hz maximum are marked in the averaged curves, thus indicating that consistent maxima (consistent selectivities) are found in these frequency ranges during the spindle sleep stage. (The concept of consistent selectivities is explained in section 7.9.)

c) SLOW WAVE SLEEP STAGE

During the slow wave sleep stage, the amplitude characteristics of all the studied nuclei showed two important common deviations from the characteristics of the waking stage: (1) prominent maxima of amplitude in the low frequency range between 1-3 Hz became apparent in all the curves, and (2) maxima in frequency ranges higher than 20 Hz became either highly attenuated or disappeared completely. This was seen even in the nuclei of the inferior colliculus and mesencephalic reticular formation, where high frequency mechanisms were dominant during the waking stage (Fig. 7.11).

Fig. 7.14A and B shows the amplitude characteristics of the nuclei studied. These amplitude characteristics were obtained from simultaneously recorded and selectively averaged evoked potentials by using the TRFC-Method (Transient Response Frequency Characteristics) described in section 3.2. Along the abscissa is the input frequency in logarithmic scale, along the ordinate the potential amplitude $|G(j\omega)|$ in relative units. The curves are normalized in such a way that the amplitude at 0 Hz is equal to 1 (or 20 log 1=0).

Acoustical Cortex

Maxima in the frequency range of 1-3 Hz and maxima in a broad frequency range covering alpha and beta ranges (7-40 Hz) were present in all the amplitude characteristics of the acoustical cortex (GEA) (alpha-beta filter). The maximum around 40 Hz which was present during the waking stage (Fig. 7.11) was absent, and the maximum between 50-80 Hz was either highly attenuated or non-existent. The maximum between 8 and 40 Hz with peaks at 12-15 Hz was usually the dominant maximum, the delta maximum being less prominent (Fig. 7.14A and B).

Medial Geniculate Nucleus

The amplitude frequency characteristics of the
medial geniculate nucleus were similar to those of the
acoustical cortex during slow wave sleep: maxima at 1-3 Hz
and 7-40 Hz were observed. In this nucleus too, the high
frequency mechanisms were either highly attenuated or
missing. In some of the curves, the maximum in the delta
frequency range was the dominant one (Fig. 7.14A and B).

Reticular Formation

A maximum in the (1-3 Hz) delta frequency range
existed in all the curves. As in the case of the cortex and
medial geniculate nucleus, and alpha-beta filter in the frequency range of 8-40 Hz was always present. However, this
alpha-beta filter in the reticular formation showed narrow
filtering properties when compared to the medial geniculate
nucleus and the cortex. The 30 Hz maximum, consistent during
the waking stage (BAŞAR et al., 1975b), disappeared. The
relevant 50 Hz maximum of the waking stage was unstable during
slow wave sleep and sometimes was entirely missing. It was
sometimes shifted to 40 Hz or the higher frequencies around
60 Hz (Fig. 7.14A and B). In all cases the amplitude of the
40 or 60 Hz maximum was relatively low. However, this maximum
was not dominant during the waking stage either (Fig. 7.11).

Slow Wave Sleep Stage

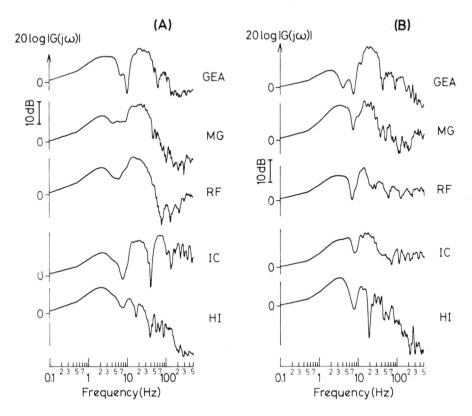

Fig. 7.14A and B Two sets of simultaneously obtained ampli-
                 tude characteristics of different brain
                 nuclei of the cat determined by the TRFC-
                 method and using the selectively averaged
                 transient responses of Fig. 7.10C respec-
                 tively. Direct computer-plottings. Along
                 the abscissa is the input frequency in
                 logarithmic scale, along the ordinate the
                 potential amplitude, $|G(j\omega)|$, in decibels.
                 The curves are normalized in such a way
                 that the amplitude at 0 Hz is equal to 1
                 (or 20 log 1=0). (After BAŞAR et al.,
                 1975c)

Inferior Colliculus

The inferior colliculus usually had amplitude characteristics similar to the characteristics of the cortex between 1 and 40 Hz. The high frequency maximum around 70-80 Hz observed during the waking stage sometimes not existent during SWS (Fig. 7.14A and B). Although, higher frequency maxima were also attenuated in the amplitude characteristics of the IC, this attenuation was not as pronounced as in other studied nuclei.

Hippocampus

The delta maximum (1-2 Hz) was usually the most prominent maximum. The maximum around the alpha-beta frequency range had narrower filtering properties in comparison to other studied nuclei (Fig. 7.14A and B).

7.8 INFORMATION OBTAINED FROM APPLICATION OF PASS-BAND FILTERS TO TRANSIENT EVOKED POTENTIALS

Fig. 7.15 shows the application of *adequately chosen* pass-band filters to the evoked potentials of the brain nuclei under study during the waking stage. (For the filtering method applied, and for the definition of pass-band filters the reader is referred to section 3.2.)

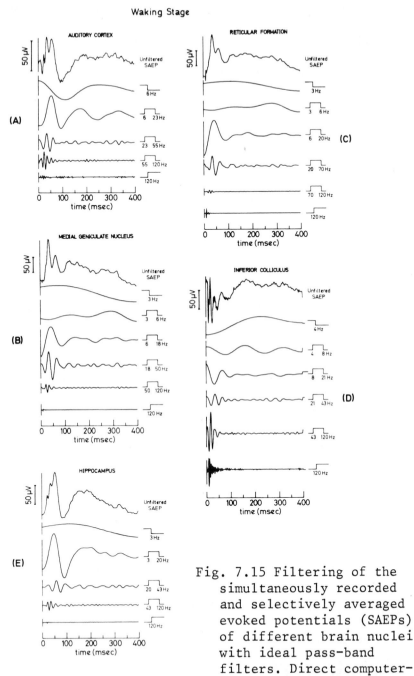

Fig. 7.15 Filtering of the simultaneously recorded and selectively averaged evoked potentials (SAEPs) of different brain nuclei with ideal pass-band filters. Direct computer-plottings. The band limits of the filters applied are shown in the right side of filtered AEPs (FAEPs). Outside these band limits the transmission is zero. The original SAEPs (of Fig. 7.10A) are shown at the top of each set (After BAŞAR et al., 1975b)

First of all, we confine our attention to the Filtered AEPs (FAEPs) of the inferior colliculus (Fig. 7.15D). According to the IC amplitude characteristic of the same evoked potential (shown in Fig. 7.11D) we define different frequency pass-bands in which the transmission reaches maximum values. Fig. 7.15D shows that in these frequency pass bands, the filtered AEPs have different time courses, but usually oscillatory waveforms.

The amplitude characteristic of the inferior colliculus (Fig. 7.11D) showed that the most prominent maxima were located at around 80 Hz and higher than 100 Hz, at around 180 Hz. The maxima centered around 12 Hz and around 7 Hz were less prominent. The pass-band filtered components obtained from the transient responses carried approximately the same information. High frequency (43-120 Hz and 120-∞ Hz) components were comparable in their magnitudes and have at least 2-3 fold greater magnitudes than the lower frequency (4-8 Hz and 8-21 Hz) components.

In order to give further examples we mention the filtered responses of the hippocampal FAEPs during the slow wave sleep. The filtered component in the delta frequency range was the dominant component, whereas all other

higher frequency components had much lower magnitudes
(or amplitudes). There was no response in frequencies higher
than 40 Hz (Fig. 7.16). This finding is also in good
agreement with the information obtained from the hippocampal
frequency characteristics shown in Fig. 7.14 and, especially
Fig. 7.18.

The high frequency component of the reticular
formation at about 50 Hz and the component higher than
100 Hz were dominant components during waking stage, whereas
during SWS these components were highly attenuated (or low
in comparison to lower frequency components). The FAEPs
of Fig. 7.16 also confirm perfectly this information
revealed by the RF frequency characteristics.

During our studies, after each experimental session,
all the measured transient evoked responses were theoretically pass-band filtered and analyzed with similar
criteria, as we explained giving a few examples. The
information obtained with pass-pand filtering was always in
good agreement.

These pass-band components (of compound averaged
evoked potentials) suggest that the AEP is a result of different unitary evoked potentials originating from dif-

Slow Wave Sleep Stage

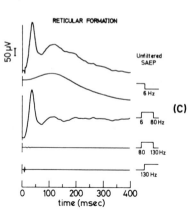

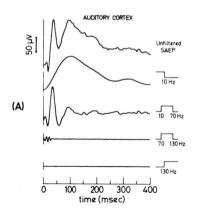

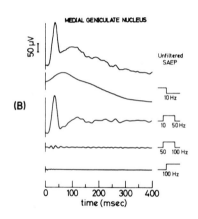

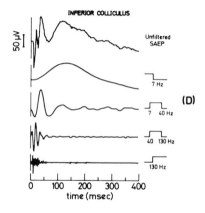

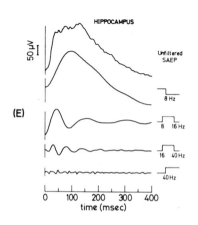

Fig. 7.16 Filtering of the simultaneously recorded and selectively averaged evoked potentials (SAEPs) of different brain nuclei with ideal pass-band filters. Direct computer-plottings. The band limits of the filters applied are shown in the right side of filtered AEPs (FAEPs). Outside these band limits the transmission is zero. The original SAEPs (of Fig. 7.10C) are shown at the top of each set (After BAŞAR et al., 1975c)

ferent neural circuits having their spontaneous activities
or frequency selectivities centered on different frequency
ranges. In fact, addition of all the different AEP (SAEP)
components (FAEPs) gives exactly the original (unfiltered)
curves.

A question which arises is the following: could the
theoretically predicted time components of AEPs (FAEPs)
shown in Figs. 7.15 and 7.16 be read as measurable components of different neural groups? What can be the
physiological correlates of these components? This
question will be treated in sections 7.14 and 7.17.

7.9 DISCUSSION OF RESULTS PRESENTED IN THE
PREVIOUS SECTIONS

Transient Evoked Potentials

A direct comporison of the results presented in
section 7.6 with previous reports is not possible since
earlier results of evoked potentials were usually obtained
by conventional averaging techniques and not with the
selective averaging method, as has been used in this
study. Moreover, evoked potentials of the studied nuclei
were mostly investigated using clicks (impulse functions)
and not step functions as was the case in our study.

However, the evoked responses shown in Figs. 7.10A, B and C have, in principle, great similarity to the auditory evoked potentials measured by HERZ (1965), HERZ et al. (1967), HALL and BORBELY (1970), WEBSTER (1971) and WICKELGREN (1968). In spite of the methodological differences, the different waves depicted in evoked potentials in the GEA, MG, RF, IC and HI which were obtained by selective averaging show at first glance great similarity to earlier results. Our previous AEP results on the same nuclei also showed resemblances in the time domain, and theoretical filtering analysis showed that the number of components was decreased and that selective averaging provided us with more consistent and stable data. Also the responses were more smooth although we used a minimum number of sweeps.

Amplitude Frequency Characteristics: Consistent Selectivities

We must emphasize that the amplitude characteristic curves presented in Fig. 7.11A-E are not frequency characteristic curves in the classical systems theory configuration. Since the stages of the brain change continuously, it is very difficult (and sometimes impossible) to get homogeneously measured, invariant averaged evoked potentials. Therefore, the curves which we present give a probabilistic description of the frequency ranges in which maxima of

potentials (or maximal selectivities) are expected and of

how the maxima are influenced or frequency shifted during

different stages of sleep and behavior. According to these

considerations, obtaining the mean value curves of amplitude

characteristics from different cats and experiments would

result in loss of information and would not help in the

study of the instantaneous selectivities. We computed the

mean value amplitude characteristic curves of all our

experiments. Fig. 7.17 shows the mean value amplitude

characteristic curves of 16 experiments on 9 cats. Despite

the large number of experiments (and the accordingly

expected reduction of information) a number of distinct

maxima are seen in the curves of Fig. 7.17: 12-14 Hz and

40 Hz maxima in the acoustical cortex; 4 Hz, 12-14 Hz and

50 Hz maxima in the medial geniculate nucleus; 2-4 Hz,

10-14 Hz, 30 Hz and 50 Hz maxima in the reticular formation;

40 Hz maximum in the hippocampus; 70 Hz and 180-220 Hz

maxima in the inferior colliculus. We call these maxima,

which always exist in the amplitude characteristics and

which are clearly revealed by mean value curves (in spite of

information reduction), the *consistent maxima* or the

consistent selectivities. In other words, the probability

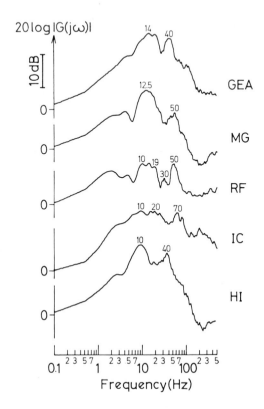

Fig. 7.17 Mean value curves of simultaneous amplitude charac-
          teristics of different brain nuclei obtained from
          19 experiments on 9 cats with auditory stim-
          ulation during the waking stage. Direct computer-
          plottings. Along the abscissa is the input fre-
          quency in logarithmic scale, along the ordinate
          the mean value potential amplitude, $|G(j\omega)|$, in
          decibels. The curves are normalized in such a
          way that the amplitude at 0 Hz is equal to 1 (or
          20 log 1=0). (After BAŞAR et al., 1975b)

for maximal signal transfer through the consistent selec-

tivity channels mentioned above is always existent in all

experimental conditions during the waking stage. We should

note that the plateau between 10-20 Hz, which is seen in

the curves of the inferior colliculus, is due to the fact

that a variable maximum between 8 and 20 Hz was observed

in all the averaged experiments (see also section 7.7).

Since the hippocampal theta maximum also changed in fre-

quency from experiment to experiment, no distinct peak,

but rather a shoulder, can be seen in the mean value curve

of Fig. 7.17.

In section 7.7 we have already described the consis-

tent selectivities during spindle sleep stage (Fig. 7.12).

During SWS the following consistent maxima can be indicated

(Fig. 7.18). In all the nuclei a maximum between 1 and 3 Hz

is seen. The most important 1-3 Hz maxima are seen in the

MG nucleus and in the hippocampus. In these nuclei this

delta maximum is often the dominant one, while in the

inferior colliculus this maximum is less relevant. The

maxima around 80-100 Hz in the cortex and 70 Hz in the

inferior colliculus, which are also seen during the waking

stage, remain almost unchanged during SWS. The 180 Hz

maximum of the inferior colliculus is also a consistent

maximum during SWS. The higher frequency maxima above 40 Hz

are absent in the RF. The alpha-beta filter described in

the previous section is among the consistent selectivities.

This alpha-beta filter has narrower bands in the reticular

formation.

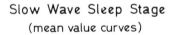

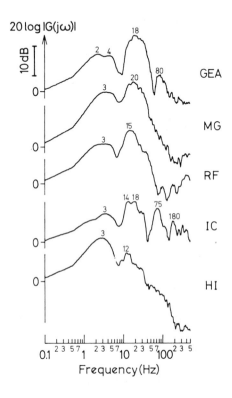

Fig. 7.18 Mean value curves of simultaneous amplitude
characteristics of different brain nuclei of the
cat obtained from 16 experiments with auditory
stimulation during the slow wave sleep stage.
Direct computer-plottings. Along the abscissa is
the input frequency in logarithmic scale, along
the ordinate the mean value potential amplitude,
$|G(j\omega)|$, in decibels. The curves are normalized
in such a way that the amplitude at 0 Hz is
equal to 1 (or 20 log 1=0). (After BAŞAR et al.,
1975c)

Pass-Band Filtering Results Support the Amplitude
Characteristics

The method of theoretical ideal filtering helps the
investigator of evoked potentials to obtain a detailed analysis of the components in defining the frequency channels
of different waves. In section 7.8 we have used the filtering method merely to check the accuracy of the amplitude
characteristics obtained by the TRFC-Method. We have seen
that the findings with the magnitudes of filtered components
were, relatively compared, in the same range of the amplitude maxima in the frequency characteristics.

However, this kind of use of the filtering results
is not the only purpose in applying this method, which we
called the theoretical isolation method (see section 3.2).
The reader is referred to the use of the filtering method
in the understanding of the circulatory phenomenon (section
4.9) and the predicted smooth muscle reverberatory circuits
(section 5.4). During the investigations on the brain's
electrical activity we will use the theoretical filtering
twice more. This method will help in the understanding and
interpretation of evoked potentials in general (see section
7.14). Moreover, the oscillatory waveforms which we obtained
by pass-band filtering will help further toward the under-

standing of neural processes (or subcomponents) which underly
the sensory evoked potentials.

Application of pass-band filters with different cutoff frequencies provided us with the same information
obtained with the amplitude frequency characteristics. For
example, the amplitude characteristics of the inferior
colliculus of Figs. 7.11 and 7.17 gave the same information
as that obtained by applying pass-band filters (see
section 7.8). The method of amplitude frequency characteristics and the theoretical filtering method are different methods. The fact that both methods provide us with
approximately the same information gives us new insights:
as we have repeatedly mentioned (BAŞAR, 1974; BAŞAR and
UNGAN, 1973), the TRFC-Method is only an approach because
of the nonlinearity of brain responses. However, the
theoretical filtering method does not apply the Fourier
(or Laplace) transform to the evoked responses. Therefore
it is a more suitable method for nonlinear systems.
Accordingly, the fact that both methods give approximately
the same results allows us to evaluate the amplitude characteristics as very reliable findings in spite of nonlinearities
of the biological system under study.

C. TRANSMISSION CHARACTERISTICS THROUGH THE BRAIN
   NEURAL NETWORKS

7.10 PROBLEMS

In this chapter we confine our attention to simultaneously and selectively obtained frequency characteristics from different structures of the brain. The structures studied were chosen from the cortical area (GEA), thalamus (MG), reticular formation (RF), midbrain (IC), and from the limbic system (HI), i.e. anatomically and functionally different centers of the brain.

What will the simultaneously obtained frequency characteristics add to our knowledge of brain potentials? "How can we obtain fundamental aspects of neurodynamics in order to reach a better understanding of the intersensory communication mechanisms?" The last very important question was asked by FESSARD (1961), who emphasized the necessity to determine the system's characteristics of the brain. He stated:

> "For the time being, it seems that we should do
> better to try to clear up such principles as
> seem to govern the most general transformations-
> or transfer functions- of multiunit homogeneous
> messages during their progression through neural
> networks. Some knowledge of that sort should at
> any rate precede any speculation about the way
> two (or more) multiunit homogeneous messages

of different modalities communicate with each
other to give rise to an integrated pattern of
neural activity a method representing a more
analytical and up to now, an easier approach
than the pattern to pattern transformation
matrix just alluded to."

In determining simultaneous frequency characteristics
from such diverse structures of the brain, both from a
physiological and anatomical point of view, we are confronted with such a problem. As we have explained, the
interconnections between the centers studied are very
complicated. Furthermore, neurons onto which different
sensory messages can converge are often, in the awake
animal, in a state of a quasi-permanent repetitive firing,
a consequence of sustained depolarization due to an
incessant bombardment by afferent impulses from all directions.

To the problems outlined by FESSARD (1961) we add
the following point of view; the study of evoked potentials
is, in one sense, nothing more than an application of
deterministic input signals to a black box which has
intrinsic electrical activities as well as selectivities. If
we have any right to analyze transient responses of the
brain systems (or subsystems) which show intrinsic activity,
(sometimes regular, sometimes irregular), we should also

try to obtain at least a rough representation of their main dynamic features. We go further with our questions: is it possible to obtain something regular from a system (brain) which usually shows highly irregular and variable activities? Will it be possible to derive (determine) some general laws and common dynamic features from hundreds or thousands of different evoked potentials from electrodes located in different brain structures during different waking and sleep stages? Do the signal transmissions in the brain obey some general transfer rules which can be determined from evoked potentials? These questions pose the main purpose of our discussion on brain potentials. Consequently we were led to choose different functional brain structures and study their simultaneous responses to the same stimulation modality.

7.11 COMMON SELECTIVITIES

We define *selectivity* as the ability of brain networks to facilitate or activate electrical activity (or communication) within determined frequency channels when stimulation signals are applied to the brain.

We define *the ratio of common selectivities* through a number of brain nuclei as the following ratio (regardless of the relative magnitude of each existing channel):

$$R = \frac{\sum\limits_{i} S_i}{N}$$

where:

  R: the ratio of common selectivities,

  N: the total number of the relevant amplitude maxima (selectivity channels) multiplied by the number of the nuclei studied,

  i: the index of the selectivity channels,

  S_i: the number of nuclei showing the specific selectivity channel, i, in their amplitude characteristics.

As an example, we shall explain the common selectivities of the simultaneously obtained amplitude characteristics of Fig. 7.19A using a matrix representation as follows:

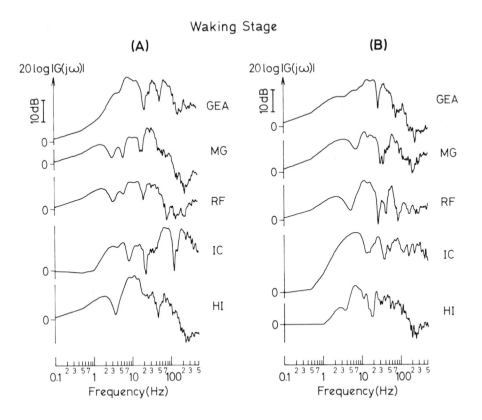

Fig. 7.19 Two sets of simultaneously obtained amplitude
characteristics of different brain nuclei of
the cat determined by the TRFC-Method and using
the selectively averaged transient responses of
Fig. 7.10A respectively. Direct computer-
plottings. Along the abscissa is the input frequency in logarithmic scale, along the ordinate
the potential amplitude, $|G(j\omega)|$, in decibels.
The curves are normalized in such a way that
the amplitude at 0 Hz is equal to 1 (or
20 log 1=0). (After BAŞAR et al., 1975b)

Approximate center frequencies of
selectivity channels

	1.5 Hz	5 Hz	10 Hz	30 Hz	80 Hz	180 Hz
GEA	0	0	1	1	1	0
MG	1	1	1	1	0	0
RF	1	1	1	1	0	0
IC	0	1	1	0	1	1
HI	1	0	1	1	1	0

(Studied nuclei)

In this example, there are 6 relevant selectivity
channels and the number of nuclei studied is 5. Therefore,
N=5x6=30. We take into account only those selectivities
which have the most relevant features. The reader will
certainly confirm also the fine structural similarities
when comparing the amplitude characteristics of all these
nuclei. The elements of the matrix are either 1 or 0
depending on whether a specific selectivity channel
exists in the corresponding nuclei or not. Hence,
the sum of each column gives the number of nuclei having
this specific selectivity channel (i.e. S_i). The above
formulated ratio of common selectivities is computed
as follows from the rough considerations on the simul-

taneously recorded curves of Fig. 7.19A:

$$R = \frac{3 + 3 + 5 + 4 + 3 + 1}{30}$$

$$R = 0.63 \quad (63\%)$$

In other words, the ratio of common selectivities was 63% in the GEA, MG, RF, IC and HI during the experiment presented in Fig. 7.19A. This ratio varied between 46% and 67% in 19 experiments performed. The mean value of the ratio of synchronized selectivity was 56% during the waking stage. Accordingly, we can state that the ratio of common selectivities is highly significant in the studied brain structures.

The *ratio of common selectivities* varies between 75% and 90% in all the experiments performed during SWS. The mean value of this ratio is 80% for this sleep stage. The mean value curves of amplitude characteristics in Fig. 7.18 which are the average of 16 experiments performed during SWS, give a ratio of 76%. One sees that this ratio is higher in comparison to the waking stage, indicating a better congruency of the consistent selectivities during slow wave sleep.

We assumed the brain stage to remain almost

unchanged (or stationary) during a short recording session

by obtaining selectively averaged evoked potentials, and

accordingly conjectured that the pass characteristics of

all the nuclei under study reflected unchanged behavior

during this period. We can conclude that a regulatory

mechanism exists which regularizes the transfer charac-

teristics of all the studied nuclei during a specified

brain stage. Our question as to *whether the signal*

transmission in the brain obeys some general transfer

rules" is answered by the foregoing considerations.

If summarized, there exist regularities, common regulative

processes (although not perfect ones, as we see from the

examples of Fig. 7.19) in different brain nuclei, as

revealed by the significance of common selectivity bands

in their pass characteristics, despite the complexity

of the system under study (see the block schema in Fig. 7.3).

How do these amplitude maxima (selectivity bands)

occur? Do they simply reflect filtering characteristics

of the studied nuclei, or are they due to resonance

phenomena? These points are discussed in the next section

7.12.

7.12 SELECTIVITY CHANNELS (AMPLITUDE MAXIMA), RESONANCE PHENOMENA AND FACULTATIVE PACEMAKER THEORY

First, we consider in detail the simultaneously recorded power spectra of spontaneous activity in all the studied nuclei.

Here it should be emphasized that the amplitude frequency characteristic is a different function from the autospectrum. In order to find the frequency characteristics of a system (or the transfer function of a system), deterministic input signals should be applied to the input of this system, while the autospectrum is obtained by measuring the oscillations in the output of this system. The autospectrum of a system can show maxima of the power density function in different frequencies without application of deterministic input signals, provided that the output has measurable oscillatory behavior. But the frequency characteristics of a system cannot be measured without application of deterministic input signals. The amplitude characteristics here present the predicted behavior of the system under study if sinusoidally modulated input signals (sound signals) were applied as stimulation.

The measurement in the output of the electrical

circuit of Fig. 7.20 does not show oscillatory potential

changes without application of time variant input signals.

However, when we apply deterministic signals to the input

of this circuit, a resonant maximum of 18 Hz can be

obtained in the amplitude frequency characteristics

(Fig. 7.20) by suitable choice of R, L and C values.

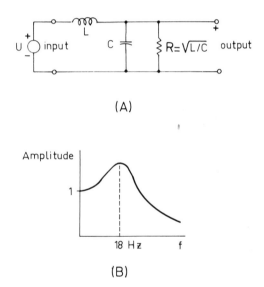

Fig. 7.20 Schematical drawing of an R, L, C circuit
         (A) producing a resonance maximum in the
         amplitude characteristic (B) when deterministic
         input signals are applied. (After   BAŞAR and
         ÖZESMİ, 1972)

In order to understand the occurrence of amplitude

maxima in the frequency characteristics, we have to try

to find a relation between autospectra and amplitude

frequency characteristics. Since the brain is a system

which shows spontaneous electrical activities, it is expected that the signal evoked in the brain by external stimuli must undergo some interactions with these spontaneous activities. Amplitude characteristics of a system containing intrinsic oscillations must contain responses which originate through those interactions. *Resonance phenomena* can be expected when an oscillatory physical or biological system is forced by external input signals.

Are the amplitude maxima in various areas of the brain due to resonance phenomena or do they represent simple non-resonant selectivities? We will try to answer these questions as follows:

Fig. 7.21A shows samples of simultaneously obtained power spectra of the studied brain nuclei. These power spectra are typical spectra sampled during the recording session, during which we obtained the amplitude characteristics of Fig. 7.19A. (These power spectra were computed using the Welch-Method presented in section 7.3.) Dominant peaks are seen in the range of 3-4 Hz in almost all the curves. The 3-4 Hz maxima in the MG and HI power spectra were the most relevant in all experiments, as confirmed by the mean value curves of 20 experiments

(Fig. 7.21B). Less relevant peaks of power spectral density function in the beta frequency range (18-35 Hz) are also seen. In the MG power spectra, where spontaneous theta activity masks all other higher frequency activities, power spectra with a dominant theta peak were observed. It is important to emphasize that in the vicinity of 9-12 Hz, where there is a dominant maximum in the frequency characteristics, there is a valley depicted by the power spectra (Fig. 7.21A and B). For comparison of amplitude characteristics with power spectra we have chosen three frequency ranges:

   i) Frequency range lower than 8 Hz (theta - delta range)

In the frequency range lower than 8 Hz, a very good correlation between power spectral density function and amplitude characteristics exists in almost all the experiments. Fig. 7.22 illustrates such an example in the case of the hippocampus. As one sees, the dominant and double peaking theta activity revealed by the power spectrum is reflected in the amplitude characteristic curve.

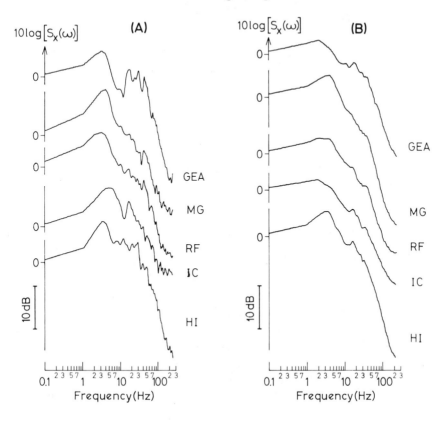

Fig. 7.21 (A): Power spectral density functions computed
by means of the Welch-Method and obtained
from the simultaneous spontaneous activities
of different brain nuclei recorded during
the same session where the amplitude characteristics of Fig. 7.19A were obtained.

(B): Mean value curves of the power spectral
density functions obtained from 19 experiments on 9 cats. Direct computer-plottings.
Along the abscissa is the frequency in logarithmic scale, along the ordinate the power
spectral density, $S_x(\omega)$, in decibels. The
curves are normalized in such a way that the
power at 0 Hz is equal to 1 (or 10 log 1=0).
(After BAŞAR et al., 1975b)

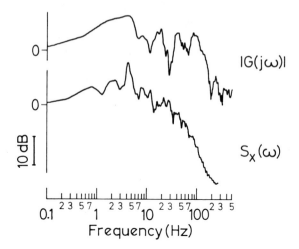

Fig. 7.22 A typical amplitude characteristic of the
          hippocampus (upper curve) and the power spectral
          density function computed from the spontaneous
          activity of the same nucleus (lower curve) which
          were obtained during the same experimental
          session. Direct computer-plottings. Along the
          abscissa is the frequency in logarithmic scale,
          along the ordinate the potential amplitude,
          $|G(j\omega)|$, for the upper curve and the power
          spectral density, $S_x(\omega)$, for the lower curve,
          both in decibels. (After BAŞAR et al., 1975b)

ii) Frequency range around 10 Hz

Valleys (minima) are observed in the range of 10 Hz

(Fig. 7.21A and B) in the power spectra. Comparison of the

amplitude characteristics of Fig. 7.19 with the power

spectra of Fig. 7.21 shows that no important correlation

exists between the power spectra and amplitude charac-

teristics in the 10 Hz (alpha) frequency range.

iii) Frequency range higher than 20 Hz

In the frequency range higher than 20 Hz a good correlation between the amplitude characteristics and power spectra was observed. However, the following point should be noted: in the power spectra, maxima near the beta frequency are usually less pronounced than the theta maxima. On the contrary, in the amplitude characteristics, the amplitude maxima around 20 Hz, as well as in frequencies higher than 20 Hz, are relatively high when compared to the amplitude maxima in lower frequency ranges (below 10 Hz). This result was supported by ideal filtering findings in section 7.8.

No relevant peaks (or relevant spontaneous activity) were recorded in the power spectra of the inferior colliculus nor of the reticular formation in the higher frequency ranges (above 20 Hz), although dominant maxima were seen in the amplitude characteristics of RF and IC (Figs. 7.11A and 7.19). In order to avoid the masking of low frequency components, we filtered out frequencies lower than 50 Hz and chose a shorter sampling interval of 50 μsec during the recording of IC spontaneous activity. Such a power spectrum compared with the amplitude characteristic of IC is given in Fig. 7.23B in order to show that the spontaneous and evoked activities have almost the same frequency bands in high frequencies. This comparison proves that the relevant high frequency amplitude maxima of IC is due to resonance phenomena resulting from the interaction of stimulus signals with the very low voltage spontaneous activity. A similar comparison of power spectra and amplitude characteristics of RF allows one to reach the same conclusion for this nucleus.

Taking into consideration the foregoing results, we define three different kinds of resonance in the brain nuclei:

1) *Weak resonances*

2) *Strong resonances*

3) *Alpha resonances*

1) Weak resonances:

The maxima of the amplitude characteristics in the frequency range less than 8 Hz (0-8 range) have magnitudes of the same order in the power spectra of spontaneous activity. The theta spontaneous activities of the hippocampus and of the medial geniculate nucleus are decoded from the transient evoked responses, as the amplitude characteristics

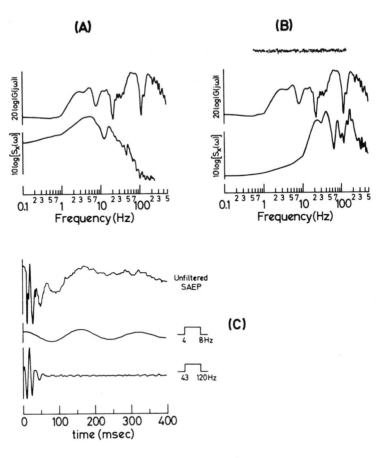

Fig. 7.23 An illustrative explanation of the strong resonance
phenomenon at frequencies higher than 20 Hz demonstrated for the inferior colliculus.
(A): The amplitude characteristic, $|G(j\omega)|$, and the
power spectral density function, $S_x(\omega)$, obtained in
the same experimental session during which the spontaneous activity shown at the top was recorded.
(B): The power spectral density function, $S_x(\omega)$,
computed from the high-pass filtered (3 dB fre-
quency=50 Hz) and further amplified spontaneous
activity (shown at the top). The amplitude charac-
teristic, $|G(j\omega)|$; is also given here for com-
parison.
(C): The original SAEP (at the top) and its two components (FAEPs) obtained by the theoretical filtering method. One low frequency (4-8 Hz) and one high
frequency (43-120 Hz) component are presented for
comparison of their magnitudes. (After BAŞAR et al.,
1975b)

and ideally filtered time components show. As the magnitude of the electrical response in this low frequency range is not increased upon stimulation, we define this phenomenon as a "weak resonance". We should bear in mind that weak resonances may simply be due to unstable time-locking phenomena, rather than to resonant behavior in the broad sense.

2) Strong resonances:

The maxima (or peaks) in the amplitude characteristics which lie in the frequency range higher than 20 Hz, have considerably higher magnitudes in comparison to the magnitude of the power spectral function of spontaneous activity of the same frequencies. (Compare amplitude characteristics and power spectra of Figs. 7.19 and 7.21A.) These kinds of resonances are especially well demonstrated by the examples in Fig. 7.23. Very low-voltage spontaneous activities resonate upon input stimuli and give highly intense responses in the form of evoked potentials. We call these kinds of resonances "strong resonances". Although we only point out the example of IC (Fig. 7.23), in all the nuclei, peaks lying in frequencies higher than 20-30 Hz are due to strong resonances. The peaks in the amplitude characteristics are much higher for strong resonances than the peaks in the power spectra. This fact is also demonstrated in the time domain with ideal filtering results (Fig. 7.23C).

One must be careful in comparing power spectra and amplitude frequency characteristics. A direct comparison of both functions is not possible, since the power spectrum reflects the intrinsic activity of a system and the amplitude characteristics represent the response of the system to an excitation. However, we can compare both functions in considering the relative magnitudes of various peaks which are revealed by these functions. In other words, it is not possible to compare the magnitudes of 70-80 Hz maxima of the power spectrum and of the amplitude characteristic, but we may state that the 70-80 Hz activity is less significant in the power spectrum of IC in comparison to theta activity, while in the amplitude characteristic the 70-80 Hz maximum is more significant than the response in the theta frequency range (Fig. 7.23A).

Of course, the fact that the 70-80 Hz maximum of the power spectrum is less significant does not exclude the possibility of the existence of ample 70-80 Hz spikes in the spontaneous activity of the inferior colliculus. In fact, spikes with large magnitudes were observed in the IC-spontaneous activity (in the RF-activity too).

However, the existence of ample high frequency spikes does
not necessarily increase the 70-80 Hz peak in the power
spectrum. The explanation for this can be found in the
probabilistic nature of the power spectral density function.
Nonstationary and randomly distributed spikes are eliminated
or highly attenuated in the power spectra. This attenuation
is even more pronounced when the power spectra obtained are
averaged (see Fig. 7.21B), because these high frequency
spikes do not have consistent frequencies. The excitation
of the system (in this example, IC) with an input signal
should *regularize*, *time-lock* and therefore *increase the
magnitude* of the existing and randomly distributed spontaneous spikes. As a matter of fact, such an increase in
the relative potential amplitude is obviously seen by
comparing the pass-band filtered AEPs (4-8 Hz and 43-120 Hz
components) presented in Fig. 7.23C.

*We also want to indicate the similarity of these
considerations with resonance phenomena in the production
of elementary particles in high energy physics experiments.
The excitation of nuclear targets with high energy radiation
(or high energetic particles) elicits strong resonance
phenomena, and elementary particles, which are usually
not detected (because they are not abundant and are*

*randomly distributed without excitation), can be produced
and measured upon excitation.*

    3) Alpha resonance:

The question as to how the maxima of amplitude characteristics in the alpha frequency (8-14 Hz) range occur
becomes puzzling on observation of the corresponding power
spectra. As we have shown in Fig. 7.21A and B, during the
waking stage, power spectral *valleys* are usually seen in
the alpha frequency range, while *maxima* in the 8-14 Hz
frequency range dominate almost all the amplitude characteristics in every nucleus (Fig. 7.19). According to this
finding it can be hypothesized that discharges in the alpha
frequency range are elicited upon stimulation and give rise
to a resonance phenomenon that also lies in the alpha
frequency range.

This point of view is already included in the
facultative pacemaker theory formulated by ANDERSEN and
ECCLES (1967) and extended by ANDERSEN and ANDERSSON (1968).
According to the *facultative pacemaker theory*, all major
thalamic nuclei have the ability to control an appropriate
part of the cortex. In other words, it is assumed that when
rhythmic activity is found in a thalamic nucleus, a corre-

sponding rhythm will be recorded in the appropriate "on line"
cortical region. Our observations of the alpha-maximum
(alpha selectivity) in the MG-nucleus and acoustical cortex
show that thalamo-cortical transmission reaches a maximum
in the alpha frequency range, thereby supporting in part
the above theory. ADRIAN (1941), BREMER and BONNET (1950)
found in the medial geniculate nucleus rhythmic activity
in response to a click. The frequency of the evoked activity
was around 10/sec. We mentioned that our findings support
in part the *facultative pacemaker theory*. This theory
makes at least two different assumptions: (1) there exists
a signal transmission between thalamus and cortex in the
alpha frequency range, and (2) the alpha pacemaker elicited
by stimulation is located in the thalamus.

Since the alpha peaks are missing in the power
spectra obtained when no stimulation signal is applied to
cats moving in an isolated room and appear after the
application of stimuli, the above theory is partly supported.
However, our results give no idea of the site of the alpha
pacemaker. On the other hand, if we take a look at happenings
in the midbrain and in the reticular formation and limbic
system of the cat, we see that prominent alpha maxima also
occur during the waking stage. Moreover, as our studies

during sleep stages have shown, the frequency ranges and magnitudes of maxima change during sleep (BAŞAR et al., 1975c). Therefore, we find it necessary to suggest serious consideration of the abstract features of the dynamics of brain structures to investigators working toward a general brain signal transmission hypothesis. This theory (or working hypothesis) should be extended to different structures of the brain and should also encompass the frequency shifts of the maximal selectivities in different waking and sleep stages.

4) Resonance during sleep stages. *Alpha resonance during spindle sleep stage.*

Fig. 7.24 shows the simultaneous power spectra obtained from the spontaneous activities of the nuclei under study during SWS stage. These curves were computed using the Welch-Method given in section 7.3. As we see, the prominent maxima are centered in the 1-3 Hz frequency range. Less relevant minor peaks between 10-20 Hz are also seen. The mean value curves of the power spectra from 16 experiments (Fig. 7.24B) approximately confirm the course of the curves from the individual experiment of Fig. 7.24A. We want only to indicate here that the occurrence of selectivities in the 1-3 Hz frequency range might be due to

weak resonance phenomena, while the selectivities higher
than 10 Hz are certainly due to strong resonance phenomena.
In the spontaneous activity, the delta waves already have
large amplitudes and mask the existing high frequency
activities as supported also by the power spectral density
functions.

We should point out that the phenomenon of alpha
resonance becomes more important when we study transition
and sleep stages. This is especially marked during the stage
where 12-14 Hz spindles appear in the cortical areas. During
this stage, a prominent 12-14 Hz maximum is seen in the
cortical amplitude characteristics (Figs. 7.12 and 7.13).
Therefore, this alpha maximum can certainly not be explained
with the same assumptions which we made on the occurrence of
alpha maxima during the waking stage. One might tend to
explain the alpha resonance in this case either as a simple
time locking phenomenon and/or a weak resonance. In this
place we only mention the occurrence of alpha channel as a
consistent amplitude maximum through rather tentative
assumptions. However, the alpha channel covering the frequency range between 8-14 Hz seems to us as a channel in
which various resonance phenomena ought to occur, depending

Slow Wave Sleep Stage

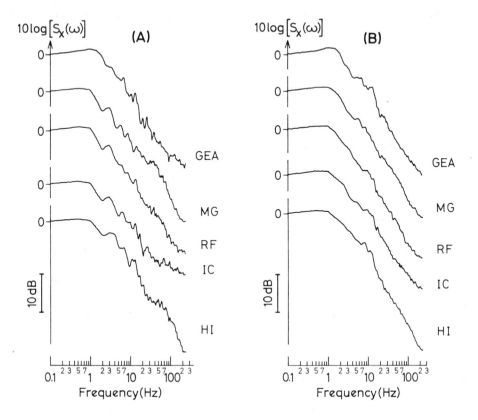

Fig. 7.24 (A): Power spectral density functions computed by
               means of the Welch-Method and obtained from
               the simultaneous activities of different nu-
               clei recorded during the slow wave sleep stage
               where the amplitude characteristics of Fig.
               7.14 were obtained.
         (B): Mean value curves of the power spectral density
               functions obtained from 16 experiments during
               the slow wave sleep stage. Direct computer-
               plottings. Along the abscissa is the frequency
               in logarithmic scale, along the ordinate the
               power spectral density, $S_x(\omega)$, in such a way
               that the power at 0 Hz is equal to 1 (or
               10 log 1=0). (After BAŞAR et al., 1975c)

on the nature of experiments, stimulation modalities and
on the behavioral state of the experimental animal. Therefore,
the alpha resonance phenomenon merits comprehensive consideration and should be a matter of more detailed experimental and theoretical analyses in both frequency and
time domains.

In this section we described different types of resonance phenomena as we deduced them by measurements. The
reader is referred to Chapter 6 where we study the resonance
phenomena with the help of a model-circuit in an analytic
manner. In section 6.4 a model-circuit is given, with the
help of which the responses of a system having intrinsic
oscillations to external forcing signals are studied. In
section 6.5 the nonlinear effects and consequences resulting
from the excitation of a self-oscillating model circuit are
correlated with the brain responses, as we tried to classify
in the present section in the form of resonances and time-
locking phenomena. The sections 6.4 and 6.5 are very important for the analyzer of brain signals, especially if he
would understand the concept of resonance and apply this
concept to the interaction of signals in the brain. The
reader may read section 6.5 independently of Chapter 7;
during the reading he will be referred to appropriate parts

of the present section.

7.13 SUGGESTIONS AND COMMENTS FOR INVESTIGATORS WORKING TOWARD THEORIES OF SIGNAL TRANSMISSION IN THE BRAIN

The general features of the dynamics of brain potentials, which are deduced immediately from the investigations presented, can be described as follows:

(1) Stimulation of the brain with peripheral input signals elicits compound potentials in various structures of the brain. These potentials consist of different components having different frequencies and different magnitudes. It is predicted that these components usually have the form of damped sinusoids (see sections 7.14 and 7.16).

(2) *Principle of Resonant Selectivities*. There exists an important relationship between the spontaneous rhythmic activities and the evoked potentials. The evoked response components result either from interactions with spontaneous activity (*weak* and *strong resonances*) or they are elicited upon stimulation (*alpha resonance*) (see section 7.12).

(3) *Principle of Congruency of Pass Characteristics.*
There exists an important congruency in the selectivity
bands of the studied nuclei (GEA, MG, RF, IC, HI). In
order to describe this congruency we introduce the concept
of *the ratio of common selectivities* (see section 7.11). The
ratio of common selectivities is 56% in the waking stage.
During slow wave sleep the ratio of common selectivities has
a much higher value (80%).

(4) The *alpha selectivity* is the most relevant
selectivity in most of the experiments and nuclei during
the waking stage.

(5) During sleep stages, the alpha selectivity
is no more relevant. A significant congruency in the
1-8 Hz frequency range is observed in all the nuclei. Selectivities in the *delta* frequency range become more prominent
in all the nuclei during SWS. In the spindle sleep stage
selectivities in the *theta* frequency range are the most
marked and consistent selectivities, being common in all
the nuclei.

(6) During slow wave sleep, selectivities (and/or
resonant maxima) in frequencies higher than 40 Hz are either
attenuated or have completely disappeared. From this fact
it can be concluded that the firing rates of the neurons

are decreased during SWS.

The principles and/or rules stated above indeed explain only in an abstract manner the dynamic properties of important brain structures. However, despite the abstract character of the above description, we may state that these principles constitute an important working frame (a base for a working hypothesis) for investigators who want to formulate hypotheses on signal transmission in the brain, as well as for investigators trying to build brain models. In other words, brain models and hypotheses on signal transmission in the brain must be compatible with and should not disagree with the rules stated or with the frequency characteristics presented in this chapter. Dynamics of future brain models should fit together with the characteristics provided in the present chapter.

Recently LOPES DA SILVA et al. (1974) formulated a hypothesis suggesting that alpha-rhythms may be assumed to be signals generated by neuron populations with frequency selective properties when they are submitted to a random input. Thus neural networks with the same design and frequency selectivity may exist in different brain areas (cortical and thalamic). This hypothesis is, for example, a compatible hypothesis with the brain dynamics mentioned

above and does not disagree with the rules stated or with

the frequency characteristics presented in this chapter.

D. RULES FOR THE UNDERSTANDING OF THE POTENTIALS
   EVOKED IN THE BRAIN

7.14 INTERPRETATION OF BRAIN EVOKED POTENTIALS

The method of averaged evoked potentials (AEPs) is
common in the study of electrical activity of the brain.
Usually the averaged evoked response is described in terms
of several arbitrarily defined components such as peak
(wave) latencies, wave magnitudes, etc. These arbitrarily
defined components depend generally upon the location of
the recording electrode, behavioral state or sleep stage
of the subject under study and upon nature of the stimulating
signal. Therefore, the interpretation of these arbitrarily
defined components is very difficult and generally does
not allow comparisons between evoked potentials of different brain structures or between evoked potentials
obtained under different experimental conditions.

The following analysis brings a new point of
view to the understanding of time courses of evoked potentials. Fig. 7.25A shows one of the typical hippocampal
evoked potentials, and Fig. 7.25B shows the amplitude
characteristics obtained using the transient evoked response
of Fig. 7.25A.

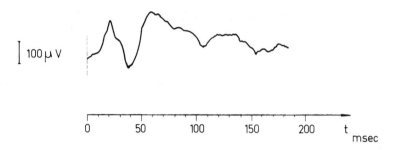

Fig. 7.25A Response evoked in the right dorsal hippocampus
          of the cat by an auditory stimulation in the
          form of a step function (tone burst of 2000 Hz
          and of 2 sec duration). Upward deflections
          indicate negativity of the hippocampus electrode.
          128 responses averaged by means of an averaging
          computer. (After BAŞAR and UNGAN, 1973)

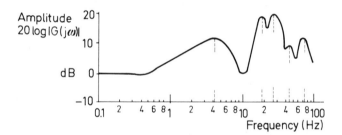

Fig. 7.25B Amplitude frequency characteristic computed
          using the transient evoked response of Fig. 7.25A.
          Along the abscissa is the frequency in logarithmic
          scale, along the ordinate the relative amplitude
          in decibels. (After BAŞAR and UNGAN, 1973)

*Contribution of Different Evoked Potential Components
to the Original AEP and Reconstruction of the Original
AEP Starting from the Components:*

Stop-band filters are filters which provide attenuation
in a desired frequency band such that the output is negligible compared to the input. For example, a stop-band filter
between 10 and 20 Hz acts in such a way that the frequency
output between 10 and 20 Hz is negligible compared with
the input. An ideal stop-band filters allows zero transmission,
i.e. provides infinite attenuation for frequencies within
the band limits. (For definitions of different filters see
section 3.2.)

The filtered AEPs (FAEPs) obtained by applying
pass-band and stop-band filters covering the same frequency
ranges are shown together in Fig. 7.26. One can easily
follow the influence of various frequency components upon
a single wave and also see how different waves are affected
by the same oscillatory response component. The entire AEP
is divided into time sections T_1, T_2, T_3, T_4 and T_5
according to time points where positive and negative peaks
(or waves) are seen.

Section T_1. The overall slope of this part (time
section) is mainly determined by the component of 0-10 Hz,

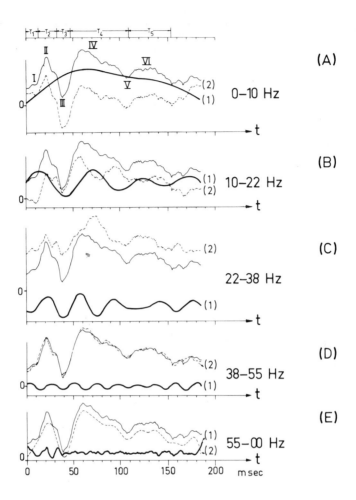

Fig. 7.26 Filtering of the hippocampal AEP shown in Fig. 7.25A
         with different stop-band and pass-band filters.
         Curves denoted with (1) are FAEPs (filtered AEPs)
         obtained with application of pass-band filters.
         Curves denoted with (2) (dashed curves) are
         FAEPs obtained with application of stop-band
         filters. The band limits (shown in the right side
         of AEPs) of applied filters are chosen according
         to minimal values of the hippocampal amplitude
         characteristics shown in Fig. 7.25B. The original
         AEP is shown for comparison with all the FAEPs.
         Time sections T_1....T_5 are shown at the top of
         the illustration. (After BAŞAR and UNGAN, 1973)

since other activity patterns cancel each other except

small variations in the 38–55 Hz and 55–∞ Hz components

(see curve A(2)). In hippocampal evoked potentials with

less significant theta components a positive peak (I) is

seen at about 10 msec. By the application of a 0–10 Hz

stop-band filter the appearance of peak I is seen

(curve A(2)).

Section T_2. Wave II is caused mainly by a 22–38 Hz

component (curve C(2)). It is also affected by the 10–22 Hz

component to some extent at around 20 msec. The shoulder

on the decreasing slope of wave II results from the second

negative wave (at 33 msec) of the 55–∞ Hz component

(curve E(1)).

Section T_3. Wave III is the result of 10–22 Hz,

22–38 Hz and 38–55 Hz frequency bands. All these oscilla-

tory components (curves B(1), C(1), D(1)) have time-coinci-

dent minimal values giving a distinct negative wave at

approximately 40 msec.

Section T_4. Wave IV is higher than wave II because

of the large amplitude of the 0–10 Hz component at about

60 msec. Application of a stop-band filter of 0–10 Hz

demonstrates this fact (curve A(2)). The components of

10-22 Hz and 22-38 Hz also contribute significantly to
the formation of wave IV. The 22-38 Hz component alone
(curve C(1)) could give rise to two negative waves at
58 and 93 msec and to one positive wave at about 75 msec,
as is the case in curve B(2). However, the 10-22 Hz
component compensates both peaks at 58 msec and 93 msec.
Therefore, in the time section T_4 only the rapid increase
of the AEP and a slow gradual decrease with the fluctuations
originating from a component of 38-55 Hz is seen. These
considerations again show that wave IV (like wave II) is a
compound wave.

Section T_5. The relatively small and flat wave VI
is raised at about 125 msec mainly by a 10-22 Hz component
(curves B(1) and B(2)). Its decrease is compensated at
140 msec by the 22-38 Hz component. This latter activity
gives a downward slope to the evoked potential at 150 msec
with a contribution of 0-10 Hz component. The 38-55 Hz
component also has a small effect in this section.

Consequences: The example shown here points out
exactly how the grossly recorded evoked potentials are
influenced and formed by different frequency components.

The fact that it is very difficult to obtain evoked potentials having always exactly the same shape can be understood clearly by consideration of the above. Since the equilibrium of contribution from different components changes perpetually, stability of AEPs can not be expected.

What are the biological correlates of the oscillatory components of evoked responses? In recent studies by HOROWITZ (1972) evoked potentials resembling damped sinusoids were elicited in the hippocampus of the cat under relatively light pentobarbital anesthesia upon electrical stimulation of the fornix. We had obtained similar oscillatory potentials in the hippocampus (see Fig. 7.26). The existence of such an evoked response, which is very similar to one of hippocampal time components, provides experimental support for our predictions.

AEPs and Post Stimulation Time (PST) histograms for pyramidal cells measured by HOROWITZ et al. (1973) are shown in Fig. 7.27. This type of oscillatory behavior indicates that single units as well as neural populations within the hippocampus exhibited damped sinusoidal activity for single-shock stimulation of the dorsal fornix. (Anatomical knowledge is given in Fig. 7.5.) The histogram in Fig. 7.27B shows successive peaks with decreasing

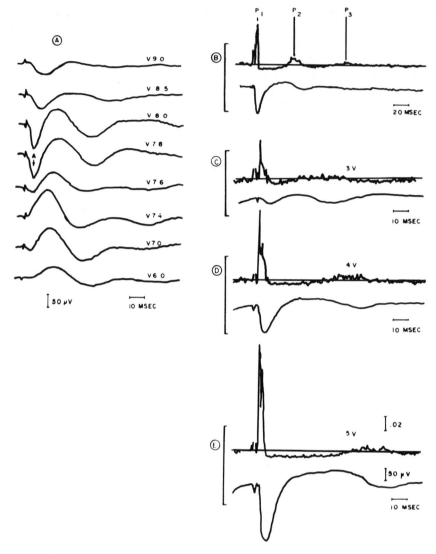

Fig. 7.27 Driven pyramidal cell recorded at site A6, L5,
        V7.8 (coordinates follow those of SNIDER and
        NIEMER, 1961). Waveforms in set A show changes
        in AEPs on a vertical tract through the pyramidal
        cell layer at A6, L5. Paired PST histogram and
        AEP of tracing B recorded over 250 msec interval
        to show three peaks P_1, P_2, and P_3. Traces C, D,
        and E were obtained for stimulation with
        3-, 4-, 5-volt (0.01 msec) pulses, respectively.
        For each PST histogram 400 transients were ave-
        raged, and the probability of pyramidal cells
        firing is plotted versus time. (After HOROWITZ
        et al., 1973)

amplitudes and increasing dispersion; such a sequence of
peaks was also predicted by model calculation (HOROWITZ et
al., 1973).

FREEMAN (1972b) also measured oscillatory responses
in the olfactory bulb of the cat upon electrical stimulation
of the lateral olfactory tract, and of the primary olfactory
nerve. His results showed damped oscillatory responses in
different frequency ranges (Fig. 7.28). The findings of
FREEMAN (1972a), HOROWITZ (1973) and coworkers in different
brain structures support also our semi-theoretical predictions. For further component analysis on firing frequencies of pyramidal neurons the reader is referred to
section 7.17.

*We have to emphasize here once more, that we did
not decompose the evoked potential's waveform into waves
with some arbitrary method. The evoked potentials were
not decomposed into some arbitrarily chosen Fourier components; with pass-band filtering we selected components
which were already detected in the amplitude frequency
characteristics. Our filters are chosen adequate
to the amplitude characteristics. Therefore, hope for the
existence of such oscillatory waveforms reflecting discrete
neural activities does exist, and this hope is enhanced with*

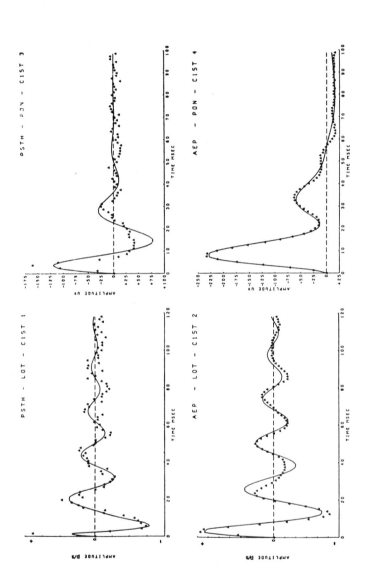

Fig. 7.28 PST histograms (above) of a single mitral cell and AEPs (below) of granule cells upon LOT (left) or PON (right) stimulation are fitted with curves for predicted responses given by FREEMAN (1972). There is phase lag of the AEP from the PST histogram of about one quarter cycle. LOT, lateral olfactory tract; PON, primary olfactory nerve. (After FREEMAN, 1972a)

the findings of HOROWITZ et al. (1973), FREEMAN (1972b) and

coworkers.

7.15 DO THE AEPs OF THE BRAIN HAVE AMPLITUDE
MODULATION WAVEFORM COMPONENTS?

We filtered evoked responses of different structures
of the brain with pass-band filters over a period of 1 sec.
In nearly all of the filtered averaged evoked potentials
(FAEPs) of the medial geniculate nucleus, reticular formation, inferior colliculus and hippocampus we obtained oscillatory waveform patterns with an amplitude modulation (AM)
shape: Fig. 7.29A and B show examples of simultaneously
recorded evoked responses of the medial geniculate nucleus
and the reticular formation in the same cat. Fig. 7.29C and
D show the averaged evoked potentials filtered with pass-
band filters of 33-42 Hz. (The amplitude characteristics of
the MG nucleus and the reticular formation which were
obtained using the transient evoked responses of Fig. 7.29A
and B had shown resonance maxima between 33 and 42 Hz.)

Since the application of pass-band filters causes amplitude modulation artifacts, we studied the artifacts produced by application of these filters with theoretical modeling (BAŞAR et al., 1973), and we have seen that these artifacts

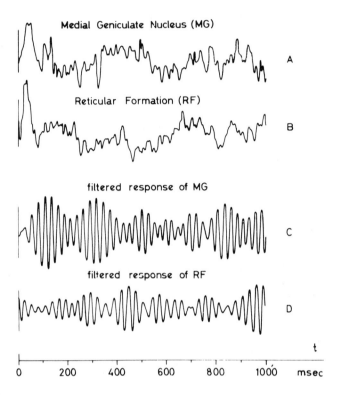

Fig. 7.29 Simultaneously recorded evoked responses (AEPs)
          of the medial geniculate nucleus and the reticular
          formation in the same cat (A and B). The same AEPs
          filtered with pass-band filters of 33-42 Hz are
          shown below (C and D). (After BAŞAR et al., 1973)

are small and that they could be neglected. Moreover, if

the nonregular AM-patterns of Fig. 7.29C and D were due

only to filtering artifacts, the time courses of the

MG-response and RF-response would show the same modulation

patterns. But the FAEPs of the medial geniculate nucleus

and of the reticular formation clearly exhibit different

modulation shapes. Moreover the AM-pattern due to the

artifact of the pass-band filter has a different modulation

frequency and negligibly low amplitudes (BAŞAR et al., 1973).

Therefore, we tend to emphasize once more the existence of

modulatory waveform patterns in the evoked potentials of

the brain. Since the process of modulation involves

multiplying a function x(t) by higher frequency sinusoids,

our findings here are in agreement with earlier results

(BAŞAR, 1972b) predicting the possibility of multiplicative

signal transmission in the brain. We will not mention the

further possibility of a nonlinear signal transmission

hypothesis in this section. These considerations are not

within the scope of this chapter. The reader is referred to

sections 6.4 and 6.5.

7.16 PRINCIPLES FOR THE ANALYSIS AND UNDERSTANDING OF EVOKED POTENTIALS

Examples of filtered AEPs and the amplitude charac-

teristics obtained during different brain stages provide

us with material for the interpretation and analysis of

AEPs in general.

1. The AEPs are compound evoked potentials which

are generated by superposition of responses of homogeneous

neural groups. The elementary evoked potentials which give

rise to the form of compound AEPs usually have oscillatory

character. (These can be damped oscillations as well as

oscillatory patterns having amplitude modulation waveform.)

2. The existence of a number of peaks (waves) with different latencies in the time course of an evoked potential does not necessarily indicate the existence of different functional structures or neural groups giving rise to these waves.

In the example of Fig. 7.26 it is clearly seen that the beta component alone has influence on different waves in the time course of the evoked potential. It does not influence a unique wave. In other words, in order to resolve a particular activity, it is not sufficient and justifiable to examine a single peak. The whole response must be frequency analyzed in order to avoid possible deceptive interpretations.

3. If the time course of an evoked potential has a particular wave in a certain behavioral state and if this wave disappears during other behavioral or sleep stages, the disappearance of this wave does not mean necessarily that a neural group ceases its activity during this stage. On the contrary, another neural group could cause the disappearance of the wave under question. In other words, the disappearance of a peak in the time course of AEPs

could be due to an active phenomenon.

4. As a consequence of the previous principles, (1) and (2), it can be stated that if an AEP does not have a large number of waves, this fact does not mean that the AEP has a simple functional structure. Different activities can compensate each other in such a way that these activities do not result in significant waves in the time course of the AEP.

5. Slope and slope changes and the entire time course of evoked potentials carry the whole information concerning different activities and frequency selectivities of brain structures rather than the number and latencies of the waves. Therefore, existence of different mechanisms can be confirmed only by systems theoretical criteria (such as frequency characteristics or filtering results) and not by simply counting the number or measuring the latencies of waves.

6. If a transient evoked potential has a smaller number of waves and/or if the waves of this AEP have different latencies compared to another AEP of a different behavioral condition, both AEPs may have amplitude characteristics with the same elements with more or less attenuation.

7. The existence of only a few resonant-frequency systems (with different attenuations or gains) in substructures of the brain can give rise to a number of varieties of transient evoked responses. The best demonstration of this fact is given by the study of transient responses of the medial geniculate nucleus and reticular formation: although the transient responses of these nuclei have different courses, their amplitude characteristics contain similar maxima; only the attenuations of maxima are different.

8. The time courses of AEPs reflect the spontaneous activities of the brain. In other words, the course of the AEPs can also serve as an indicator of changes in spontaneous activities of the nucleus under study.

The reversal of the Laplace transform (section 3.2) is of the following form:

$$c(t) = \frac{2}{\pi} \int_0^\infty \frac{Re\{G(j\omega)\}}{\omega} \sin \omega t \, d\omega$$

This reversal transform states that for a given transfer function, $G(j\omega)$, (or frequency characteristic) the corresponding step response (response in the time domain)

can be evaluated. So far, if the course of the amplitude
frequency characteristics is different, it is expected that
the transient response of the system must be different.
In fact, when spontaneous activity of a nucleus changes,
the amplitude characteristics change too. This information
(the change of the spontaneous activity) is contained in
the transient AEP.

The relationship between spontaneous activity and
evoked potentials were classified for the time being in
three different groups:

1) Weak Resonances,

2) Strong Resonances,

3) Alpha Resonance,

(see also section 7.12).

9. Signal transmission represented with amplitude
characteristics reaches maximal values during sleep stages
in lower frequency ranges of 4-5 Hz or 1-2 Hz. This shift
of maximal transmission occurs in all the nuclei studied
synchronously.

In section 7.12 of this chapter we have seen that the
evoked activity should be considered to be an electrical
variation which undergoes interactions with the ongoing

(spontaneous) activity. These interactions are described as resonance or time-locking phenomena. How can these resonance or time-locking phenomena occur from an analytical point of view? This question is answered by the model experiments described in sections 6.4 and 6.5, where the reader will find a probabilistic approach to the explanation of resonance phenomena described in the present chapter. By careful consideration of the model experiments of section 6.5, a better insight into the interpretation of evoked potentials through resonance and time-locking phenomena may be gained .

E. SUGGESTIONS FOR FURTHER COMPONENT ANALYSIS

7.17 GOING OUT OF THE SYSTEM. SEARCH THROUGH
     NEURAL GROUPS

In Chapter 4 (section 4.8) we have already seen the
advantages of the rule "going out of the system", demonstrated in the study of the circulatory autoregulation mechanism. We will try now to apply the same rule in order to
find ways to identify the neural groups of the brain giving
rise to evoked activity.

In previous sections, where we studied the amplitude
frequency characteristics in the auditory pathway, reticular
formation and hippocampus, we have already used this rule
without mentioning this application: we did not study single
nuclei, considering them as independent neural systems.
Instead, we determined simultaneously the system properties
of different brain structures from various functional and
anatomical areas of the brain. This task helped us to
formulate rules on signal transmission in the brain
(sections 7.10, 7.11, 7.12 and 7.13). The results from study
of the simultaneous dynamics of different brain nuclei
revealed to us the concept of *common selectivities* through
brain neural networks (see section 7.11).

In the present section we will go further. We will
try to identify the neural correlates of some of the
measured components presented, using the amplitude characteristics.

First of all, let us consider the following
Gedankenexperiment (Experiment of Thought): let us suppose
that we are performing an experiment with a gross electrode
implanted in a brain structure which contains three different types of neural groups, N_p, N_s and N_g (Fig. 7.30).
The gross electrode measures activities of neural groups
N_p, N_s and N_g.

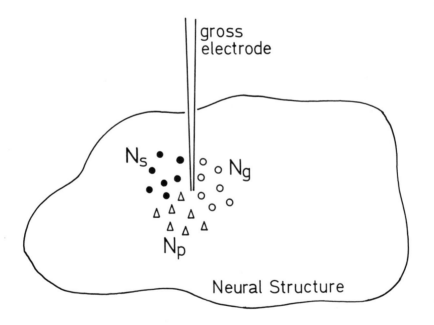

Fig. 7.30 (For explanation see text)

We assume further the following experimental knowledge as established:

   Neurons N_p fire with a frequency x upon stimulation
           by a signal A

   Neurons N_s fire with a frequency y upon stimulation
           by a signal A

   Neurons N_g fire with a frequency z upon stimulation
           by a signal A.

In other words, upon stimulation by the signal A
(which may be a direct or peripheral stimulation) the
neural system shown in Fig. 7.30 will respond with the
firing of the various neural groups (groups N_p, N_s and N_g)
which exist in the system.

If the firing rates (or firing frequencies) of different neural groups are experimentally established, as
we supposed above, then upon application of the stimulation
signal, we should be able to identify the different neural
components comprising the compound evoked potential.
At the least, we can make assumptions about the neural
correlates of the response patterns.

In order to explain this train of thought in a more
concrete manner, we will give an example in the analysis of

the anatomical organization of the cerebral cortex. Micro-

scopic analysis of the appearance of cross sections of

cortex obtained from different regions of the cortex

constitutes the study of cytoarchitectonics (science of

architecture of cells).

Briefly, the layers from the surface inward may be

named and described as follows (THOMPSON, 1967):

"1. *Molecular layer* (plexiform layer). Many
fibers but only a few cells, mostly horizontal
cells of Cajal and granule cells.

2. *External granular layer* (layer of small
pyramids). Mostly small pyramidal cells and
Golgi Type II cells.

3. *Medium pyramid layer.* Medium-sized and
larger pyramidal cells.

4. *Internal granular layer.* Mostly Golgi Type
II granule cells with fewer smaller pyramids.

5. *Large pyramid layer.* Medium or large pyramids.

6. *Spindle cell layer* (fusiform layer). Mostly
spindle cells.

The names of the cells most commonly found in
various layers are simply descriptive of their
appearance {see Fig. 7.31}. In terms of interconnections, the various types of cells can be
divided into four basic groups (LORENTE DE NO,
1938):

1. Small cells with horizontal dendrites and
axons are called horizontal cells of Cajal in
layer 1 and spindle cells in layer 6 (axons
of the latter bend and penetrate into white
matter).

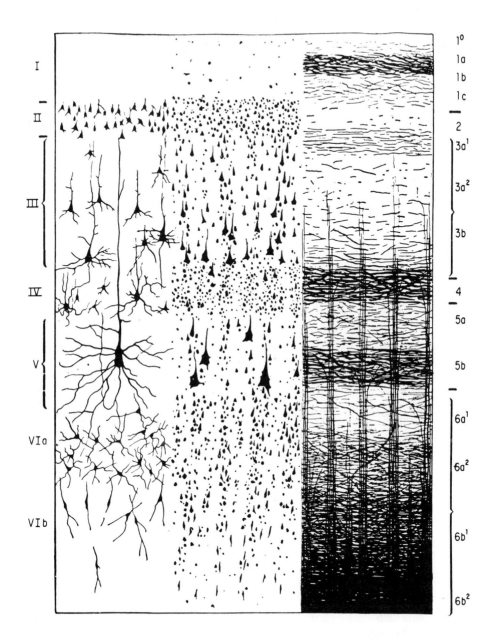

Fig. 7.31 Schematic histological characteristics of the six
          layers of the cerebral cortex. A few examples of
          typical nerve cells are shown on the left, the
          distribution of cell bodies in the middle, and the
          distribution of fiber processes on the right.
          (From RANSON and CLARK, 1959, after BRODMANN)

2. Granule cells (stellate cells) are cells
with short branching axons and many branched
dendritic trees. They include the granule
cells of layer 1 and the Golgi Type II cells
of layers 2 and 4.

3. Pyramidal cells are pyramid shaped cells
which send axons down into white matter below
the cortex and long apical dendrites toward
the cortical surface. In addition they have
many short dendrites nearer the cell body.
Pyramids are found primarily in layers 2, 3,
and 5.

4. Cells sending axons toward the surface of
the cortex. Although not named as such above,
these cells are found in essentially all layers
of the cortex."

Although the details of organization vary considerably

from place to place in the cortex, the basic points listed

above appear to hold.

The cytoarchitectonics of the auditory cortex was

recently studied in detail by SOUSA-PINTO (1973):

"The cortical layers II, III and IV are very
densely populated by relatively uniform, round
or stellate cells with 20 to 30 μ perikaryal
diameter. The separation between these three
layers, which is not possible in Nissl stained
sections, becomes visible in 1 to 3 μ thick
sections of plastic embedded material. The
nerve cells in layer II are randomly disposed,
whilst they form in layer III loose rounded
cellular groups, and in layer IV vertical cylinders which have 50 to 60 μ in outside diameter
and a cell poor centre. These cylinders are
best visible in 100 μ thick Nissl preparations,
cut parallel to the pial surface. The cylinders
may extend into layer V, which is comparatively
cell poor. The VIth layer contains numerous
round, stellate or fusiform cells with 20 to 30 μ

in diameter.

The IIIrd and Vth layers have few pyramidal perikarya which are small. Large or giant pyramidal cells are not found in A I.

The overall thickness of the cortex in the convexity of A I is 2000 μ, measured in sections of plastic blocks. The thickness of the 6 layers is 200 to 250 μ for layer I; 300 μ for layer II; 300 μ for layer III; 300 to 400 μ for layer IV; 350 μ for layer V; and 400 μ for layer VI.

In preparations stained for myelin sheaths A I is characterized by the presence of a very dense plexus of fibres running in all directions in the IVth, Vth and VIth layers. This plexus obscurs the radiations of Meynert, giving a characteristic appearance to A I, since these radiations are prominent in the neighbouring cortical areas.

In preliminary studies of Golgi rapid preparations of A I the cell types commonly present in other cortical areas were found. Pyramidal cells have small perikarya, and very long (600 μ) horizontal basal dendrites. Modified pyramidal cells (star pyramids) are the main cellular element in layer II and constitute one of the main sources of efferent fibres of A I. Several types of stellate cells were found including a particular cell type, found very often in the IVth layer, with a very long horizontal axon.

The specific thalamic afferents were identified as fibres with 5 or 8 μ in diameter, which run obliquely and sinuously through the VIth and Vth layers of A I. These fibres give off many branches with 1 to 2 μ in diameter, which pass to the IVth layer where they give off very thin sinuous branches, ending in small terminal knobs. The ramification of one of these fibres may spread horizontally over 800 μ, at the level of the IVth layer."

After this detailed description of the cytoarchitectonics of the cortical structures we want to draw
the attention of the reader again to the use of a *Gedankenexperiment* as explained in the beginning of this section.
We have described experiments on dynamics of brain potentials in the auditory cortex (see sections 7.6 and 7.7).
The general cytoarchitectonics of the cerebral cortex,
especially the organization of the auditory cortex, revealed
the existence of pyramidal cells. Pyramidal cells are also
existent in the hippocampus (see section 7.4, and Fig. 7.6A).
Moreover, from the experiments of BOUDREAU (1966) and
HOROWITZ et al. (1973) we know that pyramidal cells fire
with a frequency of around 40 Hz. Let us consider the consistent selectivities given in section 7.9 (Fig. 7.17).
We see the existence of marked 40 Hz peaks in the amplitude
characteristics of the acoustical cortex and of the
hippocampus. Therefore we now have in our hands the following facts, which may allow us a tentative assumption:

Existence of pyramidal cells in the auditory cortex

Existence of pyramidal cells in the hippocampus

Existence of 40 Hz selectivity in the cortical frequency characteristics

Existence of 40 Hz selectivity in the hippocampal
frequency characteristics

Knowledge of the fact that pyramidal neurons fire
with a frequency of 40 Hz.

According to our *Gedankenexperiment* this package of
information may lead us to suppose that the *40 Hz selectivity*
of both the cortex and hippocampus do reflect the pyramidal neuron characteristics.

This was just one example. The investigator of the
dynamics of brain potentials will certainly find various
similar possibilities. The cerebral cortex and the cerebellar
cortex especially are excellent structures for this kind of
investigation. Responses of various types of neural groups
can also be explored in a more efficient manner by implanting
several electrodes in locations where the density of neural
groups vary upon the place of the electrode. For example,
responses from different cortical layers having different
neuronal structures can give a much better idea of the
neural processes underlying the brain's evoked potentials.

7.18 SELECTIVE BLOCKING OF BRAIN STRUCTURES WITH NEMBUTAL

In order to go further in applying the biological
systems analysis program outlined in Chapter 3 (see Fig. 3.2)
experiments were performed with the purpose of selective

blocking of the brain's substructures. The cats were anaes-
thetized with Nembutal (35 mg/kg). Fig. 7.32 illustrates
mean value curves of simultaneously obtained amplitude
characteristics in the auditory pathway, reticular formation,
medial geniculate nucleus and hippocampus from cats under
Nembutal anaesthesia. When these curves are compared with
amplitude characteristics of the waking stage (Fig. 7.17)
the following important changes are noticed: the alpha
maxima during waking stage have disappeared. Instead,
dominant maxima in the frequency range of 7-8 Hz have
appeared in all the nuclei. The cortical selectivities have
all-pass characteristics. The 50 Hz maximum in the reticular
formation has become a marked selectivity, while the 50 Hz
selectivity of the medial geniculate nucleus remains marked
during Nembutal stage.

The barbiturates have a specific depressant effect
on the brain stem portion of the reticular activating system. Therefore, barbiturates obviously can either depress
brain activity or even cause sleep. Yet, it is especially
interesting that barbiturate anaesthesia *does not block
transmission* in most of the specific sensory systems and
also *does not block* the function of the thalamic portion
of the reticular activating system (GUYTON, 1971).

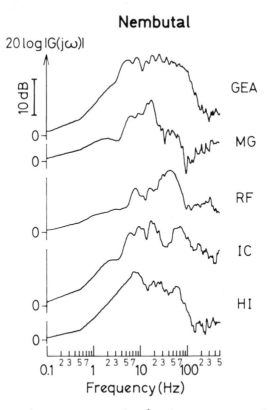

Fig. 7.32 Mean value curves of simultaneous amplitude
characteristics of different brain nuclei
of the cat obtained from nine experiments
with auditory stimulation during Nembutal
anaesthesia. Direct computer-plottings. Along
the abscissa is the input frequency in logarithmic scale, along the ordinate the mean
value potential amplitude, $|G(j\omega)|$, in
decibels. The curves are normalized in such
a way that the amplitude at 0 Hz is equal
to 1 (or 20 log 1=0). (BAŞAR, GÖNDER and
UNGAN, unpublished observations)

The above results and the effect of barbiturates lead us to formulate that thalamo-reticular communication occurs mostly in the 50 Hz frequency channel.

Summing up the considerations presented in these last two sections, we are led to consider the 40 Hz activity of the cortex and of the hippocampus as responses of pyramidal neurons, the 50 Hz activity of the reticular formation and of the medial geniculate nucleus as the frequency range of the communicative channel of the thalamo-cortical system.

These explanations are tentative assumptions; they are only first approaches, combining systems analysis, cytoarchitectonics and application of pharmacological agents. It can be expected that further application of the biological systems analysis program (especially the use of more specific pharmacological agents, lesion and ablation techniques) would allow a more profound systems approach to the study of the dynamics of the brain.

7.19 DYNAMICS OF POTENTIALS IN THE CAT VISUAL PATHWAY

In order to apply the rule *"going out of the system"* experiments similar to those performed in the auditory pathway were undertaken. During the investigation of the cat visual pathway, the experimental setup and the methods used were the same (section 7.3). Recording electrodes were placed in the occipital cortex (area 17) (OC), lateral geniculate nucleus (LG), reticular formation (RF), superior colliculus (SC) and hippocampus (HI). (For functional organization of the visual pathway the reader is referred to section 7.4).

The stimulation signals consisted of intense visual step functions with a duration of about 3 sec. These visual step functions were generated with the help of an optic stimulator made in our laboratory.

Fig. 7.33 shows simultaneously recorded and selectively averaged transient evoked responses from the visual pathway of the cat to light stimulation during the waking stage. Fig. 7.34 illustrates a set of typical amplitude characteristics in the visual pathway. The amplitude frequency characteristics were computed using the selectively averaged transient responses similar to those of Fig. 7.33 and the TRFC-Method described in section 3.2.

Fig. 7.35 illustrates mean value curves of 12 experiments using 6 different cats. Usually three different

Visual Pathway

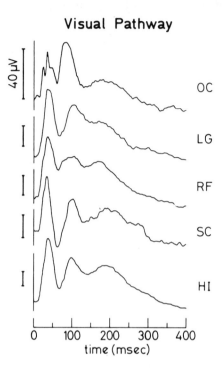

Fig. 7.33 A typical set of simultaneously recorded and
        selectively averaged evoked potentials in dif-
        ferent brain nuclei of chronically implanted
        cats, elicited during the waking stage by light
        stimulation in the form of step function. Direct
        computer-plottings. Negativity upwards. (BAŞAR,
        GÖNDER and UNGAN, unpublished observations)

amplitude maxima were registered in all these brain struc-

tures studied: 2-3 Hz frequency range, 18-22 Hz frequency

range and 70 Hz frequency range. Selectivities in these

frequency ranges are *consistent selectivities* as the mean

value curves of Fig. 7.35 show. (For the definition of

consistent selectivities, see section 7.9).

Visual Pathway

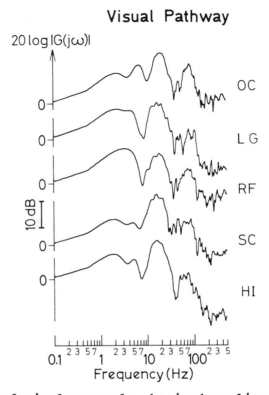

Fig. 7.34 A set of simultaneously obtained amplitude charac-
        teristics of different brain nuclei of the cat
        determined by the TRFC-Method and using the selec-
        tively averaged transient responses similar to
        those in Fig. 7.33. Direct computer-plottings.
        Along the abscissa is the input frequency in
        logarithmic scale, along the ordinate the poten-
        tial amplitude, $|G(j\omega)|$, in decibels. The curves
        are normalized in such a way that the amplitude
        at 0 Hz is equal to 1 (or 20 log 1=0). (After
        BAŞAR, GÖNDER and UNGAN, unpublished observations)

LOPES DA SILVA et al. (1970) recorded potentials

evoked by sinusoidally modulated light from the lateral

geniculate nucleus and occipital cortex of unanaesthetized

dogs. They found selectivities in the range of 20 Hz in both

of these nuclei (OC and LG), thus supporting our results

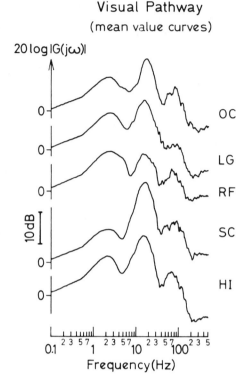

Fig. 7.35 Mean value curves of simultaneous amplitude char-
teristics of different brain nuclei of the cat
obtained from eight experiments with light stimulation during the waking stage. Along the
abscissa is the input frequency in logarithmic
scale, along the ordinate the mean value poten-
tial amplitude, $|G(j\omega)|$, in decibels. The curves
are normalized in such a way that the amplitude
at 0 Hz is equal to 1 (or 20 log 1=0). (After
BAŞAR et al., 1975b)

obtained by using light step functions and the TRFC-Method.

We should also mention here that SPEKREIJSE (1966) and

REGAN (1968) found selectivities in the higher frequency

range of 50-60 Hz in studying the human evoked responses

to sinusoidal light stimuli. However, we are not willing

yet to compare responses from human scalp electrodes with responses of deep recording electrodes.

Since the experiments in the visual pathway which we describe in this section are preliminary and undetailed investigations, we are not able to achieve further component analysis. However, we want to mention an important finding concerning the retinal transfer characteristics. MAFFEI (1969) simultaneously stimulated the center and periphery of the receptive field of an "on" ganglion of the cat retina with sinusoidally modulated light. This author found an amplitude maximum at 2 Hz. The similarity of 2 Hz selectivities in our results brings one to the idea that these selectivities may result from retinal sources.

In the future these kinds of considerations may help brain investigators to achieve further and more profound analyses.

F. DISCUSSION OF METHODS

7.20 SELECTIVE AVERAGING AND WIENER FILTERING

Fig. 7.36 shows evoked potentials of the cat inferior colliculus which were obtained by four different techniques. In this figure, curve A shows the conventional AEP, curve B shows the selectively averaged EP, curve C shows the Wiener filtered estimate of the AEP and curve D shows the AEP estimated by Wiener filtering of only the epochs selected for curve B. All these techniques were applied using the same inferior colliculus recordings of the same experimental section. At first glance all four evoked potentials show similar time courses, but a critical analysis reveals the following differences:

a) The short latency-wave complex I (which is composed of waves I', I" and I"') of the conventional AEP (curve A) is non-existent in the Wiener filtered evoked potential (curve C). In the selectively Wiener filtered evoked potential (i.e., in the evoked potential which is computed using selected single EPs only) the short latency wave complex is more marked (curve D). The short latency wave complex I is most marked in the selectively averaged evoked potential (SAEP) shown as curve B.

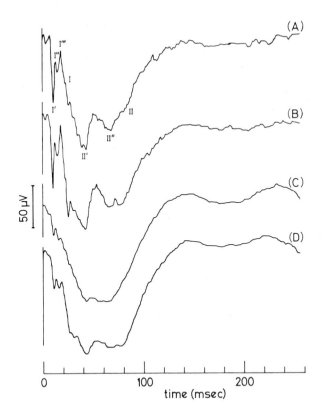

Fig. 7.36 The averaged evoked potentials obtained by four
         different techniques using the EP epochs recorded
         during the same experimental session from cat
         inferior colliculus. (A): Conventional averaging,
         (B): Selective averaging, (C): Wiener filtering,
         (D): Wiener filtering of epochs selected for
         curve B. Note that the higher frequency wave com-
         plexes I and II, which have strikingly large mag-
         nitudes in curves A and B, are reduced to a minimum
         with the application of Wiener filtering of (curves
         C and D). Upward deflections indicate negativity of
         the recording electrode. (After BAŞAR et al., 1975a)

   b) Positive waves II' and II" (of wave complex II)

are more marked in the selectively averaged evoked potential

(curve B) in comparison to the Wiener filter estimate evoked

potential (curve C).

c) Wiener filter estimate of the evoked potential
(curve C) and the selectively averaged evoked potential
(curve B) contain less noise in comparison with the conventionally averaged evoked potential (curve A).

The selective averaging method has several important
advantages over *the conventional (classical) on-line averaging procedure.* Firstly, the recordings can be played back
and all the epochs, where a movement artifact was monitored,
can be eliminated. During our experiments we always watched
the movements of the cat with the aid of the closed circuit
TV scope (this monitoring during experiments can be avoided
using a video tape recorder). Usually, the recording of
30-40 single evoked potentials are sufficient to obtain
a response which is free from noise.

The elimination of only a small number of the evoked
potential periods makes it possible to obtain an AEP with
a minimal number of stimuli. However, the most important
advantage of *a posteriori selective averaging* is that this
method enables the investigator to select evoked potentials
during defined waking and sleep stages. Selective averaging
allows averaging in *almost stationary periods.* Classical
on-line averaging allows the investigator to obtain AEP

recordings during defined stages also. However, it is not usually possible to avoid recording during a short transition stage. For example, the appearance of only a few spindles or slow waves in the corticogram causes enormous changes in the entire course of the AEP for all the nuclei under study. Moreover, using the conventional on-line averaging techniques does not allow us to play back the recording and to eliminate the epochs containing movement artifacts or nonstationary background activities. As a result of this, we usually obtain highly similar selectively averaged evoked potentials from the same cat whereas the AEPs using the classical on-line averaging may show considerable deviations.

The disadvantage of selective averaging is that the experimenter requires a highly sophisticated measuring system and longer computation times. However, this time consumption should not be considered as a severe disadvantage of selective averaging, because this off-line method provides, in turn, the possibility to discard only those epochs during which a movement artifact or a transition stage takes place. Every other epoch is evaluated and no properly recorded EP is wasted. But if the classical on-line averaging is used, when a movement artifact or a transition stage occurs at any phase of the measurement, the resultant AEP is deteriorated, hence, all the adequate EPs averaged and the time spent for that measurement are wasted.

As far as the amplitude characteristics are concerned, better results are always obtained by taking into account only the selected epochs. This fact can be seen by comparing the amplitude characteristics presented in Fig. 7.37. In the amplitude characteristics of the AEPs obtained by selected epochs (curve B) the frequency bands are distinguished more clearly than is the case for curve A which is computed from the AEP obtained by classical averaging.

The Wiener filter estimates of evoked potentials presented in this book are quite simple and smooth when compared to those obtained by usual and selective averaging methods (Fig. 7.36). The high frequency components (wave complexes I and II) existing in the selectively averaged evoked potentials of the inferior colliculus (curve B in Fig. 7.36) are reduced to a minimum or are almost non-existent in the Wiener filter estimate of the evoked potential. This fact is confirmed in ideal-filtered high frequency components of both evoked potentials (Fig. 7.38).

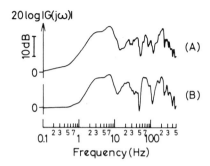

Fig. 7.37 Amplitude frequency characteristics computed from
the upper two AEPs of Fig. 7.36. Curves A and B are
obtained using the conventional AEP and the selectively averaged EP respectively. Along the abscissa
is the frequency in logarithmic scale, along the
ordinate the relative amplitude in decibels. Note
that the frequency bands formed by different amplitude maxima are distinguished more clearly in curve
B than in curve A. (After BAŞAR et al., 1975a)

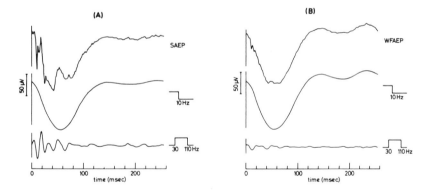

Fig. 7.38 Filtered AEPs (FAEPs) of the selectively averaged
EP and the Wiener filter estimated AEP obtained
by the method of ideal filtering. (A): Selectively
averaged EP (SAEP) (curve B of Fig. 7.36) and its
two filtered components in the frequency ranges of
0-10 Hz and 30-110 Hz. (B): Wiener filter estimated
AEP (WFAEP) (curve C of Fig. 7.36) and its core-
sponding components in the same frequency ranges as
above. Note the slight magnification of 0-10 Hz
component and drastic suppression of 30-110 Hz
component due to the Wiener filtering process.
(After BAŞAR et al., 1975a)

These high frequency components (which are also described
in sections 7.8 and 7.9) are certainly not due to some
artifacts since we obtained similar responses from the
inferior colliculi of about 15 cats. In section 7.12
we have shown that this response may be due to a strong
resonance phenomenon. On the other hand, it is shown that
this high frequency component cannot be due to instrumental
noise or instrumental artifacts since the evoked potential
of the medial geniculate nucleus does not show any high
frequency component such as the IC component (section 7.9).
The fact that the Wiener filter causes information loss
is shown in the example of Fig. 7.36 (curve C). The
application of the Wiener filter to selected evoked potential epochs (some epochs of the averaged evoked potential
of curve A) causes the appearance of the waves. In other
words, due to the use of the selected epochs, the information loss caused by Wiener filtering in the higher frequency
range is reduced. This loss is due to the fact that Wiener
filtering gives an artificial weight to the power spectral
component which already has the largest amplitude, and
conversely, supresses those components with relatively
small spectral magnitudes. Another handicap of this filtering method is that it cannot eliminate the interferences

due to hum or any periodical noise originating from instruments. The disturbances due to these types of noise, which have consistent frequencies and magnitudes throughout the experiment, are even emphasized by this method although they are randomly phased with the stimulus.

From these considerations we deduced the selective averaging procedures to give more reliable information than the Wiener filter. Moreover, the computing time is significantly lower and the number of evoked potential epochs used is reduced to a minimum. Therefore, in the experiments described in this chapter, a posteriori selective averaging was used, and not the Wiener filtering method.

7.21 TRFC-METHOD

As we have seen in Chapter 4, the use of the TRFC-Method was necessary during the autoregulation studies in order to obtain systems frequency characteristics (see section 4.11). Alternatively, the application of sinusoidally modulated signals would have been very time-consuming; the life times of the heart and kidney preparations made such a method experimentally difficult. During the brain experiments, where we work with chronically implanted cats, we do not have the problem of short preparation life time

of the heart and kidney preparations, but we have the
problem of continuous change of waking and sleep stages
instead. Accordingly, measurement time becomes an important
problem. Since it is extremely difficult to obtain homo-
geneously-measured and almost-constant transient evoked
responses, experiments with sinusoidal input signals would
be quite impossible to analyze since the experimenter must
have almost-stationary on-going brain activity in the cat
and must be able to maintain steady-state experimental
conditions during a long recording period. Using sinusoidal
input stimuli the experimenter would be continuously changing,
artificially, the experimental conditions by changing the
frequency of the stimulation. To obtain amplitude frequency
characteristics simultaneously from five different nuclei
during three different waking and sleep stages would require
enormous experimental times, within which it is certainly
not reasonable to expect steady-state experimental conditions,
i.e. almost-constant on-going brain activity. The problem
of steady-state experimental conditions is quasi-optimally
realized by applying TRFC-Method to selectively averaged
evoked potentials. The frequency characteristics obtained
in this way present, indeed, responses obtained where the
brain activity stages are almost constant. It is almost

impossible to maintain such invariant experimental conditions using sinusoidally modulated input stimuli.

The nonlinear nature of the brain responses may be
raised here again as an objection to the use of the TRFC-
Method, but the following arguments support our recommen-
dation of the TRFC-Method despite the nonlinearity of the
system:

1. The model experiments of Chapter 6 have shown
that the types of nonlinearities seen in brain responses
do not cause serious obstacles if the experimenter is
interested in the determination of dominant selectivity
bands and if he discards minor peakings detectable in
the amplitude frequency characteristics (compare the
results and discussion presented in section 6.6).

2. Results from the application of the theoretical
filtering method support the findings obtained by the
TRFC-Method. This point will be discussed in the following section.

3. Measurements of amplitude frequency characteristics
in the visual cortex and lateral geniculate nucleus using
sinusoidally modulated light as the stimulus (LOPES DA
SILVA et al., 1970) gave similar results to those obtained

using the TRFC-Method (compare section 7.19).

Accordingly, we may assume that nonlinearities do not cause an essential obstacle for the application of the TRFC-Method. For nonlinear problems of biological systems the reader is referred to Chapter 6 of this book.

7.22 THEORETICAL IDEAL FILTERING METHOD (THEORETICAL ISOLATION METHOD)

The theoretical ideal filtering method provides us with at least three basic pieces of information:

1. By theoretical pass-band filtering we obtain evoked potential components which usually have an oscillatory character. In comparing the magnitudes of these components we can try to check the reliability and accuracy of the results revealed by amplitude frequency characteristics. Examples of this kind of comparison, which basically supports the results revealed by amplitude characteristics, are given in section 7.8. TRFC-Method and the method of theoretical filtering are different methods. The fact that TRFC-Method and the filtering method both provide us with similar information brings to the EEG worker new concepts: as mentioned earlier, the TRFC-Method is only an approach because of the nonlinearity of brain responses. But the

filtering method does not apply the Fourier (or Laplace) transform to the evoked responses and is a more suitable method for nonlinear systems. Therefore the obtaining of similar results with both methods is very promising for future needs. We should emphasize that best results could be obtained by applying both TRFC and filtering methods.

2. By applying pass-band and stop-band filters alternatively to the evoked potentials, the investigator can obtain results which help him to derive rules and principles for the interpretation of evoked potentials (see section 7.14).

3. The components of evoked potentials, which have the form of damped sinusoids, are confirmed in experimental findings published by FREEMAN (1972b) and HOROWITZ et al. (1973). We may therefore assume that the theoretical isolation method is a good tool for component prediction in the analysis of biological systems.

One should also seriously consider the amplitude modulation waveforms predicted by theoretical filtering as elementary waveforms of the brain's evoked potentials (see Fig. 7.29).

7.23 POWER SPECTRA AFTER WELCH

The amplitude characteristics presented in this
chapter were obtained from selectively averaged evoked
responses rather than from simple evoked potentials. We
are therefore more justified in making comparisons with
power spectra which are averaged over a number of segments of a longer period of brain's spontaneous activity.
To this end, the Welch-Method presents a good approach
to comparing the on-going activity of the brain with
the evoked responses, as we did in evaluating the experiments presented in this chapter.

7.24 APPLICATION OF PHARMACOLOGICAL AGENTS

In this chapter (section 7.18) we have given only
one example concerning the use of pharmacological agents.
We described experiments where evoked potentials were
recorded with cats under Nembutal anaesthesia. Our results
led us to consider the 50 Hz frequency channel as the
frequency channel where the thalamo-reticular communication
occurs. Since we have used only one pharmacological agent
this method of selective blocking is obviously less developed
as yet in our studies.

7.25 GOING OUT OF THE SYSTEM

The method of going out of the system served us in the studies of the present chapter in our effort to identify one neural group giving rise to different evoked potential components (section 7.17).

Moreover the fact that we do not study only one brain structure, but various structures simultaneously, led to the concept of common selectivities through brain neural networks. This concept provides an important framework for investigators working on theories of signal transport in the brain.

G. CONCLUDING REMARKS

The experiments described in this chapter reveal noteworthy findings and concepts in the study of rhythmic and evoked potentials of the brain, especially concerning the important relationship between the evoked and rhythmic activities. The description of various experiments in sections 7.5 to 7.10 leads the investigator to formulate some general features of the dynamics of brain potentials, which are deduced directly from the experiments (sections 7.11, 7.12 and 7.13). In section 7.13 we state that brain models and hypotheses on signal transmission in the brain must be compatible with the rules derived from experiments. Dynamics of future brain models should fit together with the characteristics provided in the present chapter.

Further investigations should link these abstract principles with the underlying physiological and neural processes. In other words, not only the frequency position of these selectivities, but also the neural groups giving rise to these selectivities must be investigated in further studies. Brief examples in the form of *Gedankenexperiments* are given in section 7.17.

The method of averaged evoked potentials is common in the study of electrical activity of the brain. Usually,

interpretation of evoked potential components is very difficult. The analysis given in section 7.14 allows a new
method of interpretation of evoked potentials. According
to this analysis, in section 7.16 principles for the understanding of evoked potentials are given. Moreover, evoked
potential components resembling damped sinusoids are predicted. The existence of such components were supported by
the experiments of FREEMAN and HOROWITZ described in section
7.14.

One of the most important features of this chapter
is the fact that the investigator is always confronted with
the problem of interaction of stimuli with the spontaneous
activity of the brain. Resonance phenomena play an important
role in interpreting the amplitude frequency characteristics
and the evoked potential components. Resonance phenomena,
such as those resulting from a "forced self-oscillatory
biological system," are handled separately in sections 6.4
and 6.5 of the previous chapter. Therefore the reader who
would have a more profound idea of probabilistic resonance
phenomena and also of the understanding of evoked potentials
should read sections 6.4 and 6.5, where a relaxation oscillator is driven with various input signals.

REFERENCES

Adrian, E.D.: Afferent discharges to the cerebral cortex from peripheral sense organs. J. Physiol. (Lond.) 100, 159-191 (1941).

Altman, J., R.L. Brunner, and S.A. Bayer: The hippocampus and behavioral maturation. Behavioral Biology 8, 557-596, Abstract No. I- 225R (1973).

Andersen, P. and S.A. Andersson: Physiological Basis of the Alpha Rhythm. Appleton-Century-Crofts, New York (1968).

Andersen, P. and J.C. Eccles: Inhibitory phasing of neuronal discharge. Nature (Lond.) 196, 645-647 (1967).

Başar, E.: A study of the time and frequency characteristics of the potentials evoked in the acoustical cortex. Kybernetik 10, 61-64 (1972a).

Başar, E.: Remarks on mathematical signal processing by the brain during rhythmic neurophysiological stimulation. Int. J. Neuroscience 4, 71-76 (1972b).

Başar, E.: Biological systems analysis and evoked potentials of the brain. T.-I.-T. J. Life Sci. 4, 37-58 (1974).

Başar, E., A. Gönder, Ç. Özesmi, and P. Ungan: Dynamics of brain rhythmic and evoked potentials. I. Some computational methods for the analysis of electrical signals from the brain. Biol. Cybernetics 20, 137-143 (1975a).

Başar, E., A. Gönder, Ç. Özesmi, and P. Ungan: Dynamics of brain rhythmic and evoked potentials. II. Studies in the auditory pathway, reticular formation, and hippocampus during the waking stage. Biol. Cybernetics 20, 145-160 (1975b).

Başar, E., A. Gönder, Ç. Özesmi, and P. Ungan: Dynamics of brain rhythmic and evoked potentials. III. Studies in the auditory pathway, reticular formation, and hippocampus during sleep. Biol. Cybernetics 20, 161-169 (1975c).

Başar, E., and Ç. Özesmi: The hippocampal EEG activity and a systems analytical interpretation of averaged evoked potentials of the brain. Kybernetik 12, 45-54 (1972).

Başar, E., and P. Ungan: A component analysis and principles derived for the understanding of evoked potentials of the brain: studies in the hippocampus. Kybernetik 12, 133-140 (1973).

Başar, E., P. Ungan, and Ç. Özesmi: Oscillatory components of evoked potentials of the brain. Digest of the 10. Int. Conf. Med. Biol. Eng. Dresden, (1973).

Benoit, J.: Hypothalamic-hypophyseal control of the sexual activity in birds. Gen. comp. Endocr. Suppl. 1, 254-274 (1962).

Borg, E.: Nonlinear dynamic properties of somato-motor reflex system. A model study. Acta Physiol. Scand. 87, 15-26 (1973).

Boudreau, J.C.: Computer measurements of hippocampal fast activity in cats with chronically implanted electrodes. Electroenceph. clin. Neurophysiol. 20, 165-174 (1966).

Brady, J.V.: Motivational-emotional self-stimulation. In, D.E. Sheer (Ed.): Electrical Stimulation of the Brain. Univ. of Texas Press, Austin, Texas (1961).

Brady, J.V.: Psychophysiology of emotional behavior. In, A.J. Bachrach (Ed.): Experimental Foundations of Clinical Psychology. Basic Books, New York (1962).

Brazier, M.A.B.: The Electrical Activity of The Nervous System. The Williams and Wilkins Company, Baltimore (1968).

Brazier, M.A.B., and D.O. Walter: Evaluation of bioelectrical data from brain, nerve and muscle, I. In, A. Rémond (Ed.): Handbook of Electroencephalography and Clinical Neurophysiology. Elsevier Publishing Company, 4, (1972).

Bremer, F., and V. Bonnet: Intérprétation des réactions, rhythmiques prolonguées des aires sensorielles de l'écorce cérébrale. Electroenceph. Clin. Neurophysiol. 2, 384-400 (1950).

Brodal, A.: The Reticular Formation of the Brain Stem, Anatomical Aspects and Functional Correlations. Olive and Boyd Company, London (1957).

Caton, R.: The electric currents of the brain. Brit. Med.
    J. II, 278 (1875).

Chang, H.-T.: The evoked potentials. In, J. Field (Ed.):
    Handbook of Physiology. Volume 1, 299-314 Amer. Physiol.
    Society, Washington, D.C. (1959).

Fessard, A.: Brain potentials and rhythms. In, J. Field
    (Ed.): Handbook of Physiology. Volume 1, 255-259 Amer.
    Physiol. Society, Washington, D.C. (1959).

Fessard, A.: The role of neuronal networks in sensory com-
    munication within the brain. In, W.A. Rosenblith (Ed.):
    Sensory Communication. M.I.T. Press, Massachusetts (1961).

Freeman, W.J.: Linear analysis of the dynamics of neural
    masses. Ann. Rev. Biophys. Bioeng. 1, 225-256 (1972a).

Freeman, W.J.: Measurement of oscillatory responses to
    electrical stimulation in olfactory bulb of cat.
    J. Neurophysiol. 35, 762-779 (1972b).

French, J.D., J. Verzeano, and H.W. Magoun: An extralemniscal
    sensory system in the brain. Arch. Neurol. Psychiat. 69,
    505-518 (1953).

Galambos, R.: Suppression of auditory nerve activity by
    stimulation of efferent fibres to cochlea. J. Neurophysiol.
    19, 424-437 (1956).

Gardner, E.: Fundamentals of Neurology. W.B. Saunders Company,
    Philadelphia (1952).

Grossman, S.P.: A Textbook of Physiological Psychology.
    John Wiley and Sons, Inc., New York (1967).

Guyton, A.C.: Textbook of Medical Physiology. W.B. Saunders
    Company, Philadelphia (1971).

Hall, R.D., and A.A. Borbely: Acoustically evoked potentials
    in the rat during sleep and waking. Exp. Brain Res. 11,
    93-110 (1970).

Hernández-Peón, R.: Reticular mechanisms of sensory control.
    In, W.A. Rosenblith (Ed.): Sensory Communication. M.I.T.
    Press, Massachusetts (1961).

Herz, A.: Cortical and subcortical auditory evoked potentials
    during wakefulness and sleep in the cat. In, K. Akert,
    C. Bally, and J.P. Schadé (Eds.): Sleep Mechanisms.
    Elsevier Publishing Company, Amsterdam (1965).

Herz, A., F. Fraling, I. Nieder, and G. Farber: Pharmaco-
    logically induced alterations of cortical and subcortical
    evoked potentials compared with physiological changes
    during the awake-sleep cycle in cats. Electroenceph.
    Clin. Neurophysiol. Suppl. 26, 164-176 (1967).

Horowitz, J.M.: Evoked activity of single units and neural
    populations in the hippocampus of the cat. Electroenceph.
    Clin. Neurophysiol. 32, 227-240 (1972).

Horowitz, J.M., W.J. Freeman, and P.J. Stoll: A neural
    network with a background level of excitation in the cat
    hippocampus. Int. J. Neurosci. 5, 113-123 (1973).

Kappers, C.V.A., G.C. Huber, and E.C. Crosby: The Comparative
    Anatomy of the Nervous System of Vertebrates. Macmillan
    Company, New York (1963).

Lopes da Silva, F.H., A. Hoeks, H. Smits, and L.H.
    Zetterberg: Model of brain rhythmic activity. The alpha-
    rhythms of the thalamus. Kybernetik 15, 27-37 (1974).

Lopes da Silva, F.H., A. van Rotterdam, W. Storm van Leeuwen,
    and A.M. Tielen: Dynamic characteristics of visual evoked
    potentials in the dog. I. Cortical and subcortical poten-
    tials by sine wave modulated light. Electroenceph. Clin.
    Neurophysiol. 29, 246-259 (1970).

Lorente de Nó, R.: Cerebral cortex: cytoarchitecture. In,
    J.F. Fulton (Ed.): Physiology of the Nervous System. Oxfor
    Oxford University Press, New York (1938).

Maffei, L.: Dynamics of retinal receptive fields. In:
    Proceedings of Conference on Systems Analysis Approach
    to Neurophysiological Problems. Brainerd, Minn (1969).

Magoun, H.W., and S.W. Ranson: The afferent path of the
    light reflex. A review of the literature. Arch. Ophthal.
    13, 862-874 (1935).

Matoušek, N.: Frequency and correlation analysis. In,
    A. Rémond (Ed.): Handbook of Electroencephalography
    and Clinical Neurophysiology. Volume 5, Part A. Elsevier
    Publishing Company (1973).

Monnier, M.: Functions of the Nervous System. Volume 1.
    Publishing Company, Amsterdam (1968).

Moruzzi, G.: The sleep-waking cycle. Reviews of Physiology
    64, 1-165 (1972).

Nauta, W.J.H.: Hippocampal projections and related neural
    pathways to the midbrain in the cat. Brain 81, 319-340
    (1958).

Nauta, W.J.H.: Neural associations of the amygdaloid complex
    in the monkey. Brain 85, 505-520 (1962).

Nogawa, T., K. Katayama, Y. Tabata, T. Kawahara, and
    T. Ohshio: Visual evoked potentials estimated by "Wiener
    Filtering". Electroenceph. Clin. Neurophysiol. 35,
    375-378 (1973).

Özesmi, Ç., and E. Başar: Dynamics of potentials evoked in
    the auditory pathway and reticular formation of the cat.
    Studies during waking and sleep stages. Kybernetik 16,
    27-35 (1974).

Powell, E.W.: Limbic projections to the thalamus. Exp. Brain
    Res. 17, 394-401 (1973).

Pribram, K.H., and L. Kruger: Functions of the "olfactory
    brain". Ann. N. Y. Acad. Sci. 58, 109-138 (1954).

Ranson, SW., and S.L. Clark: The Anatomy of the Nervous
    System. Saunders, Philadelphia (1959).

Regan, O.: A high frequency mechanism which underlies visual
    evoked potentials. Electroenceph. Clin. Neurophysiol.
    25, 231-237 (1968).

Snider, R.S., and W.T. Niemer: A Stereotaxic Atlas of the
    Cat Brain. The Univ. Chicago Press (1964).

Sousa-Pinto, A.: The structure of the first auditory cortex
    (AI) in the cat. I. Light microscopic observations on its
    organization. Arch. Ital. Biol. III, 112-137 (1973).

Spekreijse, H.: Analysis of EEG responses in man evoked by
    sine wave modulated light. Thesis, Univ. Amsterdam (1966).

Thompson, R.F.: Foundations of Physiological Psychology.
    Harper and Row Company, New York (1967).

Thompson, R.F., and M.M. Patterson: Bioelectric Recording
    Techniques. Academic Press, New York (1973).

Ungan, P.: Systems theoretical analysis of potentials evoked
    in the cat auditory cortex. Thesis, Hacettepe Univ.,
    Ankara (1974).

Valdman, A.V.: Pharmacology and Physiology of the Reticular
    Formation. Progress in Brain Res. Volume 20, Elsevier
    Publishing Company, Amsterdam (1967).

Walter, D.O.: A posteriori "Wiener Filtering" of average
    evoked responses. Electroenceph. Clin. Neurophysiol.
    Suppl. 27, 61-70 (1969).

Webster, W.R.: The effects of repetitive stimulation on
    auditory evoked potentials. Electroenceph. Clin. Neuro-
    physiol. 30, 318-330 (1971).

Welch, P.D.: The use of the fast Fourier transform for the
    estimation of power spectra. IEEE Trans. Audio and
    Electroacoustics, AU-15, 2, 70-73 (1967).

Wickelgren, W.O.: Effects of state of arousal on click evoked
    responses in cats. J. Neurophysiol. 31, 757-768 (1968).

Chapter 8

An Overview

In previous chapters of this book we have studied the dynamics of various biological systems such as the peripheral circulatory system (Chapter 4), smooth muscles (Chapter 5) and various structures of the brain (Chapter 7). We have described experiments which show the investigator how to obtain new results and new points of view concerning the biological systems under study. We have also attempted to give an extended functional classification concerning the nonlinearities observed in biological systems (Chapter 6).

In the present chapter we will handle the general features and general consequences which we obtained in studying these various biological systems. We will discuss the general implications, especially the three groups below:

(1) Methodological key-points which are immediately derived from the application of the biological systems analysis program (presented in Chapter 3).

(2) Usefulness of the biological systems analysis program.

(3) Some general concepts which result from the study of various biological systems.

8.1 BIOLOGICAL SYSTEMS ANALYSIS PROGRAM:
GENERAL DISCUSSION OF THE METHODS AND RULES

Although the applied rules and methods of the biological systems analysis program were discussed in detail in different chapters of this book, in this section we will try to summarize the discussions so that the reader can have a more general idea of the usefulness and reliability of the methods. We will discuss these methods in the same order as given in the biological systems analysis program (Fig. 3.2).

a) Method of Transient Response Analysis

In section 3.2 we stated that the greatest disadvantage of this method stems from the fact that distinct components of the system studied are not visible in the transient response. In Chapters 4 and 7 we have seen that when two, three or more components exist in the system response, the observer cannot distinguish these components without further analysis. Especially in the analysis of brain evoked responses, the study of peaks, peak latencies and peak numbers of the transient responses is a disadvantage for the investigator in that it may lead to misinterpretations (sections 7.14 and 7.16). Simple-looking system transient responses sometimes have a large number of components, and vice versa, a large number of peaks in the transient response do not necessarily reveal the existence of a large number of systems components.

b) Method of Frequency Characteristics

During the experiments described in different chapters of this book, the frequency characteristics of the studied biological systems were not obtained directly by application of sinusoidal input signals, but by using the TRFC-Method presented in section 3.2. Therefore we will not discuss here the techniques of the frequency characteristics method. In the following paragraphs, in the discussion of the TRFC-Method, we will see how the direct measurement of the frequency characteristics may be replaced by the TRFC-Method. The usefulness and importance of the frequency characteristics will be handled in section 8.2.

c) Transient Response-Frequency Characteristics

Method (TRFC-Method)

This method, described in detail in section 3.2, was used in the study of various biological systems: kidney and coronary system, smooth muscles and the brain (Chapters 4, 5 and 7). Although the Fourier transform (the mathematical procedure of the method) is valid only for linear systems, in section 3.2, we recommended the application of this method in spite of the nonlinear behavior of biological systems, especially since the direct measurement of biological frequency characteristics takes up so much time, and errors resulting from the length of measurements are larger than the errors due to system nonlinearities. In fact, experiments described in Chapters 4, 5 and 7 confirmed this view: the use of the TRFC-Method was necessary during the autoregulation studies in Chapter 4, since by direct measurement of the frequency characteristics of the kidney we were not able to obtain complete curves. The isolated heart preparation has a short life time, and as the heart beats spontaneously, the frequency characteristics of the coronary system could be determined only by the use of the TRFC-Method (section 4.6).

During the brain experiments, where we work with chronically implanted cats, we do not have the problem of short preparation life time as with the heart and kidney systems, but we have the problem of continuous change of waking and sleep stages instead (sections 7.5, 7.6 and 7.7). Accordingly, measurement time becomes an important problem. As we explain in detail in section 7.21, the problem of steady-state experimental conditions is quasi-optimally solved by applying the TRFC-Method to selectively averaged evoked potentials. The frequency characteristics obtained with the TRFC-Method present, indeed, responses obtained where the brain activity stage is almost constant.

The nonlinear nature of biological systems' responses was raised as an objection to the use of the TRFC-Method (sections 7.21 and 6.6). This important objection was discussed in different sections of the book (sections 6.6, 7.9, 7.19, 7.21). To summarize, we assume that nonlinearities do not cause an essential obstacle for the application of the TRFC-Method. The reliability of the TRFC-Method was also shown to be confirmed by the use of a theoretical ideal filtering method as we will mention again below.

d) Theoretical Isolation Method (TI-Method)

An important methodological use of the theoretical ideal filtering method is its application to the brain evoked potentials in order to check the accuracy and the reliability of TRFC-Method. In sections 7.14, 7.15 and 7.16 we have seen that by theoretical pass-band filtering, we obtain evoked potential components which usually have an oscillatory character. In comparing the magnitudes of these components we can check the reliability of the results revealed by amplitude characteristics. Examples of this kind of comparison, which basically support the results of amplitude characteristics, are given in section 7.8.

A similar use of the filtering method was given in the studies of smooth muscle contractions, where the results of theoretical filtering were used to support the data obtained by power spectra analysis (section 5.7).

8.2 BIOLOGICAL SYSTEMS ANALYSIS PROGRAM: APPLICATION

In this section we will attempt to summarize and to discuss in general what the biological systems analysis program brings into light from the biological view point. In section 3.1, in presenting the biological systems analysis program, we assumed that not the application of single methods, but the combination of different methods (systems theoretical and biological methods both) would give efficient results to elucidate the black boxes studied. In establishing such a research program we assumed that its application would provide the investigator with useful information on the biological nature of the phenomena. This view will be discussed below.

a) Frequency Characteristics and the TRFC-Method

As we have often stated in this book, the determination of frequency characteristics of a biological system is usually of basic importance to the investigator trying to identify the dynamic components of the studied mechanism. The direct measurement of the frequency characteristics is not always possible to realize since the experimental procedures often require long measuring times. This difficulty can be reduced by using the TRFC-Method, as was the case in various experiments described in this book. In section 4.11, we formulated the following rule as the most important concept in the examination of the frequency characteristics of a biological system: given a mechanism which is supposed to be responsible for the occurrence of a defined biological phenomenon, let us suppose that we are able to measure the time and frequency characteristics of the proposed mechanism.

If this mechanism takes longer to occur than the studied biological phenomenon, we would not be justified in discussing this mechanism as the causal factor. For the understanding of dynamical phenomena in biology, comparison of time and frequency characteristics of mechanisms which are predicted to be (or to work) in coordination is necessary.

The example in Chapter 4 shows that to identify the role of contracting smooth muscle as the causal factor in autoregulation, the determined frequency characteristics were necessary to elucidate the black box under study. We used several of the biological systems analysis program simultaneously and in combination, in order to understand the studied phenomena: power spectral analysis, theoretical filtering, nonlinear behavior, application of pharmacological agents and "going out of the system". The combinations of these methods and what these combinations bring will be treated further in the following paragraphs.

In the experiments of Chapter 7, where dynamics of various structures of the brain are analyzed with systems theory methods, amplitude frequency characteristics of studied brain nuclei serve again as the most important key for understanding brain signal transport. As was the case in the examination of the peripheral circulatory system in Chapter 4, the determination of amplitude frequency char-

acteristics alone helps the investigator only to a certain ex-

tent toward understanding the observed phenomena. Only after

determination of the power spectra (section 4.7), going out

of the system (section 4.8) and application of the theoret-

ical filtering method (section 4.9) can the investigator

acquire a more profound knowledge. In the case of the brain

however, because of the complexity of the system, the exper-

imenter is not yet able to formulate a more concrete working

hypothesis, as was the case in the phenomenon of autoregu-

lation presented in Chapter 4.

b) Theoretical Isolation Method (TI-Method)

The theoretical isolation method (or the theoretical

ideal filtering method) was used in the brain experiments

(Chapter 7), in the smooth muscle experiments (Chapter 5)

and for the discussion of the circulatory autoregulation

phenomena. Besides its technical contribution, which was

emphasized once more in the previous section 8.2, this

method made two important conceptional contributions to the

analysis of electrical signals from the brain. In section

7.14 the simultaneous application of pass-band and stop-band

filters helped the investigator in the interpretation of

transient evoked responses and in the obtaining of rules

and principles for the analysis of transient evoked potentials. This interpretation helped further to the discussion
of resonance phenomena in section 7.12. The second contribution was an important prediction concerning the oscillatory
waveforms of evoked potential components. In fact, the discussion in section 7.14 points out that evoked responses similar to the theoretically predicted oscillatory components
have been measured in homogeneous neural groups. The experiments by FREEMAN (1972b) and HOROWITZ et al. (1973) which
were described in section 7.14 (Figs. 7.27 and 7.28), strongly
support the prediction from theoretical ideal filtering.

Moreover, through the application of the theoretical
isolation method, the conceptional knowledge of "different
stages of smooth muscle contraction" and the concept of "the
equilibrium of strengths of different rhythmic components" is
arrived at. This concept, in turn, led the investigator to
assume "contractile reverberation circuits in smooth muscles"
(section 5.7). In Chapter 4, the investigator observes the
course of smooth muscle components acting in phase or
counter-phase, in order to develop a multicomponent myogenic
hypothesis of the circulatory autoregulation phenomenon.

These considerations above (explained in detail
elsewhere in this book) show that the adequate use of the

theoretical isolation method can be very useful for achieving component analyses, for physiological interpretations and for predictions concerning the phenomena under study.

c) Combination of Methods: Frequency Characteristics and "Going Out of the System"

We will repeat here again as a leading theme of biological systems analysis the following: for the understanding *of dynamical phenomena in biology, comparison of time and frequency characteristics of mechanisms which are predicted to be (or to work) in coordination is necessary.* The best example of this is the comparison of the smooth muscle amplitude characteristics with the amplitude characteristics of the autoregulating kidney and of the coronary system of the heart (sections 4.8 and 4.9). The dynamics of smooth muscle contractions serve as a key to the understanding of the circulatory autoregulation phenomena. In Chapter 4 the investigator determines the dynamics of the peripheral circulatory organs; he then determines the dynamics of smooth muscle, which are supposed to give the causal effect for the vasoconstriction phenomena. In other words, the experimenter goes out of the systems under study (kidney and coronary system); after examining the smooth muscles, he is better able to study the primary system.

In Chapter 7 we also have examples of the rule of "going out of the system". The introduction of common selectivities establishes a working frame in order to develop model concepts for signal transport in various brain structures (section 7.11). This is an important use of the method "going out of the system" since common rules cannot be established of studying only a unique brain center. Again, the search for neural groups as the responsible mechanism for the 40 Hz selectivity in the hippocampus and the cortex presents an example of the use of the rule of "going out of the system" (see section 7.17).

Usually all the studied biological systems are not completely *black boxes*; they are rather *grey boxes*; since at the beginning of the experiments we already know a lot about their anatomical structure and their physiological functions (definition of the grey box in Chapter 2). For example, we know that the kidney has nephrons, and we know that the kidney vascular system has smooth muscle cells in the vascular wall (section 4.3). We know that the hippocampus has pyramidal cells; we know about cortical organization (section 7.17). Going out of the system is possible only when based on the information obtained from grey boxes.

d) Combination of Methods: Frequency Characteristics
  and Power Spectra

The method of power spectra and the method of frequency characteristics have been used separately in the
analysis of many biological systems. In various chapters
of this book these two methods were used simultaneously or
alternatively for each biological system:

(1) The spontaneous flow oscillations in the kidney
were analyzed with power spectra; the frequency characteristics of the same system were also determined using
pressure stimulation as the input (sections 4.6 and 4.7).
Comparison of power spectra with the amplitude characteristics of the self-oscillating and autoregulating kidney led
the investigator to develop a working hypothesis where the
self-oscillatory character of flow in the kidney plays a
major role (section 4.9). Without the use of the power spectra results, such a working hypothesis could not be developed with the frequency characteristics alone.

(2) In the analysis of smooth muscle dynamics, the
power spectra method and the frequency characteristics
method were also used simultaneously. The considerations in
section 5.8 showed that the smooth muscle response to passive
stretch had frequency components which lay in the same

frequency bands as those of the intrinsic mechanical activity of smooth muscle. However, the investigators learned that the higher frequency component (or the amplitude maximum) in the vicinity of 0.1 Hz had a relatively larger magnitude in comparison to the power spectra obtained using the spontaneous mechanical activity. This finding led the investigator to assume that passive stretch of smooth muscles augments the smooth muscle oscillations (section 5.8). This is again an important physiological result which could be obtained only by applying the methods of both power spectra and frequency characteristics.

(3) Experiments similar to those of the kidney and of smooth muscles were also undertaken for the analysis of electrical signals from the brain. The comparison of the power spectra of the spontaneous activity in various structures of the brain with the amplitude frequency characteristics of those structures upon sensory stimulation led the investigator to formulate different types of resonance phenomena in brain responses. An efficient component analysis could be achieved only by considering the frequency components which exist in the on-going and evoked activities of the brain (section 7.12). As was the case for smooth muscles, higher frequency components, which were depicted

as weak components in the power spectra of the spontaneous
activity, appeared often as dominant maxima in the amplitude
frequency characteristics obtained upon stimulation (strong
resonance phenomena described in section 7.12).

The considerations above, which were described in
detailed manner in corresponding chapters of the book,
taught us, certainly, important points about special problems under study. Furthermore, from these considerations we
want to deduce a conceptional knowledge concerning the study
of biological systems in general: biological systems are
usually self-oscillating systems. Therefore experiments
starting with the aim of obtaining the frequency characteristics of the studied system should be accompanied with measurements of the power spectra of the intrinsic oscillations of the same system in order to determine the components
resulting from the genuine oscillation and the components
resulting from different types of resonance phenomena.

*e) Combination of Methods: Frequency Characteristics
and Application of Pharmacological Agents*

Application of pharmacological agents to the studied
biological system and thereafter the determination of the
frequency characteristics of the same system was realized
only twice during the experiments described in this book.

In the study of the circulatory autoregulation phenomena, the kidney and the coronary system of the rat heart were perfused with a solution containing the vascular smooth muscle paralyzing agent, papaverine (section 4.6). Upon the use of papaverine, the physical and biological components of the frequency characteristics of the kidney and the coronary systems could be identified, since the biological systems were reduced to functioning with only their hydrodynamic properties. This identification enabled the investigator to interpret the amplitude characteristics, discarding the low-pass effects resulting from the passive properties of the studied organs (section 4.8).

During the studies on the electrical signals from the brain we described experiments where evoked potentials were recorded with cats under nembutal anaesthesia. Our results led us to consider the 50 Hz frequency channel as a channel where the thalamo-reticular communication occurs (section 7.24). Although pharmacological agents were not often applied in the brain experiments described in Chapter 7, we want to emphasize here the usefulness of combining both methods, frequency characteristics and selective blocking with application of pharmacological agents as an efficient component analysis method.

8.3 GENERAL COMMENTS OR REMARKS

In different chapters of the book we have described various experiments with the purpose of gaining new insights to various physiological phenomena. Although our first aim was to find answers to different physiological questions, some general features common to all studied phenomena were also detected. We will discuss here briefly some of these common features which were derived from the experiments.

Rhythmicity in Biological Systems, Resonance, Control and Communication, Nonlinearities

In studying the various biological systems we have seen that the systems under study have intrinsic oscillations. It is a well known fact that a large number of biological systems (perhaps all) have intrinsic rhythmic behavior. There are excellent books on the study of rhythmic biological phenomena (for example BÜNNING, 1963). However, the response of a self-oscillating biological system to a forcing signal and its relation to *control based on rhythmicity or comminication achieved by rhythmicity* are problems less discussed in the literature. Few attempts are made (IBERALL, et al., 1971; HYNDMAN, 1974; VON HOLST, 1939). In the present book we have tried to fill this gap which usually exists in the study of biological systems, and we will emphasize that the investigator has to consider this aspect of biological systems in performing his experiments. The reader who wants to consider carefully this view, must be familiar with the results of Chapters 4, 5, 6 and 7.

In section 4.9 we developed a new myogenic concept of the circulatory autoregulation. The working hypothesis, which we called "multicomponent vasomotion theory of auto-regulation", was based on the findings of vascular autooscil-lations and vascular smooth muscle autooscillations. The rhythmic behavior of the biological system under study elim-inated the obstacles of the classical myogenic theory of autoregulation. The vascular autooscillations were shown to be characteristic of autoregulation (the findings by BAŞAR (1970) and BAŞAR and WEISS (1968), already have pointed out such a possibility).

IBERALL et al. (1971) attempted to postulate that the generation of oscillations of particular periods may be an intrinsic characteristic of the regulatory processes of the biological system. Control of the state of the internal milieu by dynamic fluctuations has been described as *homeokinesis*. IBERALL et al. (1971) state as follows:

> "When be began our 1962 review of control in the
> biosystem, we quickly found the central prin-
> ciple in biology enunciated as homeostasis, or

homeostatic regulation. This represented a
regulation of the internal variables in the
system - its fluxes and potentials - independent of conditions external to the complex
organism. It seemed clear to us that to achieve
such regulated states would require mechanisms
involved in dynamic regulation or control. It
was such description that we found lacking in
the biological literature, except for a few
isolated instances. (For example: the modelling
of Danziger and Elmergreen of thyroid function
and of Yates and Urquhart of adrenal function).

Having our own observations on the oscillating
nature of metabolic processes to add to the
known periodic nature of heart beat, breathing,
EEG, the alternation of rest and wake, we began
to trace out a broader spectrum of periodic
phenomena involving autonomous oscillators in
the complex biological spectrum. For example,
we have found these in other metabolic con-
stituents in blood - blood sugar, blood gases
(oxygen and CO_2), lactate, free fatty acids,
even in the file of red cells in capillaries.

Seeking function and structure beyond these
oscillatory processes, we then expected to be
confronted with the identification of the
regulators and controllers. However, it finally
dawned on us, as we uncovered the ubiquity of
large amplitude oscillations, that in toto the
network chains from which the oscillations
emerged likely made up the biological system.
Coupled with mechanisms embodying their control
algorithms, functionally they represented a
dynamic scheme of regulation within the body
for which we have proposed the name homeokinesis.

Homeokinesis denotes the scheme of mediation
of the operating conditions of a large but
compact collection of autonomous coupled oscillators, mainly by inhibition or release
from inhibition, so that their mean state
provides the near constancy of the internal
variables."

Our explanation of the autoregulation is in accordance with the concept of IBERALL and coworkers. Additionally, the autoregulation hypothesis of section 4.9 is involved also with external excitations: i.e. the investigator deals also with the control response of a self-oscillatory system upon stimulation. Here also as a result of our observation, we recommend the search for the role of intrinsic oscillation of a biological system when this system performs a control operation.

As a further important point, we want to emphasize the role of the intrinsic oscillation of a biological system in the response of the system to external stimuli. As we have seen in the example of frequency characteristics of smooth muscles (section 5.8) and in the evoked potentials of the brain (section 7.12) the response of a self-oscillatory biological system is influenced markedly by its genuine oscillation. In other words, the resonance phenomena play a basic role in the signal transport (or communication) in biological systems. Not only in the signal transport problems, but in the analysis of coupled structures, the self-oscillatory behavior plays an important role, since one of the components of a compound system can strongly influence the other components: the magnet effect (a component forcing another to its own rhythm) and harmonic entrainment are examples of this kind. For a profound analysis the reader is referred to sections 6.4 and 6.5 of this book. The investigator of biological systems should always remember the problem of the external stimulation of a self-oscillatory biological system. To him, we recommend the application of the ideas in Chapter 6, including the use of the model concepts given in sections 6.4 and 6.5. However, as we have already pointed out, every investigator should build his own model for each special system under study.

Consideration of phenomena such as the nonlinearities seen in biological systems, forcing of a self-oscillatory model system with external signals and the resulting *resonance or time-locking* phenomena, *mutual influence of coupled oscillators and harmonic entrainment,* as we have studied in detail in Chapter 6, are important common problems arising from the analysis of biological systems. Therefore, we want to attract the special attention of the biological systems investigator to keep in mind the following facts when studying a problem:

(1) Various components or mechanisms are usually responsible for the occurrence of control and communication in a biological system.

(2) In biological systems, various components performing a function usually show self-oscillatory behavior. These components may be coupled or at least may be arranged in such a way that they affect each other (different smooth muscle components in the vasculature, various neural groups).

Coupled oscillators may act as low-pass, high-pass or band-pass filters, according to the frequency of external forcing signals. Forced coupled oscillators in the functioning organism therefore act as important devices which regularize communication in the living system. Coupled, oscillatory smooth muscles and coupled, oscillatory neural structures can be given as important examples of active filters which regularize communication within the animal and human body. Accordingly we assume that the self-oscillatory behavior of biological structures or organisms is one of the most important factors in the regularization of communication and coordination in the living organism.

(3) All biological systems have at least two different kinds of components: physical and biological.

According to these facts, for every special biological system under study the common problems outlined above should be taken seriously into consideration. The common phenomena which can be derived from the model experiments of Chapter 6 (time-locking, resonances, harmonic entrainment, magnet-effect, interaction of the input signal with the active response) are effects which result from the concepts of physics. And, although one might comment that biological systems function in their own special way, we want to emphasize here that *biological mechanisms too must function in the frame of physical laws, and despite the special structure of living systems, many phenomena in biology are based on physical processes.*

REFERENCES

Başar, E.: Circulatory Autoregulation and Vascular Autooscil-
    lations. International Conference at Titisee on "Problems
    of Muscular Circulation" 30./31 October, (1970). {Arzneim.
    -Forsch. (Drug Res.) 366-376 (1971)}

Başar, E., und Ch. Weiss: Analyse des Frequenzganges druck-
    induzierter Änderungen des strömungswiderstandes isolierter
    Rattennieren. Pflügers Arch. 304, 121-135 (1968).

Hyndman, B.W.: The role of rhythms in homeostasis. Kybernetik
    15, 227-236 (1974).

Iberall, A., M. Weinberg, and A. Schintler: General Dynamics
    of the Physical Chemical Systems in Mammals. NASA Report
    Cr-1806 (1971).

von Bünning, E.: Die Physiologische Uhr. Springer Verlag
    Berlin (1963).

von Holst, E.: Die relative Koordination als Phänomen und
    als Methode Zentralnervöser Funktionsanalyse. Ergebn.
    Physiol. 42, 228-306 (1939).

Chapter 9

Conclusion

9.1 WHAT THIS BOOK TRIES TO ATTAIN

In this book, by applying systems analysis, we tried to understand scientifically various biological phenomena. We have studied problems in the circulatory system, the smooth muscles and the brain. In the study of all these systems a common course was pursued. Experiments followed the statement of the problem. Firstly the system to be studied was considered as a black box. According to the nature of the studied process, either the spontaneous rhythmic behavior or the response of the system to stimulation signals was analyzed in the beginning as abstract signals. Till this point the analysis was an approach common to all technical, physical or biological systems. Then the concept of "grey box" was used; this means, the experimenter

tried to collect what was known about the biological structure of the system and to discuss the accordance of various
anatomical or physiological findings already acquired with
new abstract results obtained by using systems theory tools.
This last step usually allowed the investigator to formulate
new points of view or some working hypotheses concerning
the biological and physical nature of the studied special
system or phenomenon. However, this approach did not consist
only of trials with the aim of elucidating the special
phenomena under study; the investigator tried to derive
knowledge common to various living (and also to physical)
systems as well. This is certainly a difficult task and
general considerations or common rules derived through an
analysis restricted only to the study of a few problems is
somewhat limited.

The *"Biological Systems Analysis Program"* is also
a product of the study of various phenomena presented in this
book. Although the program is given at the beginning of the
book, this program was developed during the studies of
various systems described in different chapters. To give
an example we will mention the chronological development in
the application of the theoretical isolation method presented
in the third chapter. At first, this method was used a priori

with the aim of understanding the evoked potentials of the

brain; then it was also applied to the circulatory auto-

regulation phenomenon, although the autoregulation studies

were started long before (about five years earlier) the

brain experiments presented in this book. In other words,

this method developed during more recent studies in brain

research, provided an important feedback to a circulatory

phenomenon which had already been studied with systems anal-

ysis. This was also our rationale in starting a book like

this. Methodological and conceptional developments reached

during systems analysis of biological systems should provide

feedback to the study of other or related biological systems.

Therefore, the book should not be considered as a collection

of studies on various separate biological phenomena, but a

treatise of biological systems theory which steps toward a

new physiology.

9.2 CYBERNETICS IN THE SENSE OF NORBERT WIENER

Following the rationale given in the foregoing

section, we want to point out that the scientific approach

of the present book is developed in the sense of NORBERT

WIENER who introduced the concept of cybernetics to the

sciences. What is cybernetics? The subtitle of NORBERT

WIENER's book CYBERNETICS (1961) reads as follows:

Control and Communication in the Animal and the Machine.
HASSENSTEIN (1971) tries to determine what the two terms
"control" and *"communication"* have in common: both terms
involve signals, or (where a written code is used) symbols;
in a control loop, signals pass from the detecting element
and the reference input to the final control element; in
information transmission and data processing, signals carry
the information in the form of signals or symbols. Cybernetics
is then the science of information. However, the aim of
NORBERT WIENER was not to limit the concept of cybernetics
only to such an abstract formulation: he discovered functional similarities between technical processes and living
organisms, and felt the need to develop a common terminology
and set of concepts to describe similar phenomena in various
areas. Accordingly the concept of cybernetics as a separate
branch goes back to the idea of the conformity of functional
principles in physical sciences, technology and biology.
WIENER's aim was ultimately to understand scientifically,
with the aid of systems concepts, the common phenomena in
physical sciences, technology and biology. To elucidate the
biological black box was certainly one of the aims of WIENER.

The attempt at solving problems stemming from living
systems with common systems concepts, is what biological

cybernetics is concerned about. Accordingly, biological

systems analysis may be distinguished as a vital tool of

cybernetics.

The biological systems analysis program introduced

in this book is a step toward the development of a general

methodology in the analysis of living systems. As we stated

at the beginning of the book, this program is not the best

and most perfect that one may consider. It should be

extended and ameliorated during further research and with

the contributions of investigators from the fields of both

biology and mathematical sciences. We also want to emphasize

that the team work of biologists and mathematicians must

also be in the sense of WIENER (1961), who stated:

> "The mathematician need not have the skill to
> conduct a physiological experiment, but he must
> have the skill to understand one, to criticize one,
> and suggest one. The physiologist need not be
> able to prove a certain mathematical theorem,
> but he must be able to grasp its physiological
> significance and to tell the mathematician for
> what he should look."

9.3 TOWARD A NEW PHYSIOLOGY

If we could only investigate all of the questions

proposed which are related to the topics treated in this

book, we would be able to write a book of five times

the content of the present one. Furthermore, if we

remember that we have studied only a few topics within the
vast area of physiology, the possibility of this type
approach to all the physiological phenomena should emerge
as an essential key to their understanding. The term "physiological phenomena" is used in order to express the most
complicated of biological phenomena (compound phenomena),
where many different biological processes are involved. All
the biological processes contribute to physiological function
or performance: the anatomical structure of living systems,
molecular processes which end in biochemical reactions or
endocrinal implications contribute at the last end to the
physiological function.

Furthermore, in order for physiology to develop
further, definitions of adequate "biological variables"
or "generalized biological coordinates" are needed which,
as in the physical sciences, are not expressed in subjective
terms. The only way to meet this need seems to be to link the
physical and biological sciences by trying to fill the
peculiar gap between them and to establish a common language
between them. This task is indeed a difficult one,
especially in regard to the rigid conventions accumulated
throughout the rather isolated development of the biological
sciences. The origin of many conventions in physiology may

be traced back to early periods when description was non-mathematical. Therefore some basic conceptual changes in physiology, meaning the establishment of a new physiology, are necessary. An effective approach to this problem should be the expansion of the few attempts already made to apply general systems theory to the various research areas of living systems. The author hopes that the studies presented in this book constitute, in this sense, a step forward.

REFERENCES

Hassenstein, B.: Information and Control in the Living Organism. Chapman and Hall Ltd. London (1971).

Wiener, N.: Cybernetics. M.I.T. Press and John Wiley and Sons, Inc., New York (1961).

AUTHOR INDEX

Adrian, E.D., 322
Altman, J., Brunner, R.L., Bayer, S.A., 256, 259
Andersen, P., Andersson, S.A., 321
Andersen, P., Eccles, J.C., 321
Ashby, W.R., 9, 13

Barlow, J.S., 223
Başar, E., 198, 237, 239, 277, 300, 406
Başar, E., Eroğlu, C., 156, 157, 162
Başar, E., Eroğlu, C., Ungan, P., 105, 136, 140, 144, 151,
    164, 165
Başar, E., Gönder, A., Özesmi, Ç., Ungan, P., 39, 253, 270,
    271, 272, 274, 275, 276, 279, 282, 283, 286, 287, 289,
    293, 296, 298, 305, 313, 314, 317, 323, 325, 364, 367,
    371
Başar, E., Özesmi, Ç., 237, 310
Başar, E., Ruedas, G., Schwarzkopf, H.J., Weiss, Ch., 73, 74,
    77, 79, 81, 165, 183
Başar, E., Tischner, H., Weiss, Ch., 73, 185, 226
Başar, E., Ungan, P., 37, 38, 300, 332, 334
Başar, E., Ungan, P., Özesmi, Ç., 341, 342, 343
Başar, E., Weiss, Ch., 32, 75, 76, 77, 78, 88, 89, 90, 91,
    97, 107, 164, 165, 226, 406
Bayliss, W.M., 59, 105
Bendat, J.S., Piersol, A.G., 42, 46
Benoit, J., 266
Berne, R.M., 68
Blesser, W.B., 30
Borg, E., 173, 239
Boudreau, J.C., 356
Bozler, E., 130
Brady, J.V., 255, 257
Brazier, M.A.B., 250, 258, 261
Brazier, M.A.B., Walter, D.O., 244
Bremer, F., Bonnet, V., 322
Brodal, A., 266
Burnstock, G., Prosser, L.C., 99, 130, 160
Burton, A.C., 56, 62
Bülbring, E., Kuriyama, H., 154
Bülbring, E., Needham, D.M., 129
Bülbring, E., Shuba, M.F., 129, 156, 157, 162

SUBJECT INDEX

Amplitude characteristics,
see Frequency char-
acteristics

Auditory cortex, 250, 252
(Fig.), 253(Fig.),
267
see also Brain

Auditory pathway, 249-
253, 252(Fig.),
253(Fig.), 267

Autocorrelation function,
42-46
application of, 89, 90
(Fig.), 138, 139
(Fig.), 148, 149
(Fig.)

Autoregulation of circu-
lation, 53-59
cell separation hypoth-
esis, 67, 68, 116,
117
metabolic hypothesis, 68,
69, 117
multi-component vaso-
motion theory, 112-
115
myogenic hypothesis, 66,
104-106, 114-116,
119, 120
renin-angiotensin
hypothesis, 69, 70,
117-119
tissue pressure
hypothesis, 66, 67,
116
vasomotion theory, 106,
107

Basic organ specific
rhythm (BOR), 142

Beating phenomena, 207, 208
(Fig.)

Black box, 13, 14, 17-19, 400

Brain
amplitude modulation in,
341-344
common selectivities in,
303-308, 328, 349, 379
consistent selectivities
in, 295-298, 307, 362
evoked potentials, 233,
235, 242
experimental setup for,
240, 241(Fig.), 242-
246
resonance phenomena, 311,
316, 320, 326, 381
alpha, 316, 321, 326, 347
strong, 316, 317(Fig.),
318, 320, 324, 347,372
weak, 316, 318, 324, 347
ratio of common selec-
tivities in, 303-307,
328
spontaneous activity, 233-
235, 270(Fig.), 271
(Fig.), 272(Fig.)
interactions with evoked
activity, 311, 316, 326,
347, 348
waking and sleep stages of,
234, 237, 246, 269, 273,
277, 281, 284, 323

Cerebral cortex, anatomical
organization of, 354
(Fig.), 355

Clipping effect, 180, 228

Convolution integral, 36

425